Applications of Mathematics

Stochastic Modelling
and Applied Probability

26

Applications of Mathematics

François Baccelli   Pierre Brémaud

Elements
of Queueing Theory

Palm-Martingale Calculus and
Stochastic Recurrences

With 24 Figures

Springer-Verlag
Berlin Heidelberg New York
London Paris Tokyo
Hong Kong Barcelona
Budapest

François Baccelli
INRIA Sophia Antipolis
2004 Route des Lucioles, BP 93, 06902 Sophia Antipolis, France

Pierre Brémaud
CNRS, Laboratoire des Signaux et Systèmes
Plateau du Moulon, 91192 Gif-sur-Yvette, France

Managing Editors

I. Karatzas
Department of Statistics, Columbia University
New York, NY 10027, USA

M. Yor
CNRS, Laboratoire de Probabilités, Université Pierre et Marie Curie
4 Place Jussieu, Tour 56, 75252 Paris Cedex 05, France

Mathematics Subject Classification (1991):
60F20, 60F99, 60G07, 60G17, 60G35, 60G44, 60G55, 60K05, 60K10,
60K15, 60K20, 60K25, 60K30, 68M10, 68M20, 68U20, 90B05, 90B15,
90B22, 90B35

ISBN 3-540-53347-8 Springer-Verlag Berlin Heidelberg New York
ISBN 0-387-53347-8 Springer-Verlag New York Berlin Heidelberg

Library of Congress Cataloging-in-Publication Data
Baccelli, F. (François), 1954-
Elements of queueing theory: Palm-Martingale calculus and stochastic recurrences/
François Baccelli, Pierre Brémaud. p. cm. — (Applications of mathematics; 26)
Includes bibliographical references and index.
ISBN 0-387-53347-8
1. Queueing theory. 2. Point processes. I. Brémaud, Pierre. II. Title. III. Series.
QA274.8.B33 1994 519.8' 2–dc20 93-41286

Typesetting: Camera-ready copy from the authors using a Springer T$_{\mathrm{E}}$X macro package
41/3140 - 5 4 3 2 1 0 - Printed on acid-free paper

Table of Contents

Chapter 3 Formulas

Chapter 4 Stochastic Ordering and Comparison of Queues

Introduction

As long as one is interested in a single isolated queue, specific assumptions on the input flow – for instance renewal, Markov, deterministic – can produce significant results which can be exploited as useful guidelines for system design.

The technological explosion which took place in the past quarter of century in computer/communications systems, the two main fields of application of queueing theory, has been responsible for the emergence of complex systems featuring queues organized in networks. The classical specific assumptions are usually not verified for a given queue in the network, even if the original input to the system has nice properties. Still, a number of models, mostly Markovian – for instance Jackson networks or Gordon-Newell networks – tolerate analytical treatment up to a certain point and are also of engineering interest. However, it is fair to say that interesting models allowing some kind of mathematical solution form a minority.

One purpose of the present book is to present a unified view of what can be said when only very weak assumptions are made on the input to a queueing system. Typical of the kind of results that can be reached within such a framework are Loynes' stability condition for the $G/G/1/\infty$ queue, Little's conservation formula $L = \lambda W$, stochastic monotonicity and convexity results.

As its title suggests and as its size commands, the present book does not give a systematic treatment of queueing theory: instead we have tried to present the elements of the more general methods of point processes and stochastic recurrences which can be directly useful to queueing theory. These include Palm–martingale calculus, ergodic theory, Strassen's representation of stochastic orders, and coupling.

The precise content of this book is described by its subtitle: stochastic recurrences and Palm–martingale calculus.

By stochastic recurrences, we mean sequences of random variables governed by a stochastic recurrence, for instance the sequence of waiting times of successive customers in a queue. The stability of such sequences constitutes one of the central problems of queueing theory. In many situations of practical interest, one can prove or disprove stability only for special models, mostly Markovian or renewal. However, in his pioneering article of 1962 concerning the recurrence equation satisfied by waiting times, Loynes was able to prove stability for a single server, infinite capacity queue, under the natural condition that the rate of work brought into the system be smaller than the processing speed of the server. Loynes' proof did not require the usual independence assumptions. It only required the input to be stationary and ergodic. The generality of his proof provided impetus to the stability theory of stationary and ergodic systems which is still flourishing.

Loynes' theory of stability of the $G/G/1/\infty$ queue has since been refined and extended. We shall present various extensions of the basic theory to the case when the critical monotonicity assumption is not verified (a typical example is the $G/G/1/0$ queue). Borovkov's theory of renovating events provides a general method to analyze this type of systems. This theory generalizes the notion of construction points and allows one to prove the convergence in variation of non-stationary sequences to stationary limits, via coupling arguments. Another basic tool is Kingman's sub-additive ergodic theorem, which provides the stability region for open separable queueing systems, like blocking queues for instance.

In a queueing context, the stochastic recurrences arise by sampling a continuous time stochastic process at events such as the arrival or the departure of a customer, or its transfer from one queue to another. They are also called imbedded sequences, and are often used as a way for going back to the Markovian framework, when the original model is not Markovian. The pioneering work in this respect is that of Kendall who studied the $M/GI/1/\infty$ queue via imbedding at departure times. However, as is well known in continuous time Markov chain theory, the stationarity of an imbedded sequence does not imply the stationarity of the original continuous time processes and viceversa. Also, in the ergodic context, empirical averages of the continuous time process and of the imbedded sequence need not coincide.

The theory of Palm probabilities provides the natural framework for the study of relations between time averages and event averages, such as for instance Little's theorem, Brumelle's $H = \lambda G$ formula and the PASTA (Poisson Arrivals See Time Averages) property. The first chapter of the book is devoted to the aspects of Palm probabilities which are relevant to queueing theory, and in particular of the so–called Palm calculus based on Matthes' definition and Mecke's formula. In this book, the treatment is in terms of abstract shifts. This is the so-called θ_t–formalism which makes the basic rules clear and easy to use, by allowing one to remain in the same measurable space. The connection is also made between the theories of Palm probabilities and of stochastic intensities of point processes via Papangelou's Radon-Nikodým theorem and the martingale strong law of large numbers.

Once the Palm calculus and the stability theory of stochastic recurrences are available, the harvesting of the classical results of queueing theory is easy; this is the object of Chapter 3, where Little's $L = \lambda W$ formula, Brumelle's

$H = \lambda G$ formula, Kleinrock's conservation law, the PASTA principle, and their applications are given.

The constructive theory of stationary states in terms of stochastic recurrences is also a very useful tool in the theory of stochastic comparison of queues, together with the sample path approach to stochastic orders (Strassen's theorems). The corresponding theory is covered in Chapter 4, where it is applied to provide non-analytical proofs of classical monotonicity results in queueing theory, and various optimality properties, such as the optimality of the SRPT (shortest remaining processing time) discipline and the extremal properties of the FIFO (first-in-first-out) discipline. Finally, the relationship between the stochastic monotonicity of point processes and that of stochastic recurrences based on these point processes is studied, together with extensions to continuous time processes.

The general approach taken in this book has already proved fruitful in two respects: it gives simple and rigorous proofs of most classical results, and it has taken the theory one step beyond the renewal assumptions a number of situations. We have not given all the consequences of the theory, but we have illustrated it in a few examples, with the purpose of showing how the general machinery can be used and also of providing familiar context for a reader already acquainted with the classical theory of queues. For the reader wishing to obtain more information on classical topics that we have only approached, *Stochastic Networks and Reversibility*, by Frank Kelly, *Applied Probability and Queues*, by Søren Asmussen and *Stochastic Modeling and the Theory of Queues*, by Ronald Wolff are highly recommended references.

Acknowledgements

We wish to acknowledge our intellectual debt to the book *Queues and Point Processes*, by Peter Franken, Dieter König, Volker Schmidt and Ursula Arndt, which introduced us to the Palm calculus approach to queues.

The present book grew out of the authors' Lecture Notes *Palm Probabilities and Stationary Queueing Systems* (1987), Springer-Verlag, and from a graduate course taught at the École Polytechnique in the DEA *Modélisation aléatoire et statistique*, where it greatly benefited from the interaction with the students.

Our colleagues Venkat Anantharam, Serguei Foss, Armand Makowski, Masakiyo Miyazawa and Volker Schmidt deserve our sincere thanks for reading and checking the manuscript at various steps of completion.

The task of typing was diligently accomplished by Rivo Rakotosafi; Ephie Deriche also greatly contributed to the material realization of this book in many ways.

1 The Palm-Martingale Calculus of Point Processes

Introduction

The input into a queueing system can be viewed as a sequence of required service times together with the times at which these requests arrive, that is a double sequence $\{(T_n, \sigma_n)\}$ indexed by the set $\mathbb{Z}$ of relative integers, where σ_n is the amount of service (in time units) needed by customer n, who arrives at time T_n. If there are no batch arrivals, then $T_n < T_{n+1}$. Since we are interested in the stationary behavior of the system, the sequence of arrival times $\{T_n\}$ contains arbitrarily large negative times. By convention, the negative or null times of the arrival sequence will be indexed by negative or null relative integers, and the positive times by positive integers: $\ldots < T_{-2} < T_{-1} < T_0 \leq 0 < T_1 < T_2 < \ldots$.

The sequence $\{T_n\}$ is a *point process*, and the double sequence $\{(T_n, \sigma_n)\}$ is a *marked point process*, σ_n being the *mark* of point T_n. More complicated mark sequences $\{Z_n\}$ can be considered, where Z_n is an attribute of customer n including, among other possible choices, the amount of service σ_n he requires and his priority class U_n. If the queueing system under consideration is a network of queues, the mark Z_n will for instance, feature the route followed by customer n through the network and the amount of service he requires at each station along his route.

Even in the simplest models, intricate dependencies may exist among the members of the sequence $\{(T_n, \sigma_n)\}$. Of course, in the so-called elementary theory of queues, the stream of required services is of the GI/GI type, i.e. $\{T_n\}$ and $\{\sigma_n\}$ are independent sequences, $\{\sigma_n\}$ is an *i.i.d.* sequence, and $\{T_n\}$ forms a renewal process, say a Poisson process. However, suppose that the customers go through a very simple queueing system with two servers operating at unit speed, with a *first come first served* queueing discipline. The sequence of times $\{T_n'\}$ at which customers leave the queueing system, with the convention $\ldots < T'_{-2} < T'_{-1} < T'_0 \leq 0 < T'_1 < T'_2 < \ldots$ may be of a complex nature, even in the GI/GI case: customers may overtake one another, the delay incurred by a given customer is a complicated function of the past history of the input stream, etc. Suppose now that the customers, just after leaving, join a second queueing system where they require the same amount of service as in the first system. The input stream into the second system is $\{(T_n{}', \sigma'_n)\}$ where σ'_n is in general different from σ_n (due to over-taking). These remarks show that the input stream into the second system will most likely not be a GI/GI stream, except in very special cases (in particular when $\{T_n\}$ is a homogeneous Poisson process, and $\{\sigma_n\}$ is $i.i.d.$ with a probability distribution of the exponential type (Burke's theorem)).

The need for general models of input streams is apparently in contradiction with the need for analytically tractable models. This is indeed true, but only to a certain extent. In this chapter, we shall introduce the notion of stationary marked point processes. Although this class of models is very general, the theory will provide many structural results of direct interest to queueing theory. A similar situation occurs in signal theory, when only wide sense stationary signal models are considered. Such crude models, entirely described by a number (the mean) and a function (the autocorrelation function), have proved to be of undeniable engineering interest. Stationary marked point processes will be described by a number (the intensity) and a probability distribution (the Palm distribution of the marks). This suffices to produce simple and useful queueing formulas, such as Little's formula and Kleinrock's conservation law (Chapter 3). In the present chapter, we shall prepare the way by introducing an abstract formalism for the study of stationary queueing systems, the so-called θ_t-framework, and by presenting the basic theory of Palm probability and its link with the stochastic intensity approach to point processes. As a result, we shall have a versatile computational tool (which we shall call *Palm-martingale calculus*) based on Matthes' definition of Palm probability and on the martingale definition of stochastic intensity. This tool, and the existence theory for stationary states of Chapter 2, will enable us to obtain basic formulas of queueing theory in a powerful manner in Chapter 3.

1 Stationary Marked Point Processes

1.1 The Canonical Space of a Point Process on the Real Line

A *counting measure* on $\mathbb{R}$ (the real line) is a measure m on $(\mathbb{R}, \mathcal{B})$, where $\mathcal{B}$ denotes the Borel σ-field of $\mathbb{R}$, such that

(a) $m(C) \in \{0, 1, \ldots, \infty\}$ for all $C \in \mathcal{B}$,
(b) $m([a, b]) < \infty$ for all bounded intervals $[a, b] \subset \mathbb{R}$.

Let M be the set of all counting measures on $\mathbb{R}$. The σ-field on M generated by the functions $m \rightarrow m(C), C \in \mathcal{B}$, is denoted by $\mathcal{M}$. The measurable space $(M, \mathcal{M})$ is the *canonical space of point processes on $\mathbb{R}$*.

With each counting measure $m \in M$, we can associate a unique sequence $\{t_n\}, n \in \mathbb{Z}$, of $\overline{\mathbb{R}}$, such that

$$m(.) = \sum_{n \in \mathbb{Z}} \delta_{t_n}(.),$$

with $-\infty \leq \ldots \leq t_{-1} \leq t_0 \leq 0 < t_1 \leq t_2 \leq \ldots \leq +\infty$ and card $\{n \in \mathbb{Z} \mid t_n \in [a, b]\} < \infty$, for all $[a, b] \subset \mathbb{R}$. Here δ_x is the Dirac measure at $x \in \mathbb{R}$, with the convention $\delta_\infty(.) = \delta_{-\infty}(.) \equiv 0$, the measure with no mass.

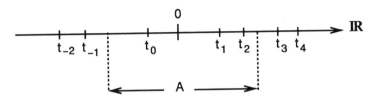

Fig. 1.1.1 A counting measure m is just a finite or countably infinite subset $\{t_n\}$ of $\mathbb{R}$. The measure $m(A)$ of the Borel set $A \subset \mathbb{R}$, is the number of indices n such that $t_n \in A$. Here, $m(A) = 3$.

The time t_n is called the n-th *point* of m. The mapping $m \to t_n$ is a random variable on $(M, \mathcal{M})$.

Note: We have taken the option not to give formal proofs concerning measurability, with the exception of Subsections 8 and 9 where predictability is introduced. For these questions, the reader is referred to Daley and Vere-Jones (1988), *Introduction to Point Processes*, Springer-Verlag, New York.

The counting measure m is called *simple* if $m(\{x\}) = 0$ or 1 for all $x \in \mathbb{R}$. Clearly m is simple if and only if $t_n < t_{n+1}$ for all $n \in \mathbb{Z}$ such that $|t_n| < \infty$. Owing to the definition of t_n, for any function $f : \mathbb{R} \to \mathbb{R}_+$, we have

$$\int_\mathbb{R} f(x) m(dx) = \sum_{n \in \mathbb{Z}} f(t_n) 1_\mathbb{R}(t_n).$$

The *translation* or *shift operator* S_t operating on M is defined for each $t \in \mathbb{R}$ by

$$S_t m(C) = m(C + t), \quad C \in \mathcal{B},$$

that is, if $m(.) = \sum_{n \in \mathbb{Z}} \delta_{t_n}(.)$, then $S_t m(.) = \sum_{n \in \mathbb{Z}} \delta_{t_n - t}(.)$.

The family $\{S_t\}, t \in \mathbb{R}$, forms a (measurable) *flow* of $(M, \mathcal{M})$ i.e.

(a) $(t, m) \to S_t m$ is measurable from $\mathcal{B} \otimes \mathcal{M}$ to $\mathcal{M}$,
(b) S_t is bijective for all $t \in \mathbb{R}$,
(c) $S_t \circ S_s = S_{t+s}$ for all $t, s \in \mathbb{R}$. In particular $S_0 = I$ (identity) and $S_t^{-1} = S_{-t}$.

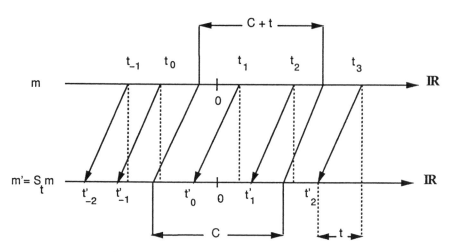

Fig. 1.1.2 The shift. Note the numbering of the points $\{t'_n\}$; we have to respect the convention $t'_0 \le 0 < t'_1$. Clearly, $S_t m(C) = m(C + t)$.

1.2 Stationary Point Processes

Let $(\Omega, \mathcal{F})$ be a measurable space. A measurable mapping N from $(\Omega, \mathcal{F})$ into $(M, \mathcal{M})$ is called a *point process*. Thus, for each $\omega \in \Omega$, $N(\omega)$ is a counting measure. For any Borel set C, let $N(C)$ be the random variable $N(\omega, C) = N(\omega)(C)$, and let T_n be $T_n(\omega) = t_n(N(\omega))$. Thus $T_n(\omega)$ is the n-th point of $N(\omega)$ and $N(C) = \sum_{n \in \mathbb{Z}} 1_C(T_n)$.
If a probability measure P is given on $(\Omega, \mathcal{F})$, then the pair (N, P) is called a *stochastic point process*.

Let $\{\theta_t\}, t \in \mathbb{R}$, be a (measurable) flow on $(\Omega, \mathcal{F})$, i.e.

(a) $(t, \omega) \to \theta_t \omega$ is measurable with respect to $\mathcal{B} \otimes \mathcal{F}$ and $\mathcal{F}$,
(b) θ_t is bijective for all $t \in \mathbb{R}$,
(c) $\theta_t \circ \theta_s = \theta_{t+s}$ for all $t, s \in \mathbb{R}$. In particular θ_0 is the identity and $\theta_t^{-1} = \theta_{-t}$.

If U and V are real-valued random variables on $(\Omega, \mathcal{F})$, we have the following composition rule

$$(1.2.1) \quad \theta_U \circ \theta_V(\omega) = \theta_{U \circ \theta_V(\omega)}(\theta_V(\omega)) = \theta_{V + U \circ \theta_V}(\omega).$$

If (N, P) is a stochastic point process such that for all $t \in \mathbb{R}, \omega \in \Omega$,

$$(1.2.2) \quad \begin{cases} N(\theta_t \omega) = S_t N(\omega) & (\text{ i.e. } N(\theta_t \omega, C) = N(\omega, C + t)), \\ P \circ \theta_t = P, \end{cases}$$

the triple (N, θ_t, P) is called a *stationary stochastic point process*, or stationary point process for short.

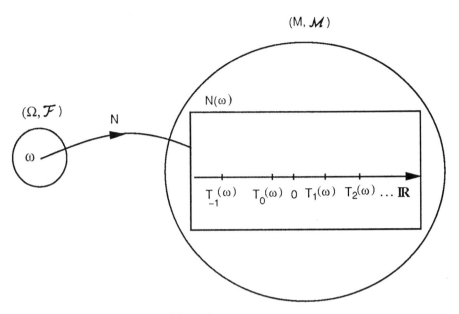

Fig. 1.2.1 A point process and its points

Property (1.2.2) is indeed stationarity in the usual sense. To see this, consider the event

$$A = \{\omega \mid N(\omega, C_1) = k_1, \ldots, N(\omega, C_m) = k_m\},$$

with $C_1, \ldots, C_m \in \mathcal{B}$, $k_1, \ldots, k_m \in \mathbb{N}$. By definition

$$\begin{aligned}
\theta_t^{-1} A &= \{\omega \mid \theta_t \omega \in A\} \\
&= \{\omega \mid N(\theta_t \omega, C_1) = k_1, \ldots, N(\theta_t \omega, C_m) = k_m\} \\
&= \{\omega \mid N(\omega, C_1 + t) = k_1, \ldots, N(\omega, C_m + t) = k_m\}.
\end{aligned}$$

Note that if 1_A denotes the indicator function of A, then

$$1_A \circ \theta_t = 1_{\theta_t^{-1} A} = 1_{\theta_{-t} A}.$$

Therefore, since $P \circ \theta_t^{-1} = P$,

$$P(N(C_1) = k_1, .., N(C_m) = k_m) = P(N(C_1 + t) = k_1, .., N(C_m + t) = k_m).$$

Example 1.2.1 *Stationary point process in canonical form.* Here $(\Omega, \mathcal{F}) = (M, \mathcal{M})$, $\theta_t = S_t$ $(t \in \mathbb{R})$, and $P = \mathcal{P}$, where $\mathcal{P}$ is a measure on $(M, \mathcal{M})$ such that $\mathcal{P} \circ S_t = \mathcal{P}$ $(t \in \mathbb{R})$. Taking N equal to the identity, we obtain a stationary point process which is said to be in canonical form, namely $(\Phi, S_t, \mathcal{P})$, where Φ denotes the identity map of M.   □

Example 1.2.2 *Superposition of independent point processes in canonical form.* Let $(M_i, \mathcal{M}_i, S_t^{(i)}, \Phi_i)$ $(1 \le i \le k)$ be k replicas of $(M, \mathcal{M}, S_t, \Phi)$ of Example 1.2.1 and let $\mathcal{P}_i$ be a probability on $(M_i, \mathcal{M}_i)$ which is $S_t^{(i)}$-invariant for all $t \in \mathbb{R}$. Define the product space

$$(\Omega, \mathcal{F}, P) = (\prod_{i=1}^{k} M_i, \bigotimes_{i=1}^{k} \mathcal{M}_i, \bigotimes_{i=1}^{k} \mathcal{P}_i)$$

and, for each $t \in \mathbb{R}$, define

$$\theta_t = \bigotimes_{i=1}^{k} S_t^{(i)},$$

with the meaning that $\theta_t \omega = (S_t^{(i)} m_i; 1 \le i \le k)$, where $\omega = (m_i; 1 \le i \le k)$. Define

$$N(\omega) = \sum_{i=1}^{k} m_i \quad \text{and} \quad N_i(\omega) = m_i \ (1 \le i \le k).$$

The stationary point process (N, θ_t, P) is called the *superposition* of the stationary point processes (N_i, θ_t, P) $(1 \le i \le k)$. $\square$

1.3 Marks of a Point Process

Let $Z = \{Z_n\}$, $n \in \mathbb{Z}$, be a sequence of measurable mappings from $(\Omega, \mathcal{F})$ into some measurable space $(K, \mathcal{K})$. It is it called a *sequence of marks* of (N, θ_t) if

(1.3.1) $Z_n(\omega) = Z_0(\theta_{T_n} \omega)$.

If moreover (N, θ_t, P) is a stationary point process, $((N, Z), \theta_t, P)$ is called a *stationary marked point process* (with marks in K).

The Shadowing Property. The motivation for definition (1.3.1) is that we want to be sure that the mark $Z_n(\omega)$ associated with $T_n(\omega)$ *follows* $T_n(\omega)$ when the underlying counting measure $N(\omega)$ is shifted.

To see how this *shadowing property* works (Z_n is the *shadow* following T_n), consider the following picture, where we have taken $Z_n = \sigma_n$, the required service of customer n, as an example.

First we shall be careful about the numbering: for instance, in Figure 1.3.1, $T_1(\theta_t \omega)$ is *not* $T_1(\omega) - t$ but $T_2(\omega) - t$, since $t \in [T_1(\omega), T_2(\omega))$. Therefore if we want σ_2 to shadow T_2 we must have $\sigma_2(\omega) = \sigma_1(\theta_t \omega)$. We shall see that this is guaranteed by the property $\sigma_n(\omega) = \sigma_0(\theta_{T_n} \omega)$. Indeed

$$\sigma_1(\theta_t \omega)) = \sigma_0(\theta_{T_1} \circ \theta_t(\omega)) = \sigma_0(\theta_{t+T_1 \circ \theta_t(\omega)}) = \sigma_0(\theta_{T_2}(\omega)).$$

Therefore $\sigma_1(\theta_t \omega) = \sigma_0(\theta_{T_2} \omega) = \sigma_2(\omega)$.

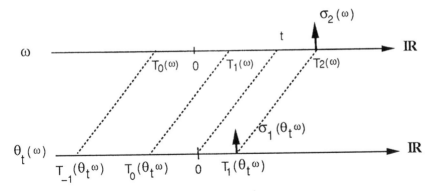

Fig. 1.3.1 The shadowing property

Example 1.3.1 *Universal marks.* Let (N, θ_t, P) be a stationary point process. Define

$$(1.3.2) \quad \widetilde{Z}_n(\omega) = \theta_{T_n(\omega)}\omega$$

or, more briefly, $\widetilde{Z}_n = \theta_{T_n}$. The sequence $\widetilde{Z} = \{\widetilde{Z}_n\}$, is called the *universal sequence of marks* of (N, θ_t) since every sequence of marks $Z = \{Z_n\}$ is of the form $Z_n = Z_0(\theta_{T_n}) = Z_0(\widetilde{Z}_n)$. The property that $\{\widetilde{Z}_n\}$ is a sequence of marks is immediate: $\widetilde{Z}_0 \circ \theta_{T_n} = \theta_{T_0} \circ \theta_{T_n} = \theta_{T_n + T_0 \circ \theta_{T_n}} = \theta_{T_n} = \widetilde{Z}_n$, since $T_0 \circ \theta_{T_n} = 0$.   □

Example 1.3.2 Let (N, θ_t, P) be a stationary point process and let $\{A_t\}, t \in \mathbb{R}$, be a non-negative process on $(\Omega, \mathcal{F})$ such that

$$(1.3.3) \quad A_t = A_0(\theta_t).$$

The formula

$$(1.3.4) \quad Z_n = \int_{T_n}^{T_{n+1}} A_s ds$$

defines a sequence of marks of (N, θ_t, P). For instance if $A_t = 1$, $Z_n = T_{n+1} - T_n$.   □

The next example introduces a family of stationary point processes of special interest in queueing theory. Indeed, as we shall see, a stationary Markov chain generates a family of stationary point processes, that is, those counting the transitions of a given type. The abstract framework is the following.

Example 1.3.3 Let E be a countable state space. For $t \in \mathbb{R}$, let $\Omega = D(\mathbb{R}; E)$ be the set of functions $\omega : \mathbb{R} \to E$ which are piecewise constant right-continuous, and with a finite number of discontinuities in any finite interval. Let $\theta_t : \Omega \to \Omega$ be defined by

(1.3.5) $(\theta_t \omega)(u) = \omega(u + t)$.

Let $\mathcal{F}$ be the σ-field generated by the coordinate mappings $X_t, t \in \mathbb{R}$ (i.e. $X_t(\omega) = \omega(t)$). Let P be a probability on $(\Omega, \mathcal{F})$ such that $P \circ \theta_t = P$, $t \in \mathbb{R}$. Define N by: $N(C)$=number of discontinuities of $\{X(t)\}$ in the Borel set C. Suppose that under P, $\{X_t\}, t \in \mathbb{R}$, is a (regular) Markov chain with infinitesimal generator $Q = \{q_{ij}\}$ and stationary distribution $\pi = \{\pi(i)\}$. Recall that $\pi'Q = 0$, where prime denotes transposition.

Let H be a subset of $E \times E - \text{diag}(E \times E)$. Let N_H be the point process counting the H-transitions of $\{X_t\}$, i.e.

(1.3.6) $N_H(C) = \displaystyle\int_C 1_H(X_{s-}, X_s)N(ds)$.

(N_H, θ_t, P) is a stationary point process. In particular for $H = E \times E - \text{diag}(E \times E)$, we have $N_H = N$ the *basic* point process of the chain, which counts all transitions. Let $\{T_n\}$ be the jump times of $\{X_t\}$, i.e. the points of the basic point process N. The formula

(1.3.7) $Z_n = X_{T_n}$

defines a sequence of marks for (N, θ_t) with values in the state space. Clearly, (N, Z) and $\{X_t\}$ are equivalent descriptions of the same object. $\square$

Example 1.3.4 *Canonical space of marked point processes.* It is somewhat easier to understand the θ_t-formalism in terms of canonical spaces. Let $(K, \mathcal{K})$ be a measurable space and define $\widetilde{M}_K$ to be the set of sequences:

(1.3.8) $\{(t_n, k_n)\}, n \in \mathbb{Z}$,

where $t_n \in \overline{\mathbb{R}}, k_n \in K$ and

(1.3.9) $-\infty \leq \ldots \leq t_{-2} \leq t_{-1} \leq t_0 \leq 0 < t_1 \leq t_2 \leq \ldots \leq +\infty$.

Define a measure μ on $(\mathbb{R} \times K, \mathcal{B} \otimes \mathcal{K})$ by

(1.3.10) $\mu(C \times L) = \displaystyle\sum_{n \in \mathbb{Z}} 1_C(t_n) 1_L(k_n), \quad C \in \mathcal{B}, L \in \mathcal{K}$.

Call M_K the set of measures μ representable by (1.3.8)–(1.3.10). Let $\mathcal{M}_K$ be the σ-field on M_K generated by the mappings $\mu \to \mu(C \times L)$, $C \in \mathcal{B}$, $L \in \mathcal{K}$. For each $t \in \mathbb{R}$, we define the operator S_t to act on a measure μ in the following manner:

(1.3.11) $S_t\mu(C \times L) = \mu((C + t) \times L), \quad C \in \mathcal{B}, L \in \mathcal{K}$.

It can be shown that $\{S_t\}, t \in \mathbb{R}$, is a flow on $(M_K, \mathcal{M}_K)$ and $\mu \to t_n, \mu \to k_n$ are M_K-measurable mappings.

Let $\mathcal{P}$ be a probability on $(M_K, \mathcal{M}_K)$ such that

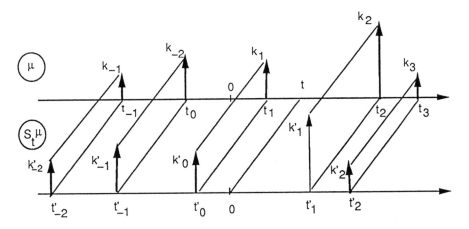

Fig. 1.3.2 Translation of a canonical marked point process

(1.3.12) $\mathcal{P} \circ S_t = \mathcal{P}$, $t \in \mathbb{R}$.

Call Ψ the identity mapping on M_K and T_n, Z_n the mappings $\mu \to t_n$, $\mu \to k_n$ respectively. Then with the identifications

(1.3.13) $\begin{cases} (\Omega, \mathcal{F}, P) \equiv (M_K, \mathcal{M}_K, \mathcal{P}), \\ \theta_t = S_t, \\ N(.) = \Psi(. \times K), \end{cases}$

we have a stationary point process (N, θ_t, P). Moreover $\{k_n\}$ is a sequence of marks associated with (N, θ_t). □

Remark 1.3.1 Let the process $\{k(t)\}, t \in \mathbb{R}$, be defined by $k(t, \mu) = k_n(\mu)$ for $t \in [t_n(\mu), t_{n+1}(\mu))$. In particular $k(0) = k_0$. Moreover, by definition of S_t,

$$k(t, \mu) = k(0, S_t\mu),$$

and therefore $k_n = k(t_n)$. More generally, a sequence of marks $\{Z_n\}$ of a point process (N, θ_t) has the canonical form

(1.3.14) $Z_n = Z(T_n)$,

for some stochastic process $\{Z(t)\}$, that is,

(1.3.15) $Z(t) = Z_n$ for $t \in [T_n, T_{n+1})$.

The process $\{Z(t)\}$ so defined is called the *canonical t-process associated with the sequence of marks* $\{Z_n\}$ of (N, θ_t). □

The θ_t-Framework and Compatibility. The θ_t-framework consists of
- a measurable space $(\Omega, \mathcal{F})$ and a measurable flow $\{\theta_t\}$ defined on it
- a probability measure P that is θ_t-invariant for all $t \in \mathbb{R}$
- a point processes N *compatible with the flow* $\{\theta_t\}$, i.e. satisfying $N(\theta_t) = S_t N$ for all $t \in \mathbb{R}$
- a stochastic processes $\{Z(t)\}$ *compatible with the flow* $\{\theta_t\}$, i.e. satisfying $Z(t, \omega) = Z(0, \theta_t \omega)$ for all $t \in \mathbb{R}, \omega \in \Omega$.

The stochastic process $\{Z(t)\}$ can be defined in terms of a point process N (for instance $Z(t) = N((t, t + a]))$, or, vice-versa N can be defined in terms of $\{Z(t)\}$ as in Example 1.3.3. In any case, in this framework, N and $\{Z(t)\}$ are *jointly stationary*, since they are compatible with the same flow.

1.4 Two Properties of Stationary Point Processes

(1.4.1) *Independent stationary point processes have a.s. no common points*

Proof: Consider the situation described in Example 1.2.2 with $k = 2$. It will be shown that N_1 and N_2 have almost surely no common point. The proof is given when one of them (say N_1) has a finite intensity, i.e. $E[N_1(0, 1]] < \infty$. Then $E[N_1\{t\}] = 0$ for all $t \in \mathbb{R}$, by stationarity. Therefore, by Fubini's theorem

$$E[\int_{\mathbb{R}} N_1(\{s\})N_2(ds)] = \int_{M_1} \int_{M_2} \int_{\mathbb{R}} m_1(\{s\})m_2(ds)\mathcal{P}_1(dm_1)\mathcal{P}_2(dm_2)$$

$$= \int_{M_2} \int_{\mathbb{R}} [\int_{M_1} m_1(\{s\})\mathcal{P}_1(dm_1)]m_2(ds)\mathcal{P}_2(dm_2) = 0$$

and this implies $\int_{\mathbb{R}} N_1(\{s\})N_2(ds) = 0$, P-a.s. $\qquad\square$

(1.4.2) *Let (N, θ_t, P) be a stationary point process, then*

$$P(\{N(\mathbb{R}) = 0\} \cup \{N((0, \infty)) = N((-\infty, 0)) = +\infty\}) = 1.$$

Proof: Let $H_t = \{N((t, \infty)) = 0\}$. H_t increases with t, so that $\cup_{n=0}^{\infty} H_n \supset \cap_{n=1}^{\infty} H_{-n}$. Hence

$$G = \cup_{n=0}^{\infty} H_n = \{N((0, \infty)) < \infty\} \supset H = \cap_{n=0}^{\infty} H_{-n} = \{N(\mathbb{R}) = 0\}.$$

In addition $\theta_t H_s = H_{s-t}$ for all $s, t \in \mathbb{R}$, so that $P(H_n) = $ constant, for all $n \in \mathbb{Z}$. Hence $P(G) = \lim_{n \to \infty} P(H_n) = \lim_{n \to -\infty} P(H_n) = P(H)$, which together with $G \supset H$ imply $P(G - H) = 0$. A similar reasoning based on $\tilde{H}_s = \{N((-\infty, s)) = 0\}$ leads to $P(G' - H) = 0$, where $G' = \{N((-\infty, 0)) < \infty\}$. Therefore $P((G \cup G') - H) = 0$. $\qquad\square$

2 Intensity

2.1 The Intensity of a Stationary Point Process

Let (N, θ_t, P) be a stationary point process. The non-negative (possibly infinite) number

$$(2.1.1) \quad \lambda = E[N((0,1])]$$

is called the *intensity* of (N, θ_t, P). More generally, define for all $C \in \mathcal{B}$

$$(2.1.2) \quad \lambda(C) = E[N(C)].$$

From the stationarity of (N, θ_t, P), $\lambda(C + t) = \lambda(C)$ for all $t \in \mathbb{R}$, and therefore λ defines a translation invariant measure on $(\mathbb{R}, \mathcal{B})$. It is therefore proportional to the Lebesgue measure l so that

$$(2.1.3) \quad \lambda(C) = \lambda.l(C), \quad C \in \mathcal{B}.$$

Assumptions. In this monograph we shall assume that the stationary point processes under consideration have a *non-null and finite* intensity and are *simple*, i.e. $P(N\{T_n\}) > 1) = 0$ for all $n \in \mathbb{Z}$.
These assumptions will generally not be recalled in the text.

Example 2.1.1 *Rate of arrivals into a queueing system.* In queueing theory $\{T_n\}$ is the sequence of arrival times of customers into a queueing system, the intensity λ of $\{T_n\}$ is called the *arrival rate.*   □

2.2 Campbell's Measure

Let $((N, Z), \theta_t, P)$ be a stationary marked point process with marks in $(K, \mathcal{K})$. Define the random counting measure N_Z on $(\mathbb{R} \times K, \mathcal{B} \otimes \mathcal{K})$ by

$$(2.2.1) \quad N_Z(C \times L) = \int_C 1_L(Z_0 \circ \theta_s) N(ds) = \sum_{n \in \mathbb{Z}} 1_L(Z_n) 1_C(T_n),$$

where $C \in \mathcal{B}, L \in \mathcal{K}$. Observe that, by construction,

$$N_Z(\theta_t \omega, C \times L) = N_Z(\omega, (C + t) \times L).$$

The intensity measure λ_Z associated with the stationary marked point process $((N, Z), \theta_t, P)$ is the measure on $(\mathbb{R} \times K, \mathcal{B} \otimes \mathcal{K})$ defined by

$$(2.2.2) \quad \lambda_Z(C \times L) = E[N_Z(C \times L)],$$

where $C \in \mathcal{B}, L \in \mathcal{K}$. It is called the *Campbell measure of* (N, Z). Since the intensity λ of (N, θ_t, P) is finite by assumption, λ_Z is a $\sigma-$finite measure.

Indeed since $N_Z(C \times L) \leq N(C)$ and therefore $\lambda_Z(C \times L) \leq \lambda(C)$. From the θ_t-stationarity of P, we have

$$\lambda_Z((C + t) \times L) = \lambda_Z(C \times L).$$

Thus, for fixed $L \in \mathcal{K}, \lambda_Z(. \times L)$ is a shift invariant, σ-finite measure on $\mathbb{R}$ and it must therefore be proportional to the Lebesgue measure and necessarily

$$\lambda_Z(C \times L) = \lambda_Z((0, 1] \times L)l(C).$$

Let ν_Z be the measure on $(K, \mathcal{K})$ defined by

(2.2.3) $\nu_Z(L) = \dfrac{1}{\lambda}\lambda_Z((0, 1] \times L).$

Then, summarizing the above results and definitions

(2.2.4) $\lambda_Z(C \times L) = \lambda l(C)\nu_Z(L).$

Note that $\nu_Z(L)$ is the average number of points T_n in $C \in \mathcal{B}$ such that $Z_n \in L$, divided by the average number of points T_n in C. This characterization does not depend upon $C \in \mathcal{B}$ provided $l(C) > 0$.

The probability measure ν_Z is called the *Palm probability distribution of the marks Z_n*.

3 Palm Probability

3.1 Matthes' Definition in Terms of Counting

Let $\tilde{Z}$ be the sequence of universal marks (§ 1.3) associated with (N, θ_t, P) and denote by $\tilde{\lambda}$ the Campbell measure $\lambda_{\tilde{Z}}$ associated with $((N, \tilde{Z}), \theta_t, P)$. Also denote $\nu_{\tilde{Z}}$ (see Definition (2.2.3) for ν_Z) by P_N^0. Thus, recalling that the marks $\tilde{Z}_n = \theta_{T_n}$ take their values in $(\Omega, \mathcal{F})$, we see that P_N^0 is a probability measure on $(\Omega, \mathcal{F})$ defined by

(3.1.1)
$$\begin{aligned} P_N^0(A) &= \frac{1}{\lambda l(C)} E\left[\int_C (1_A \circ \theta_s)N(ds)\right] \\ &= \frac{1}{\lambda l(C)} E\left[\sum_{n \in \mathbb{Z}}(1_A \circ \theta_{T_n})1_C(T_n)\right]. \end{aligned}$$

It is called the *Palm probability of the stationary point process* (N, θ_t, P). We immediately observe that

(3.1.2) $P_N^0(T_0 = 0) = 1.$

This equality follows when taking $A = \{T_0 = 0\}$ in (3.1.1) and observing that

$$\int_C (1_{\{T_0=0\}} \circ \theta_s) N(ds) = \sum_{n \in \mathbb{Z}} 1_{\{T_0 \circ \theta_{T_n}=0\}} 1_C(T_n)$$

$$= \sum_{n \in \mathbb{Z}} 1_C(T_n),$$

since $T_0 \circ \theta_{T_n} \equiv 0$.

Let now Z be an arbitrary sequence of marks of (N, θ_t) with values in $(K, \mathcal{K})$, and let $L \in \mathcal{K}$. Taking $A = \{Z_0 \in L\}$ in (3.1.1) and observing that $1_{\{Z_0 \in L\}} \circ \theta_{T_n} = 1_{\{Z_0 \circ \theta_{T_n} \in L\}} = 1_{\{Z_n \in L\}}$, we see that

(3.1.3) $\nu_Z(L) = P_N^0(Z_0 \in L).$

Thus Formula (2.2.4) takes the form

(3.1.4) $\lambda_Z(C \times L) = \lambda l(C) P_N^0(Z_0 \in L).$

Example 3.1.1 *Traffic intensity.* Adopting the queueing theory point of view of Example 2.1.1., and taking $Z_n = \sigma_n$ (the amount of service required by the customer arriving at time T_n), we see that $\lambda_Z((0,1] \times L) = \lambda P_N^0(\sigma_0 \in L)$ is the rate of generation of services of size L, i.e. the average number of required service times of size L arriving in the queueing system per unit of time. The quantity

(3.1.5) $\rho = \lambda \displaystyle\int_{\mathbb{R}_+} x P_N^0(\sigma_0 \in dx) = \lambda E_N^0[\sigma_0]$

is called the *traffic intensity* at the input of the queueing system.   □

In order to gain some intuition as to what is going on, take (N, θ_t, P) to be the canonical stationary point process $(\Phi, S_t, \mathcal{P})$ of Example 1.2.1. Definition (3.1.1) reads

(3.1.6) $\mathcal{P}_\Phi^0(A) = \dfrac{1}{\lambda l(C)} E_\mathcal{P}\left[\sum_{n \in \mathbb{Z}} (1_A \circ S_{t_n}) 1_C(t_n)\right],$

where $A \in \mathcal{M}$.

A set $A \in \mathcal{M}$ can be viewed as a property which a given trajectory $m \in M$ does or does not satisfy. Thus $1_A(S_{t_n} m) = 1$ when the trajectory m, viewed by an observer placed in t_n, satisfies A.

It will be seen later (in § 7) that if $(\mathcal{P}, S_t)$ is ergodic,

(3.1.7) $\dfrac{1}{\lambda l(C)} E_\mathcal{P}\left[\sum_{n \in \mathbb{Z}} (1_A \circ S_{t_n}) 1_C(t_n)\right] = \lim_{N \to \infty} \dfrac{1}{N} \sum_{k=1}^N 1_A(S_{t_k} m),$ $\mathcal{P}$−a.s., where we used the relation $\lambda l(C) = E_{\mathcal{P}}[\Phi(C)]$. Therefore, in this case, $P_{\Phi}^0(A)$ is the limiting empirical frequency, under $\mathcal{P}$, with which an observer jumping from point to point, sees property A realized.

The first historical interpretation of Palm probability (to be given in § 6.2) says that

(3.1.8) $P_{\Phi}^0(A) = \lim\limits_{h \to 0} \mathcal{P}(S_{t_1} m \text{ verifies } A \mid t_1 \leq h).$

This is the local interpretation of Palm probability.

In the θ_t-framework (§ 1.3), (3.1.1) reads, with $C = (0, t]$ and $Y = 1_A$

(3.1.9) $E_N^0[Y] = \dfrac{1}{\lambda t} E\Big[\int_{(0,t]} (Y \circ \theta_s) N(ds) \Big].$

By standard monotone class arguments, (3.1.9) is true for all non-negative random variables Y of $(\Omega, \mathcal{F})$. Taking $Y = Z(0)$, where $\{Z(t)\}$ is a non-negative real-valued stochastic process compatible with the flow $\{\theta_t\}$, (3.1.9) reads

(3.1.10) $E_N^0\Big[Z(0) \Big] = \dfrac{1}{\lambda t} E\Big[\int_{(0,t]} Z(s) N(ds) \Big].$

If (P, θ_t) is ergodic, then (§ 7)

(3.1.11) $E_N^0[Z(0)] = \lim\limits_{t \to \infty} \dfrac{1}{N((0,t])} \int_{(0,t]} Z(s) N(ds), \quad P-\text{a.s.}$

On the other hand

(3.1.12) $E[Z(0)] = \lim\limits_{t \to \infty} \dfrac{1}{t} \int_{(0,t]} Z(s) ds, \quad P-\text{a.s.}$

Thus $E_N^0[Z(0)]$ is the empirical average of $\{Z(t)\}$ at *events*, or *event-average* whereas $E[Z(0)]$ is the usual *time-average* of $\{Z(t)\}$. In the queueing theory context, when N is the point process counting the arrivals in a queueing system, $E_N^0[Z(0)]$ is sometimes called a *customer-average* because it represents the point of view of a customer, whereas $E[Z(0)]$ is called a *system-average* or *continuous time-average* and represents the point of view of the system designer.

3.2 Invariance of the Palm Probability

The Palm probability P_N^0 of the stationary point process (N, θ_t, P) has its mass concentrated on $\Omega_0 = \{T_0 = 0\}$. On the other hand, on $\Omega_0, \theta_{T_n} = (\theta_{T_1})^n$ for all $n \in \mathbb{Z}$. Therefore defining

(3.2.1) $\theta = \theta_{T_1},$

we see that θ is a bijection of Ω_0 and that

(3.2.2) $\theta_{T_n} = \theta^n$ on Ω_0, for all $n \in \mathbb{Z}$.

In addition, as we shall see next:

(3.2.3) P_N^0 is $\theta - invariant$.

Remark 3.2.1 This result is expected in view of the heuristic interpretation in the previous subsection (see (3.1.7)) $\square$

Proof of (3.2.3). Take $A \in \mathcal{F}, A \subset \Omega_0$

$$| P_N^0(A) - P_N^0(\theta^{-1}(A)) | \leq \frac{1}{\lambda t} E \mid \sum_{n\in\mathbb{Z}} (1_A \circ \theta^n - 1_{\theta^{-1}(A)} \circ \theta^n)1_{(0,t]}(T_n) \mid,$$

where we have applied the defining Formula (3.1.1) with $C = (0, t]$. Since $1_{\theta^{-1}(A)} \circ \theta^n = 1_A \circ \theta^{n+1}$, we see that

$$|P_N^0(A) - P_N^0(\theta^{-1}(A))| \leq \frac{2}{\lambda t}.$$

Now letting $t \to \infty$, we obtain

$$P_N^0(A) = P_N^0(\theta^{-1}(A)),$$

for all $A \in \mathcal{F}, A \subset \Omega_0$. $\square$

Remark 3.2.2 If $\{Z(t)\}$ is compatible with the flow $\{\theta_t\}$, it is a (time)-stationary process under P, and the sequence $\{Z(T_n)\}$ is a stationary sequence under P_N^0. $\square$

3.3 Mecke's Formula

Let v be the real-valued function defined on $\Omega \times \mathbb{R}$ by

$$v(\omega, t) = 1_A(\omega)1_C(t),$$

where $A \in \mathcal{F}, C \in \mathcal{B}$. By definition of the product measures $P_N^0(d\omega) \times dt$ and $P(d\omega)N(\omega, dt)$, the defining Formula (3.1.1) reads

$$(3.3.1) \quad \lambda \int \int_{\Omega\times\mathbb{R}} v(\omega, t)P_N^0(d\omega)dt = \int \int_{\Omega\times\mathbb{R}} v(\theta_t\omega, t)P(d\omega)N(\omega, dt).$$

By standard monotone class arguments, (3.3.1) remains true for all non-negative measurable functions v from $(\Omega \times \mathbb{R}, \mathcal{F} \otimes \mathcal{B})$ into $(\mathbb{R}, \mathcal{B})$.

Formula (3.3.1) is known as the *generalized Campbell's formula*. In this book, it will be called *Mecke's formula*, in the name of its author. The original Campbell formula is obtained by specializing Mecke's formula (3.3.1) to

$$v(\omega, t) = f(t, Z_0(\omega)),$$

where $\{Z_n\}$ is a sequence of marks of (N, θ_t), with values in $(K, \mathcal{K})$. In view of (3.1.4) :

$$\lambda \int \int_{\Omega \times \mathbb{R}} f(t, Z_0(\omega)) P_N^0(d\omega) dt = \int \int_{\mathbb{R} \times K} f(t, z) \lambda_Z(dt \times dz).$$

On the other hand

$$\int \int_{\Omega \times \mathbb{R}} f(t, Z_0(\theta_t \omega)) P(d\omega) N(\omega, dt) = E\left[\sum_{n \in \mathbb{Z}} f(T_n, Z_0(\theta_{T_n}))\right]$$

$$= E\left[\sum_{n \in \mathbb{Z}} f(T_n, Z_n)\right].$$

Therefore (Campbell's formula)

$$(3.3.2) \quad E\left[\sum_{n \in \mathbb{Z}} f(T_n, Z_n)\right] = \int \int_{\mathbb{R} \times K} f(t, z) \lambda_Z(dt \times dz),$$

for all non-negative measurable functions f from $(\mathbb{R} \times K, \mathcal{B} \times \mathcal{K})$ into $(\mathbb{R}, \mathcal{B})$.

The Campbell-Little-Mecke Formula. This formula is obtained by writing Campbell's formula (3.3.2) with the help of expression (3.1.4) for Campbell's measure:

$$(3.3.3) \quad E\left[\sum_{n \in \mathbb{Z}} f(T_n, Z_n)\right] = \lambda \int \int_{\mathbb{R} \times K} f(t, z) P_N^0(Z_0 \in dz) dt.$$

Although this formula is essentially a mixture of the original Campbell's formula and of Mecke's formula, it is baptized the Campbell-Little-Mecke formula because of its relevance to Little's formula (see Chapter 3).

The generalized Campbell formula is very important in queueing theory, and as it turns out, the celebrated $H = \lambda G$ formula, popularized by the work of Brumelle, is an avatar of it (see Chapter 3).

Example 3.3.1 *The Palm-Khinchin formula.* Define the Palm function ϕ_k, $k \geq 0$, by

$$\phi_k(t) = P_N^0\left(N(0, t] = k\right).$$

Then the following formula holds

$$P\left(N(0, t] > k\right) = \lambda \int_0^t \phi_k(s) ds.$$

Proof: Observing that

$$1_{N(0,t]>k} = \int_0^t 1_{N(s,t]=k} N(ds)$$

and that

$$N(s,t] \circ \theta_{-s} = N(0, t-s],$$

we have

$$1_{N(0,t]>k} = \int_{\mathbb{R}} 1_{(0,t]}(s) 1_{N(0,t-s]=k} \circ \theta_s N(ds).$$

From the generalized Campbell's formula, the expectation of the right-hand side with respect to P is equal to

$$\lambda \int_{\mathbb{R}} 1_{(0,t]}(s) P_N^0 \left(N(0, t-s] = k \right) ds = \lambda \int_0^t P_N^0 \left(N(0, t-s] = k \right) ds$$

$$= \lambda \int_0^t P_N^0 \left(N(0, s] = k \right) ds.$$

$\square$

3.4 Neveu's Exchange Formula

Let (N, θ_t, P) and (N', θ_t, P) be two stationary point processes with finite intensities λ and λ' respectively. Note that N and N' are *jointly* stationary, in the sense that their stationarity is relative to the same quadruple $(\Omega, \mathcal{F}, P, \theta_t)$.

The following formula, called the *exchange formula*, holds :

$$(3.4.1) \quad \lambda E_N^0[f] = \lambda' E_{N'}^0 \left[\int_{(0, T'_1]} (f \circ \theta_t) N(dt) \right],$$

for all non-negative measurable functions $f : (\Omega, \mathcal{F}) \to (\mathbb{R}, \mathcal{B})$. Here T'_n is the n-th point of N'.

Proof: By the Lebesgue monotone convergence theorem, we may assume f bounded (say by 1, without loss of generality). With all such f, we associate the function

$$g \overset{\text{def}}{=} \int_{(T_0', T_1']} (f \circ \theta_t) N(dt).$$

For all $t \in \mathbb{R}_+$, we have

$$\int_{(0,t]} (f \circ \theta_s) N(ds) = \int_{(0,t]} (g \circ \theta_s) N'(ds) + R(t),$$

where $R(t)$ consists of two terms:

$$R(t) = \int_{(0, T'_+(0)]} (f \circ \theta_s) N(ds) - \int_{(t, T'_+(t)]} (f \circ \theta_s) N(ds).$$

Here $T'_+(t)$ is the first point of N' strictly larger than t.

For all $l > 0$, define

$$f_l = f 1_{\{N(T_0, T_1'] \le l-1\}}$$

and let g_l be the associated function. For these functions, each term in $R(t)$ is bounded by l, and therefore the expectations are finite. Moreover, by the θ_t-invariance of P, they have the same expectations, so that $E[R(t)] = 0$. We therefore have

$$E\left[\int_{(0,t]} (f_l \circ \theta_s) N(ds)\right] = E\left[\int_{(0,t]} (g_l \circ \theta_s) N'(ds)\right].$$

This and (3.1.9) imply (3.4.1) with $f = f_l$, $g = g_l$. Letting l go to infinity, we obtain (3.4.1). $\qquad\square$

Remark 3.4.1 By the $\theta_{T_n'}$ invariance of $P_{N'}^0$, $E_{N'}^0[(f \circ \theta_{T_n'}) N\{T_n'\}]$ does not depend upon $n \in \mathbb{Z}$, so that in (3.4.1), the integral can be taken over $[0, T_1')$ instead of $(0, T_1']$. $\qquad\square$

A special case of (3.4.1) is obtained for $f \equiv 1$, which gives

$$(3.4.2) \quad \lambda' E_{N'}^0\left[N((0, T_1'])\right] = \lambda,$$

and therefore the exchange formula takes the much expected form

$$(3.4.3) \quad E_N^0[f] = \frac{E_{N'}^0\left[\int_{(0, T_1']} (f \circ \theta_t) N(dt)\right]}{E_{N'}^0\left[N((0, T_1'])\right]}.$$

Remark 3.4.2 Formula (3.4.3) is rather intuitive in the ergodic context, if we can write

$$(3.4.4) \quad \begin{cases} E_N^0[f] = \lim_{n \to \infty} \dfrac{1}{n} \sum_{k=1}^{n} f \circ \theta_{T_k} & P-\text{a.s.} \\[2mm] E_{N'}^0[g] = \lim_{n \to \infty} \dfrac{1}{n} \sum_{k=1}^{n} g \circ \theta_{T_k'} & P-\text{a.s.} \end{cases}$$

with $g = \int_{(T_0', T_1']} (f \circ \theta_t) N(dt)$ or $g = N((T_0', T_1'])$. See § 7 for a discussion of ergodicity and the validity of (3.4.4). As a matter of fact, the heuristic proof of (3.4.3) by (3.4.4) is a familiar exercise for queueing theorists in the context, for instance, of busy cycles (see Chapter 3). This is why we also call the exchange formula the *cycle formula*. $\qquad\square$

Remark 3.4.3 Formula (3.4.3) can also be viewed as a generalization of *Wald's identity* since it reads

$$(3.4.5) \quad E_{N'}^0\left[\sum_{k=0}^{N((0, T_1'])} f \circ \theta_{T_k}\right] = E_{N'}^0\left[N((0, T_1'])\right] E_N^0[f].$$

$\qquad\square$

3.5 Miyazawa's Conservation Principle

Let $\{Y(t)\}$ be a bounded real-valued stochastic process, right-continuous with left-hand limits, and compatible with the flow $\{\theta_t\}$. Let N be a point process compatible with $\{\theta_t\}$ and with non-null finite intensity λ, and let $\{Y'(t)\}$ be a real-valued stochastic process compatible with $\{\theta_t\}$, and such that

$$(3.5.1) \quad Y(1) = Y(0) + \int_0^1 Y'(s)ds + \int_{(0,1]} (Y(s) - Y(s-))N(ds).$$

(for instance N counts all the discontinuity points of $\{Y(t)\}$ and $Y'(t)$ is the derivative of $Y(t)$ between discontinuity points). By taking expectations on both sides and using the θ_t-invariance of P, we obtain Miyazawa's formula

$$(3.5.2) \quad E[Y'(0)] + \lambda E_N^0[Y(0) - Y(0-)] = 0.$$

The above equality constitutes the (rate) conservation principle. We shall see many applications of this elementary formula in Chapter 3.

As we shall see in the next section, the inversion formula of Palm theory can readily be obtained from the conservation principle.

Remark 3.5.1 Observe that the boundedness condition for $\{Y(t)\}$ can be replaced by one of the following three conditions
(a) $E[|\,Y(0)\,|] < \infty$ and $E[|\,Y'(0)\,|] < \infty$
(b) $E[|\,Y(0)\,|] < \infty$ and $E_N^0[|\,Y(0) - Y(0-)\,|] < \infty$
(c) $E[|\,Y'(0)\,|] < \infty$ and $E_N^0[|\,Y(0) - Y(0-)\,|] < \infty$ □

4 From Palm Probability to Stationary Probability

4.1 The Inversion Formula of Ryll-Nardzewski and Slivnyak

The original (θ_t-invariant) probability can be recovered from the Palm probability. Indeed let f be a bounded non-negative random variable and define

$$(4.1.1) \quad Y(t) = \int_t^{T_+(t)} (f \circ \theta_s)ds,$$

where $T_+(t) = \inf\{T_n; T_n > t\}$. The process $\{Y(t)\}$ verifies the condition (c) of application of Miyazawa's formula (3.5.2) with

$$Y'(t) = -f \circ \theta_t, \quad Y(0-) = 0 \; P_N^0-\text{a.s.}, \quad Y(0) = \int_0^{T_1} (f \circ \theta_s)ds \; P_N^0-\text{a.s.}$$

This gives the following inversion formula which can be extended to all non-negative random variables f by monotone convergence:

$$(4.1.2a) \quad E[f] = \lambda E_N^0 \left[\int_0^{T_1} (f \circ \theta_t) dt \right].$$

In the special case $f = 1_A$, $A \in \mathcal{F}$, this formula reads

$$(4.1.2b) \quad P(A) = \lambda \int_0^\infty P_N^0(T_1 > t, \theta_t \in A) dt.$$

The next formulas are obvious consequences of the θ_{T_1}-invariance of P_N^0 and of (4.1.2a) and (4.1.2b). For instance,

$$(4.1.2a') \quad E[f] = \lambda E_N^0 \left[\int_{T_n}^{T_{n+1}} (f \circ \theta_t) dt \right]$$

and, for $f = 1_A$:

$$(4.1.2b') \quad P(A) = \lambda \int_{\mathbb{R}} P_N^0(T_n < t \leq T_{n+1}, \theta_t \in A) dt.$$

4.2 Forward and Backward Recurrence Times

Taking $f = 1$ in (4.1.2a) gives

$$(4.2.1) \quad \lambda E_N^0[T_1] = 1.$$

Let F_0 be the cumulative distribution function (c.d.f.) of T_1 under P_N^0, that is

$$(4.2.2) \quad F_0(x) = P_N^0(T_1 \leq x).$$

Letting $A = \{T_1 > v, -T_0 > w\}$ in (4.1.2b), with $v, w \in \mathbb{R}_+$, we obtain

$$(4.2.3) \quad P(T_1 > v, -T_0 > w) = \lambda \int_{v+w}^\infty (1 - F_0(u)) du.$$

In particular, taking $v = 0$, and observing that, by construction of T_1, $P(T_1 > 0) = 1$, we obtain

$$(4.2.4a) \quad P(-T_0 > w) = \lambda \int_w^\infty (1 - F_0(u)) du.$$

This shows in particular that $P(-T_0 > 0) = 1$ since $\lambda \int_0^\infty (1 - F_0(u)) du = \lambda E_N^0[T_1] = 1$. Similarly, taking $w = 0$ in (4.2.3), we obtain

$$(4.2.4b) \quad P(T_1 > v) = \lambda \int_v^\infty (1 - F_0(u)) du.$$

Thus $-T_0$ and T_1 are identically distributed under P.

The Case of Renewal Processes. Let (N, θ_t, P) be a stationary point process with finite intensity λ and P_N^0 be its Palm probability. Suppose moreover that under P_N^0, the inter-event sequence $(S_n, n \in \mathbb{Z})$ defined by

$$(4.2.5) \quad S_n = T_{n+1} - T_n$$

is i.i.d. Then (N, P_N^0) is called a *renewal process* and (N, P) a *stationary renewal process*. The existence of such a mathematical object is granted by the results of the forthcoming § 4.4.

(4.2.6) *The distribution of the sequence* $S^* = (S_n, n \in \mathbb{Z} - \{0\})$ *is the same under* P *and* P_N^0.

Proof: Let $g : (\mathbb{R}^{\mathbb{Z}}, \mathcal{B}^{\mathbb{Z}}) \to (\mathbb{R}, \mathcal{B})$ be an arbitrary non-negative measurable function. It suffices to show that

$$E[g(S^*)] = E_N^0[g(S^*)].$$

By the inversion formula (4.1.2a) :

$$E[g(S^*)] = \lambda E_N^0 \left[\int_0^{T_1} g(S^*(\theta_u)) du \right].$$

But if u is in $[0, T_1)$, then $S^*(\theta_u) = S^*$, so that

$$E[g(S^*)] = \lambda E_N^0 \left[\int_0^{T_1} g(S^*) du \right] = \lambda E_N^0 [T_1 g(S^*)]$$
$$= \lambda E_N^0[T_1] E_N^0[g(S^*)] = E_N^0[g(S^*)],$$

where we have used the independence of $T_1 = S_0$ and S^* under P_N^0.   □
Next we show that

$$(4.2.7) \quad S_0 \text{ and } S^* \text{ are } P-\text{independent.}$$

Proof: Similar computations give

$$E[f(S_0)g(S^*)] = \lambda E_N^0[f(S_0)T_1 g(S^*)]$$
$$= \lambda E_N^0[f(S_0)T_1] E_N^0[g(S^*)]$$
$$= \lambda E_N^0[f(S_0)T_1] E[g(S^*)]$$
$$= E[f(S_0)] E[g(S^*)].$$

□

Feller's Paradox. So far the following was proved : under P, $S = (S_n, n \in \mathbb{Z})$ is a sequence of independent random variables and $S^* = \{S_n\}, n \in \mathbb{Z} - \{0\})$, is i.i.d.. The question now is: has S_0 the same distribution under P and under P_N^0? The answer is negative in general : from

$$E[f(S_0)] = \lambda E_N^0[f(S_0)T_1] = \lambda E_N^0[f(S_0)S_0],$$

we obtain, with $f(S_0) = S_0$ and recalling that $\lambda E_N^0[S_0] = 1$,

$$E[S_0] = \frac{1}{E_N^0[S_0]} E_N^0[S_0{}^2].$$

Therefore, if $E[S_0] = E_N^0[S_0]$,

$$E_N^0[S_0]^2 = E_N^0[S_0{}^2].$$

The variance of S_0 has hence to be zero under P_N^0, i.e. $S_n = \text{constant}$, P_N^0-a.s. Indeed, one can check from (4.2.3) that in this particular case, S_0 has the same deterministic distribution under P and P_N^0.

Remark 4.2.1 The formula

$$(4.2.8) \quad E[f(S_0)] = E_N^0[\lambda S_0 f(S_0)]$$

is true in the general case of stationary point processes, and it states that on the σ-field generated by S_0, P_N^0 is absolutely continuous with respect to P, with the Radon-Nikodým derivative λS_0. In particular

$$(4.2.9) \quad P(-T_0 + T_1 \leq x) = \int_{[0,x]} \lambda y F_0(dy)$$

where $F_0(x) = P_N^0(T_1 \leq x)$.   □

4.3 The Mean Value Formulas

Let (N, θ_t, P) be a stationary point process with finite intensity, and let P_N^0 be the associated Palm probability. Let $\{Z_t\}, t \in \mathbb{R}$, be a stochastic process with values in a measurable space $(E, \mathcal{E})$ and such that

$$(4.3.1) \quad Z_t = Z_0 \circ \theta_t.$$

Then, for any non-negative measurable function $g : (E, \mathcal{E}) \to (R, \mathcal{B})$

$$(4.3.2) \quad E\left[g(Z_0)\right] = \frac{E_N^0\left[\int_0^{T_1} g(Z_t)dt\right]}{E_N^0\left[T_1\right]}$$

and

$$(4.3.3) \quad E_N^0 \Big[g(Z_0) \Big] = \frac{E\Big[\sum_{n\in\mathbb{Z}} g(Z_{T_n})1_{\{T_n\in(0,1]\}} \Big]}{E\Big[\sum_{n\in\mathbb{Z}} 1_{\{T_n\in(0,1]\}} \Big]}.$$

These formulas just rephrase the inversion formula (4.1.2a) and the definition Formula (3.1.1) of P_N^0.

4.4 The Inverse Construction of Slivnyak

On $(\Omega, \mathcal{F})$, define a flow $\{\theta_t\}$, $t \in \mathbb{R}$, and a point process N compatible with $\{\theta_t\}$. Let P^0 be a probability measure on $(\Omega, \mathcal{F})$ such that

$$(4.4.1) \quad P^0(\Omega_0) = 1,$$

where $\Omega_0 = \{T_0 = 0\}$. Suppose that P^0 is θ_{T_n}-invariant :

$$(4.4.2) \quad P^0(\theta_{T_n} \in .) = P^0(.), \quad n \in \mathbb{Z}.$$

Moreover assume that

$$(4.4.3) \quad 0 < E^0[T_1] < \infty.$$

We shall see that P^0 is then the Palm probability P_N^0 associated with the stationary point process (N, θ_t, P), for some probability P that is θ_t-invariant for all $t \in \mathbb{R}$. Moreover, in view of the inversion formula, P will be unique.

As required by the inversion formula, if such a P exists, it should satisfy

$$(4.4.4) \quad P(A) = \frac{1}{E^0[T_1]} E^0 \Big[\int_0^{T_1} (1_A \circ \theta_t) dt \Big].$$

Clearly (4.4.4) defines a probability P on $(\Omega, \mathcal{F})$. We must show that P is θ_t-invariant for all $t \in \mathbb{R}$, and that

$$(4.4.5) \quad P_N^0 = P^0.$$

We first remark that, on Ω_0,

$$\int_{T_0\circ\theta_{T_j}}^{T_1\circ\theta_{T_j}} (1_A \circ \theta_s \circ \theta_{T_j}) ds = \int_{T_j}^{T_{j+1}} (1_A \circ \theta_s) ds, \quad j \in \mathbb{Z},$$

and therefore, since P^0 is θ_{T_n}-invariant

$$P(A) = \frac{1}{n} \frac{1}{E^0[T_1]} E^0 \Big[\int_0^{T_n} (1_A \circ \theta_s) ds \Big].$$

Also, for any $t \in \mathbb{R}$

$$P(\theta_t A) = \frac{1}{n} \frac{1}{E^0[T_1]} E^0 \Big[\int_0^{T_n} (1_{\theta_t A} \circ \theta_s) ds \Big] = \frac{1}{n} \frac{1}{E^0[T_1]} E^0 \Big[\int_{-t}^{T_n-t} (1_A \circ \theta_s) ds \Big].$$

Therefore

$$|P(A) - P(\theta_t A)| \le \frac{1}{n} \frac{1}{E^0[T_1]} E^0 \left| \int_{T_n - t}^{T_n} 1_A \circ \theta_s ds - \int_{-t}^{0} 1_A \circ \theta_s ds \right| \le \frac{2t}{E^0[T_1]} \frac{1}{n}$$

and therefore, by letting n go to ∞, it follows that P is θ_t-invariant. Hence (N, θ_t, P) is a stationary stochastic point process. From (4.4.4), we obtain

$$E[f] = \frac{1}{E^0[T_1]} E^0 \left[\int_0^{T_1} (f \circ \theta_t) dt \right].$$

In particular

$$\frac{E[N(0, \epsilon]]}{\epsilon} = \frac{1}{E^0[T_1]} \frac{1}{\epsilon} E^0 \left[\int_0^{T_1} N((t, t + \epsilon]) dt \right].$$

It is straightforward to check that

$$\lim_{\epsilon \to 0} \frac{1}{\epsilon} E^0 \left[\int_0^{T_1} N((t, t + \epsilon]) dt \right] = 1,$$

and therefore

$$\lim_{\epsilon \to 0} \frac{E[N(0, \epsilon]]}{\epsilon} = \frac{1}{E^0[T_1]}.$$

Since $\frac{E[N(0, \epsilon]]}{\epsilon} = \lambda$, we obtain $\lambda = \frac{1}{E^0[T_1]}$ and therefore, in view of assumption (4.4.3), $0 < \lambda < \infty$. We can hence define the Palm probability P_N^0 associated with (N, θ_t, P).

By the inversion formula, for all $A \in \mathcal{M}$

$$\begin{aligned}
(4.4.6) \qquad P(\theta_{T_0} \in A) &= \lambda E_N^0 \left[\int_0^{T_1} (1_{\theta_{T_0}^{-1} A} \circ \theta_t) dt \right] \\
&= \lambda E_N^0 \left[\int_0^{T_1} 1_A dt \right] = \lambda E_N^0 [T_1 1_A]
\end{aligned}$$

since on Ω^0, $\theta_{T_0} \circ \theta_t$ is the identity for all $t \in (0, T_1]$. Using now the definition of P in terms of P^0, i.e. (4.4.4):

$$P(\theta_{T_0} \in A) = \frac{1}{E^0[T_1]} E^0 [T_1 1_A].$$

Therefore

$$E^0 [T_1 1_A] = E_N^0 [T_1 1_A], \quad A \in \mathcal{F}.$$

Since $T_1 > 0$ by construction, $P^0 \equiv P_N^0$. $\qquad \square$

Remark 4.4.1 The inversion formula (4.1.2a) receives an interesting interpretation when written in the form

$$E[f] = E_N^0 \left[\lambda T_1 \frac{1}{T_1} \int_0^{T_1} f \circ \theta_t dt \right] = E_N^0 \left[\lambda T_1 f \circ \theta_V \right],$$

where V is a random variable which, 'conditionally upon everything else', is uniformly distributed on $[0, T_1]$ (for the above to make sense, we must of course enlarge the probability space). This interpretation provides an explicit construction of P from P_N^0. First construct the probability P_0' by

(4.4.7) $dP_0' = (\lambda T_1) dP_N^0.$

Since $P_N^0(T_0 = 0) = 1$ and P_0' is absolutely continuous with respect to P_N^0, $P_0'(T_0 = 0) = 1$. The stationary probability is then obtained by placing the origin at random in the interval $[0, T_1]$, that is

(4.4.8) $E[f] = E_0'[f \circ \theta_V].$

$\square$

Remark 4.4.2 The construction in the preceding remark seems to suggest that only the distributions of T_0 and T_1 are changed when passing from the Palm to the stationary probability. This is of course not true, since these two points may condition the distribution of other random variables. What is true is that, conditionally on T_0 and T_1, P and P_N^0 are the same. In particular, if $\mathcal{G}$ is a sub σ-field of $\mathcal{F}$ such that $\mathcal{G}$ and N are P (resp. P_N^0)-independent, then $\mathcal{G}$ and N are also P_N^0 (resp. P)-independent. $\square$

Remark 4.4.3 In relation with Remark 4.4.1, we mention yet another relation between P and its Palm probability, that is,

$$\theta_{T_0} P = \lambda T_1 P_N^0$$

that is to say, for all $A \in \mathcal{F}$,

$$P(\theta_{T_0}^{-1} A) = \lambda E_N^0 [T_1 1_A].$$

Proof: This is just Equality (4.4.6). $\square$

Application: Construction of a Stationary Semi–Markov process.
A semi–Markov process on the denumerable state space E is constructed as follows.

Let $I\!P = \{p_{ij}\}$, $i, j \in E$, be a stochastic matrix on E, assumed irreducible, positive and recurrent (in short: ergodic). Its unique stationary distribution is denoted by $\pi = \{\pi(i)\}$, $i \in E$.

For each $i, j \in E$, let $G_{ij}(t)$ be a cumulative distribution function of some strictly positive and proper random variable: thus $G_{ij}(0) = 0$ and $G_{ij}(\infty) = 1$. Denote by m_{ij} the mean

$$m_{ij} = \int_0^\infty t dG_{ij}(t) = \int_0^\infty (1 - G_{ij}(t)) dt.$$

Recall at this stage that if U is a random variable uniformly distributed on $[0,1]$, $G_{ij}^{-1}(U)$ is a random variable with c.d.f. $G_{ij}(t)$ (here G_{ij}^{-1} is the inverse of G_{ij}).

Let $\{X_n\}$, $n \in \mathbb{Z}$, be a stationary Markov chain with transition matrix $I\!P$, defined on some probability space with a probability P^0, and let $\{U_n\}$, $n \in \mathbb{Z}$, be a sequence of i.i.d. random variables, defined on the same space and uniformly distributed on $[0,1]$. Assume moreover that the sequences $\{U_n\}$ and $\{X_n\}$ are independent under P^0.

Define

$$(4.4.9) \quad S_{n+1} = G_{X_n X_{n+1}}^{-1}(U_n).$$

In particular, conditionally on $X_n = i$ and $X_{n+1} = j$, S_{n+1} is distributed according to the c.d.f. $G_{ij}(t)$. Moreover, conditionally on the whole sequence $\{X_n\}$, the sequence $\{S_n\}$ forms an independent family of random variables.

We can now define a point process N by

$$(4.4.10) \quad T_0 = 0, \ T_{n+1} - T_n = S_{n+1} \qquad (n \in \mathbb{Z})$$

and the semi Markov process $\{X(t)\}$, $t \in \mathbb{R}$, by

$$(4.4.11) \quad X(t) = X_n, \ \text{for} \ T_n \leq t < T_{n+1}.$$

Observe that there is no explosion (i.e. $\lim_{n \to \infty} T_n = \infty$ and $\lim_{n \to -\infty} T_n = -\infty$, almost surely) due to the fact that $\{X_n\}$ is recurrent. It will be assumed that

$$(4.4.12) \quad E^0[T_1] = \sum_{i \in E} \pi(i) \sum_{j \in E} \int_0^\infty (1 - G_{ij}(t))dt < \infty.$$

Therefore, since $E^0[T_1] > 0$, Slivnyak's construction can be performed, and we may assume a canonical stationary framework $(\Omega, \mathcal{F}, P, \theta_t)$ with a marked point process N compatible with the shift, the mark of T_n being (X_n, U_n); and P_N^0 can be identified with the original probability P^0.

The probabilistic structure of $\{X(t)\}$, $t \in \mathbb{R}$, under the stationary probability P is the following:

Conditionally on $X_1 = j$, the process

$$(4.4.13) \quad X_2, S_2, X_3, S_3, \ldots$$

has the same distribution under P or P_N^0. Similarly conditionally on $X_0 = i$, the process

$$(4.4.14) \quad S_0, X_{-1}, S_{-1}, X_{-2}, S_{-2}, \ldots$$

has the same distribution under P and P_N^0. Moreover

$(4.4.15) \quad P(X_0 = i, \ X_1 = j, \ -T_0 > x, \ T_1 > y) = \lambda \pi(i) p_{ij} \int_{x+y}^{\infty} (1 - G_{ij}(t)) dt \ .$

The proof of the first two statements is quite similar to what we saw for renewal processes. For instance, for $n \geq 1$

$$P(X_n = i, X_{n+1} = j) = \lambda E_N^0 \left[\int_0^{T_1} 1_{X_n \circ \theta_s = i, \ X_{n+1} \circ \theta_s = j} ds \right]$$

$$= \lambda E_N^0 \left[\int_0^{T_1} 1_{X_n = i, \ X_{n+1} = j} ds \right]$$

since $s \in (0, T_1)$ implies $X_n \circ \theta_s = X_n$ for all $n \in \mathbb{Z}$. Therefore

$$P(X_n = i, \ X_{n+1} = j) = \lambda E_N^0 \left[T_1 1_{X_n = i} 1_{X_{n+1} = j} \right]$$
$$= \lambda E_N^0 \left[G_{X_0 X_1}^{-1}(U_0) 1_{X_n = i} 1_{X_{n+1} = j} \right]$$
$$= \lambda E_N^0 \left[G_{X_0 X_1}^{-1}(U_0) 1_{X_n = i} \right] p_{ij}$$
$$= \lambda E_N^0 \left[T_1 1_{X_n = i} \right] p_{ij},$$

where we have used the hypothesis $n \geq 1$, guaranteeing that X_{n+1} is conditionally independent of X_0, X_1, U_0 given $X_n = i$. Similarly (summing the last equality in j)

$$P(X_n = i) = \lambda E_N^0 \left[T_1 1_{X_n = i} \right]$$

and therefore, for $n \geq 1$,

$$P(X_{n+1} = j | X_n = i) = p_{ij} \ .$$

More generally, it can be shown with the same type of calculations that $\{X_n\}$ is a P Markov chain with transition matrix $\mathbb{P}$. Also, again with the same proof, under $P, U_1, U_2, \cdots$ are i.i.d. random variables uniform on $[0,1]$, independent of $X_1, X_2, \ldots$, and this proves the statement concerning the law of (4.4.13). As for the process (4.4.14), it suffices to reverse time, and to observe that under P_N^0, the sequence $\{X_{-n}\}$, $n \in \mathbb{Z}$, is also a Markov chain stationary and ergodic, this time with the transition matrix $Q = \{q_{ij}\}$, $i, j \in E$, given by

$(4.4.16) \quad q_{ij} = p_{ij} \dfrac{\pi(j)}{\pi(i)} \ .$

Having the distribution of (4.4.13) conditionally on $X_1 = j$ and that of (4.4.14) conditionally on $X_0 = i$, for all $i, j \in E$, it remains to give the joint law of X_0, X_1, T_0, T_1 under P. By the inversion formula the left–hand side of (4.4.15) equals

$$\lambda E_N^0 \left[\int_0^{T_1} 1_{X_0 \circ \theta_s = i, \ X_1 \circ \theta_s = j} 1_{-T_0 \circ \theta_s > x, \ T_1 \circ \theta_s > y} ds \right] \ .$$

But if $s \in (0, T_1)$, $X_0 \circ \theta_s = X_0$, $X_1 \circ \theta_s = X_1$, $-T_0 \circ \theta_s = s$, $T_1 \circ \theta_s = T_1 - s$. Therefore the last quantity equals

$$\lambda E_N^0 \left[1_{X_0 = i,\ X_1 = j} \int_0^{T_1} 1_{s > x} 1_{T_1 - s > y} ds \right]$$

$$= \lambda \pi(i) p_{ij}\, E_N^0 \left[E_N^0 \left[\int_x^\infty 1_{T_1 > y + s} ds \mid X_0 = i, X_1 = j \right] \right]$$

$$= \lambda \pi(i) p_{ij} \int_{x+y}^\infty (1 - G_{ij}(t)) dt\ .$$

Setting $x = y = 0$ in (4.4.15) gives, recalling $m_{ij} = \int_0^\infty (1 - G_{ij}(t)) dt$:

$$(4.4.17)\quad P(X_0 = i,\ X_1 = j) = \frac{\pi(i) p_{ij}\, m_{ij}}{\displaystyle\sum_{k \in E} \sum_{l \in E} \pi(k) p_{kl}\, m_{kl}}$$

and therefore

$$(4.4.18)\quad P(-T_0 > x,\ T_1 > y | X_0 = i,\ X_1 = j) = \frac{1}{m_{ij}} \int_{x+y} (1 - G_{ij}(t)) dt\ .$$

5 Examples

5.1 Superposition of Independent Point Processes

The situation is that described in Example 1.2.2 with the additional assumption

$$(5.1.1)\quad 0 < \lambda_i < \infty,\quad (1 \le i \le k),$$

where λ_i is the intensity of N_i. Recall that for each $1 \le i \le k$, $(\Phi_i, S_t^{(i)}, \mathcal{P}_i)$ is a stationary point process. We shall denote by $\mathcal{P}_i^0$ the associated Palm probability. We now prove the following formula:

$$(5.1.2)\quad P_N^0 = \sum_{i=1}^k \frac{\lambda_i}{\lambda} (\otimes_{j=1}^{i-1} \mathcal{P}_j) \otimes \mathcal{P}_i^0 \otimes (\otimes_{j=i+1}^k \mathcal{P}_j),$$

where $\lambda = \sum_{i=1}^k \lambda_i$ is the intensity of (N, θ_t, P), the superposition of the independent point processes $(\Phi_i, S_t^{(i)}, \mathcal{P}_i)$, $1 \le i \le k$.

Proof: By definition, for $A = \prod_{i=1}^k A_i$, where $A_i \in \mathcal{M}_i$

$$P_N^0(A) = \frac{1}{\lambda} E \left[\int_{(0,1]} (1_A \circ \theta_s) N(ds) \right]$$

$$= \frac{1}{\lambda} \int_{M_1} \cdots \int_{M_k} \left\{ \sum_{j=1}^k \int_{(0,1]} \left(\prod_{i=1}^k 1_{A_i} \circ S_t^{(i)} \right) \Phi_j(dt) \right\} \mathcal{P}_1(dm_1) \ldots \mathcal{P}_k(dm_k).$$

But by Fubini's theorem and the definition of Palm probability $\mathcal{P}_j^0$

$$\frac{1}{\lambda_j} \int_{M_1} \cdots \int_{M_k} \left\{ \int_{(0,1]} \prod_{i=1}^{k} (1_{A_i} \circ S_t^{(i)}) \Phi_j(dt) \right\} \mathcal{P}_1(dm_1) \ldots \mathcal{P}_k(dm_k) =$$

$$\mathcal{P}_j^0(A_j) \prod_{i=1,\ i \neq j}^{k} \mathcal{P}_i(A_i),$$

where we have taken into account the $S_t^{(i)}$-invariance of $\mathcal{P}_i$. Therefore

$$P_N^0 \left(\prod_{i=1}^{k} A_i \right) = \sum_{i=1}^{k} \left\{ \frac{\lambda_i}{\lambda} \mathcal{P}_i^0(A_i) \prod_{\substack{1 \leq j \leq k \\ j \neq i}} \mathcal{P}_j(A_j) \right\},$$

which implies (5.1.2). $\qquad\square$

Remark 5.1.1 The interpretation of (5.1.2) is the following : there is a probability $\frac{\lambda_i}{\lambda}$ that a point of the superposition comes from the i-th point process, and $(\otimes_{j=1}^{i-1} \mathcal{P}_j) \otimes \mathcal{P}_i^0 \otimes (\otimes_{j=i+1}^{k} \mathcal{P}_j)$ is the Palm probability of P associated with the i-th point process. $\qquad\square$

Example 5.1.1 If we call F_i and F_i^0 the c.d.f. of the first point of the i-th point process under $\mathcal{P}_i$ and $\mathcal{P}_i^0$ respectively, it follows from the above results that the c.d.f. G^0 of the first point of the superposition under its Palm probability is

$$(5.1.3) \quad G^0(x) = 1 - \sum_{i=1}^{k} \left(\frac{\lambda_i}{\lambda} (1 - F_i^0(x)) \prod_{\substack{1 \leq j \leq k \\ j \neq i}} (1 - F_j(x)) \right).$$

$\qquad\square$

5.2 Selected Marks and Conditioning

Let (N, θ_t, P) be a stationary point process with finite intensity, and for $U \in \mathcal{F}$, define

$$(5.2.1) \quad N_U(\omega, C) = \int_C 1_U(\theta_t \omega) N(\omega, dt), \quad C \in \mathcal{B}.$$

Example 5.2.1 If $Z = \{Z_n\}$ is a sequence of marks associated with (N, θ_t, P), with values in $(K, \mathcal{K})$ we could take $U = \{Z_0 \in L\}$ for some $L \in \mathcal{K}$. Then, since $Z_0(\theta_{T_n} \omega) = Z_n(\omega)$,

$$N_U(C) = \sum_{n \in \mathbb{Z}} 1_L(Z_n) 1_C(T_n).$$

In this case N_U counts the points of T_n with mark Z_n falling in L.   □

The point process (N_U, θ_t, P) is obviously stationary and with finite intensity (since $N_U \leq N$). Its Palm probability is given by

$$(5.2.2) \quad P^0_{N_U}(A) = \frac{1}{\lambda_U} E\left[\int_{(0,1]} (1_A \circ \theta_s) N_U(ds)\right],$$

where λ_U is the intensity of N_U. But

$$\lambda_U = E\left[\int_{(0,1]} (1_U \circ \theta_t) N(dt)\right] = \lambda P^0_N(U).$$

In addition, we have

$$E\left[\int_{(0,1]} (1_A \circ \theta_s) N_U(ds)\right] = E\left[\int_{(0,1]} (1_A \circ \theta_s)(1_U \circ \theta_s) N(ds)\right]$$

$$= \lambda P^0_N(A \cap U),$$

which gives

$$P^0_{N_U}(A) = \frac{P^0_N(A \cap U)}{P^0_N(U)},$$

that is to say

$$(5.2.3) \quad P^0_{N_U}(A) = P^0_N(A \mid U).$$

Example 5.2.2 *Traffic intensity and types of customers.* In the last example, let the marks be of the form

$$(5.2.4) \quad Z_n = (\sigma_n, U_n),$$

where σ_n is interpreted as the amount of service required by customer n, and U_n is the type of this customer : $U_n \in \{1, \ldots, I\}$. For $1 \leq i \leq I$, define the point process N_i by

$$(5.2.5) \quad N_i(C) = \sum_{n \in \mathbb{Z}} 1_C(T_n) 1_{\{i\}}(U_n).$$

The point process N_i counts the number of customers of type i. Clearly $N_i \circ \theta_t = S_t N_i$ and $N = \sum_{i=1}^{I} N_i$. The intensity of N_i is $\lambda_i = E[N_i(0,1]]$

$$(5.2.6) \quad \lambda_i = \lambda P^0_N(U_0 = i).$$

The *traffic intensity* was defined by the formula

$$\rho = \lambda E^0_N[\sigma_0].$$

In view of (5.2.3) and (5.2.6), we have

$$\lambda E_N^0[\sigma_0] = \lambda \sum_{i=1}^{I} E_N^0[\sigma_0 \mid U_0 = i] P_N^0(U_0 = i)$$

$$= \sum_{i=1}^{I} \lambda_i E_{N_i}^0[\sigma_0],$$

that is

$$(5.2.7) \quad \rho = \sum_{i=1}^{I} \rho_i,$$

where ρ_i is the traffic intensity $\lambda_i E_{N_i}^0[\sigma_0]$ for the i-th type of customer. We therefore check that *traffic intensities are additive*. □

Example 5.2.3 *Superposition of independent point processes.* The result of § 5.1 can be obtained more directly by using the theory of the present subsection: let N_i $(1 \leq i \leq k)$ be independent point processes, compatible with the flow $\{\theta_t\}$ and with finite and non-null intensities λ_i $(1 \leq i \leq k)$ respectively. Call N their superposition. From Bayes' rule:

$$P_N^0(A) = \sum_{i=1}^{k} P_N^0\left(N_i(\{0\}) = 1\right) P_N^0\left(A \mid N_i(\{0\}) = 1\right).$$

But

$$P_N^0\left(N_i(\{0\}) = 1\right) = \frac{1}{\lambda} E\left[\sum_{n \in \mathbb{Z}} 1_{(0,1]}(T_n) 1_{N_i(\{T_n\}) = 1}\right] = \frac{1}{\lambda} E\left[N_i(0,1]\right] = \frac{\lambda_i}{\lambda}.$$

Let $U = \{N_i(\{0\}) = 1\}$. Since we have $N_U = N_i$ (with the notations of (5.2.1)), we obtain

$$P_N^0\left(A \mid N_i(\{0\}) = 1\right) = P_{N_i}^0(A).$$

Therefore

$$P_N^0(A) = \sum_{i=1}^{k} \frac{\lambda_i}{\lambda} P_{N_i}^0(A).$$

□

5.3 Selected Transitions of a Stationary Markov Chain

The setting and the notations of the present subsection are the same as in Example 1.3.3. The intensity λ_H of N_H is

$$E[N_H(0,1]] = E\left[\int_{(0,1]} 1_H(X_{s-}, X_s)N(ds)\right]$$

$$= E\left[\int_{(0,1]} \sum_{(i,j)\in H} 1_{\{i\}}(X_{s-})N_{ij}(ds)\right],$$

where $N_{ij} = N_{\{(i,j)\}}$ counts the transitions from i to j. Therefore from Lévy's formula (see § 10.1)

$$\lambda_H = E\left[\int_{(0,1]} \sum_{(i,j)\in H} 1_{\{i\}}(X_{s-})q_{ij}ds\right] = \int_{(0,1]} \sum_{(i,j)\in H} P(X_s = i)q_{ij}ds,$$

that is to say

(5.3.3) $\lambda_H = \displaystyle\sum_{(i,j)\in H} \pi(i)q_{ij}.$

We assume that

(5.3.4) $0 < \lambda_H < \infty,$

so that we can define the Palm probability $P^0_{N_H}$ associated with N_H. Let now $g : E \times E \to \mathbb{R}$ be non-negative and measurable. Then

$$E^0_{N_H}\left[g(X_{0-}, X_0)\right] = \frac{1}{\lambda_H}E\left[\int_{(0,1]} g(X_{s-}, X_s)N_H(ds)\right]$$

$$= \frac{1}{\lambda_H}E\left[\int_{(0,1]} \sum_{(i,j)\in H} g(i,j)1_{\{i\}}(X_{s-})N_{ij}(ds)\right]$$

$$= \frac{1}{\lambda_H}E\left[\int_{(0,1]} \sum_{(i,j)\in H} g(i,j)1_{\{i\}}(X_{s-})q_{ij}ds\right],$$

so that finally :

(5.3.5) $E^0_{N_H}(g(X_{0-}, X_0)) = \dfrac{\sum_{(i,j)\in H} g(i,j)\pi(i)q_{ij}}{\sum_{(i,j)\in H} \pi(i)q_{ij}}.$

In particular, we have

(5.3.6) $P^0_{N_H}(X_0 = k) = \dfrac{\sum_{i/(i,k)\in H} \pi(i)q_{ik}}{\sum_{(i,j)\in H} \pi(i)q_{ij}}$

and

(5.3.7) $P^0_{N_H}(X_{0-} = k) = \pi(k)\dfrac{\sum_{i/(k,i)\in H} q_{ki}}{\sum_{(i,j)\in H} \pi(i)q_{ij}}.$

5.4 Delayed Marked Point Process

Let $(\Omega, P, \mathcal{F}, \theta_t)$ be a stationary framework, let N be a θ_t-compatible point process associated with the time sequence $\{T_n\}$, and let $\{Z_n\}$ and $\{V_n\}$ be two θ_t-compatible mark sequences, with values in $(K, \mathcal{K})$ and $(\mathbb{R}_+, \mathcal{B}(\mathbb{R}_+))$ respectively. Define the point process N' by its time sequence $\{T_n'\}$, where

$$T_n' = T_n + V_n.$$

Associate with T_n' the mark $Z_n' = Z_n$. This makes $(N', \{Z_n\})$ a marked point process which is θ_t-compatible in the sense that, if one defines the associated counting measure $N'(dt, dz)$ by

$$(5.4.1) \quad N'(C \times L) = \sum_{n \in \mathbb{Z}} 1_C(T_n') 1_L(Z_n),$$

then, for all $C \in \mathcal{B}(\mathbb{R})$, all $L \in \mathcal{K}$, all $\omega \in \Omega$ and all $t \in \mathbb{R}$,

$$(5.4.2) \quad N'(\theta_t \omega, C \times L) = N'(\omega, (C + t) \times L).$$

In order to see this, we write (5.4.1) as

$$N'(\omega, C \times L) = \int \int \int_{\mathbb{R} \times \mathbb{R}_+ \times K} 1_C(s + v) 1_L(z) N(\omega, ds \times dv \times dz),$$

where

$$N(C \times F \times L) = \sum_{n \in \mathbb{Z}} 1_C(T_n) 1_F(V_n) 1_L(Z_n).$$

Since N, $\{V_n\}$ and $\{Z_n\}$ are θ_t-compatible,

$$N(\theta_t \omega, C \times F \times L) = N(\omega, (C + t) \times F \times L).$$

Therefore

$$\begin{aligned}
N'(\theta_t \omega, C \times L) &= \int \int \int 1_C(s + v) 1_L(z) N(\theta_t \omega, ds \times dv \times dz) \\
&= \int \int \int 1_C(s + v) 1_L(z) N(\omega, (ds + t) \times dv \times dz) \\
&= \int \int \int 1_C(u - t + v) 1_L(z) N(\omega, du \times dv \times dz) \\
&= \int \int \int 1_{C+t}(u + v) 1_L(z) N(\omega, du \times dv \times dz) \\
&= N'(\omega, (C + t) \times L)
\end{aligned}$$

Denoting $N(ds \times dv \times K) = N(ds \times dv)$, we have

$$E\left[N'((0,a])\right] = E\left[\int\int 1_{(0,a]}(s+v)N(ds\times dv)\right]$$

$$= E\left[\int\int 1_{(0,a]}(s+v)\lambda ds P_N^0(V_0\in dv)\right],$$

where λ is the intensity of N (Campbell-Mecke-Little formula). But

$$\int\int 1_{(0,a]}(s+v)\lambda ds P_N^0(V_0\in dv) = \int_{\mathbb{R}_+}\left(\int_{-v}^{a-v}\lambda ds\right)P_N^0(dv)$$

$$= \lambda a\int P_N^0(dv) = \lambda a.$$

Therefore, N' has the same intensity λ as N. A similar computation gives

$$E\left[N'((0,a]\times L)\right] = E\left[N((0,a]\times L)\right],$$

so that the Campbell measures $\lambda(dt\times dz) = E[N(dt\times dz)]$ and $\lambda'(dt\times dz) = E[N'(dt\times dz)]$ are the same. In particular, from (3.1.4),

(5.4.3) $P_N^0(Z_0\in dz) = P_{N'}^0(Z_0'\in dz),$

where Z_n' is the mark associated to T_n' in the point process with associated counting measure $N'(dt\times dz)$.

6 Local Aspect of Palm Probability

6.1 The Korolyuk-Dobrushin Infinitesimal Estimates

Let (N,θ_t,P) be a stationary point process with finite intensity λ and no multiple points, and let P_N^0 be the associated Palm probability. The inversion formula (4.1.2b'), for $n = -1$, gives

$$P(N((0,t]) > 1) = P(T_2\le t) = \lambda\int_0^\infty P_N^0(u < -T_{-1}, T_2\circ\theta_{-u}\le t)du.$$

But on Ω_0, $u < -T_{-1}$ implies $T_2\circ\theta_{-u} = T_1 + u$. Therefore

$$P(N((0,t]) > 1) = \lambda\int_0^t P_N^0(u < -T_{-1}, T_1\le t - u)du$$

$$\le \lambda\int_0^t P_N^0(T_1\le t)du$$

$$= \lambda t P_N^0(T_1\le t).$$

Since $P_N^0(T_1 > 0) = 1$, this implies

(6.1.1) $P(N((0,t]) > 1) = o(t),$

where $\lim_{t \to 0} \frac{o(t)}{t} = 0$. This estimate is attributed to *Korolyuk*. We can similarly obtain *Dobrushin's* estimate

(6.1.2) $P(N((0, t]) > 0) = \lambda t + o(t)$.

Indeed, since $T_1 \circ \theta_{-u} = u$ on Ω_0,

$$P(N((0, t]) > 0) = P(T_1 \leq t) = \lambda \int_0^\infty P_N^0(u < -T_{-1}, T_1 \circ \theta_{-u} \leq t) du$$

$$= \lambda \int_0^t P_N^0(u < -T_{-1}) du$$

$$= \lambda t - \lambda \int_0^t P_N^0(-T_{-1} \leq u) du$$

$$= \lambda t + o(t).$$

6.2 Conditioning at a Point: Ryll-Nardzewski's Interpretation

The local interpretation of Palm probability is contained in the following result

(6.2.1) $\lim_{t \to 0} \sup_{A \in \mathcal{F}} | P_N^0(A) - P(\theta_{T_1} \in A \mid T_1 \leq t)| = 0$.

Proof:

$$P(\theta_{T_1} \in A \mid T_1 \leq t) = \frac{\lambda t}{P(T_1 \leq t)} \frac{P(T_1 \leq t, \theta_{T_1} \in A)}{\lambda t}.$$

From Dobrushin's estimate,

$$\lim_{t \to 0} \frac{\lambda t}{P(T_1 \leq t)} = 1.$$

From (4.1.2b), we obtain

$$P(T_1 \leq t, \theta_{T_1} \in A) = \lambda \int_0^\infty P_N^0(u < -T_{-1}, T_1 \circ \theta_{-u} < t, \theta_{T_1} \circ \theta_{-u} \in A) du$$

$$= \lambda \int_0^t P_N^0(u < -T_{-1}, A) du,$$

since $\theta_{T_1} \circ \theta_{-u}$ is the identity on $\Omega_0 \cap \{u < -T_{-1}\}$ when $u > 0$. Moreover

$$\lambda t P_N^0(A) = \lambda \int_0^t P_N^0(A) du.$$

Therefore

$$\lambda t |P(\theta_{T_1} \in A \mid T_1 \le t) - P_N^0(A)| = \lambda \int_0^t P_N^0(u \ge -T_{-1}, A) du + o(t)$$

$$\le \lambda \int_0^t P_N^0(u \ge -T_{-1}) du + o(t) = o(t),$$

where the function $t \to o(t)$ does not depend upon A.   □

Example 6.2.1 In a special case, we shall give a formulation of (6.2.1) which is appealing to intuition. Define

(6.2.2) $T_+(t) = t + \inf \{h > 0 \mid N(t, t + h] = 1\}.$

We can write

$$P(\theta_{T_1} \in A \mid T_1 \le h) = P(\theta_{T_+(0)} \in A \mid N(0, h] \ge 1).$$

From the θ_t-invariance of P:

$$P(\theta_{T_+(0)} \in A \mid N(0, h] \ge 1) = P(\theta_{T_+(t)} \in A \mid N(t, t + h] \ge 1).$$

For any process $\{X(t)\}, t \in \mathbb{R}$, compatible with $\{\theta_t\}$, and any $C \in \mathcal{B}$, this remark allows us to write

(6.2.3) $P_N^0(X(0) \in C) = \lim_{h \to 0} P(X(T_+(t)) \in C \mid N(t, t + h] \ge 1).$

Also if $\{X(t)\}$ is right-continuous with left-hand limits :

(6.2.4) $P_N^0(\triangle X(0) \in C) = \lim_{h \to 0} P(\triangle X(T_+(t)) \in C \mid N(t, t + h] \ge 1),$

where $\triangle X(t) = X(t) - (X(t-).$

A typical use of (6.2.3) arises in queueing theory, when one computes the law of the number of customers in a stationary system given that some event (departure, or arrival) occurred.   □

7 Ergodicity of Point Processes

7.1 Invariant Events

Let (N, θ_t, P) be a stationary point process with non-zero and finite intensity and let P_N^0 be the associated Palm probability. Denote θ_{T_1} by θ.

(7.1.1) *Let $A \in \mathcal{F}$ be such that $\theta_t A = A$ for all $t \in \mathbb{R}$ (i.e. A is θ_t-invariant). Then $P(A) = 1$ if and only if $P_N^0(A) = 1$.*

Proof: Suppose $P_N^0(A) = 1$. The inversion formula (4.1.2b) gives

$$P(A) = \lambda \int_0^\infty P_N^0(u < T_1, \theta_u A) du$$

$$= \lambda \int_0^\infty P_N^0(u < T_1, A) du \quad (\theta_t - \text{invariance of } A)$$

$$= \lambda \int_0^\infty P_N^0(u < T_1) du, \quad (P_N^0(A) = 1)$$

$$= \lambda E_0^0[T_1] = 1.$$

Conversely, supposing that $P(A) = 1$ and using part of the preceding computation, we obtain

$$P(A) = 1 = \lambda \int_0^\infty P_N^0(u < T_1, A) du,$$

and therefore, since $1 = \lambda \int_0^\infty P_N^0(u < T_1) du$,

$$0 = \lambda \int_0^\infty P_N^0(u < T_1, \overline{A}) du.$$

This implies $P_N^0(u < T_1, \overline{A}) = 0$, du−almost everywhere, from which we conclude that $P_N^0(A) = 1$ (recall that $T_1 < \infty$). $\square$

In a similar way, we obtain the following result:

(7.1.2) Let $A \in \mathcal{F}$ such that $\theta^{-1}A = A$ (i.e. A is θ-invariant). Then $P_N^0(A) = 1$ if and only if $P(A) = 1$.

Proof: Assume that $P(A) = 1$. Then from (3.1.8)

$$P_N^0(A) = \frac{1}{\lambda t} E[\int_{(0,t]} (1_A \circ \theta_s) N(ds)]$$

$$= \frac{1}{\lambda t} E[\int_{(0,t]} 1_A N(ds)] \quad (\theta - \text{invariance of } A)$$

$$= \frac{1}{\lambda t} E[1_A N(0,t])]$$

$$= \frac{1}{\lambda t} E[N(0,t]] \quad (P(A) = 1)$$

$$= 1.$$

Conversely when supposing that $P_N^0(A) = 1$ and when using the above computation, we obtain

$$\lambda t P_N^0(A) = \lambda t = E[1_A N((0,t])],$$

that is

$$E[1_{\overline{A}} N((0,t])] = 0, \text{ for all } t > 0,$$

which implies $P(\overline{A}) = 0$ (recall the assumption $N(\mathbb{R}_+) = \infty$). $\square$

7.2 Ergodicity under the Stationary Probability and under the Palm Probability

Let (N, θ_t, P) be a stationary point process with a finite intensity λ, and let P_N^0 be its associated Palm probability. Denote $\theta_{T_1} = \theta$.

(7.2.1) (P, θ_t) *is ergodic if and only if* (P_N^0, θ) *is ergodic.*

This is a consequence of the characterization of ergodic probabilities as extremal invariant probabilities. For instance

(7.2.2) (P_N^0, θ) *is ergodic if and only if there exists no decomposition*

$$P_N^0 = \alpha_1 Q_1 + \alpha_2 Q_2, \quad \alpha_1 + \alpha_2 = 1, \ \alpha_1 > 0, \ \alpha_2 > 0,$$

where Q_1 and Q_2 are θ-invariant probabilities.

Similarly:

(7.2.3) (P, θ_t) *is ergodic if and only if there exists no decomposition*

$$P = \beta_1 P_1 + \beta_2 P_2, \quad \beta_1 + \beta_2 = 1, \ \beta_1 > 0, \ \beta_2 > 0,$$

where P_1 and P_2 are, for all $t \in \mathbb{R}$, θ_t-invariant probabilities.

(cf. Billingsley (1965), *Ergodic Theory and Information*, Wiley, New York. pp. 38-39).

Proof of (7.2.1). Suppose for instance that (P, θ_t) is ergodic and that (P_N^0, θ) is not. Then there must be a decomposition of the type (7.2.2). Let P_1 and P_2 be the stationary probabilities associated with Q_1 and Q_2 (see § 4.4). The inversion formula applied to (7.2.2) gives

$$P = \alpha_1 \frac{\lambda}{\lambda_1} P_1 + \alpha_2 \frac{\lambda}{\lambda_2} P_2,$$

where $\frac{1}{\lambda} = E_N^0[T_1]$, $\frac{1}{\lambda_1} = E_{Q_1}[T_1]$, $\frac{1}{\lambda_2} = E_{Q_2}[T_1]$ (note that λ_1 and λ_2 must be strictly positive). Therefore (θ_t, P) is not ergodic, hence a contradiction. The proof of the converse part is based on the observation that (7.2.3) implies

$$P_N^0 = \beta_1 \frac{\lambda_1}{\lambda} P_{1,N}^0 + \beta_2 \frac{\lambda_2}{\lambda} P_{2,N}^0,$$

where $\lambda = E[N(0,1]]$, $\lambda_1 = E_{P_1}[N(0,1]]$, $\lambda_2 = E_{P_2}[N(0,1]]$. $\square$

7.3 The Cross Ergodic Theorems

Let (N, θ_t, P) be a stationary point process. It is supposed to be ergodic, i.e. (P, θ_t) is ergodic. Assume its intensity λ to be non-null and finite and let P_N^0 be the associated Palm probability. Let f be in $L^1(P)$. Since (P, θ_t) is ergodic, the event

$$A = \left\{ \lim_{T \to \infty} \frac{1}{T} \int_0^T f \circ \theta_t dt = E[f] \right\},$$

is P-almost certain. Moreover it is θ_t-invariant. Therefore by the results of § 7.1, $P_N^0(A) = 1$, i.e.

$$(7.3.1) \quad \lim_{T \to \infty} \frac{1}{T} \int_0^T f \circ \theta_t dt = E[f], \quad P_N^0 - \text{a.s.}$$

Similarly, since (P_N^0, θ) is ergodic, for all $f \in L^1(P_N^0)$,

$$B = \left\{ \lim_{n \to \infty} \frac{1}{n} \sum_{k=1}^n f \circ \theta_{T_k} = E_N^0[f] \right\},$$

is P_N^0-almost certain. It is also θ-invariant, and therefore $P(B) = 1$ by (7.2.1), i.e.

$$(7.3.2) \quad \lim_{n \to \infty} \frac{1}{n} \sum_{k=1}^n f \circ \theta_{T_k} = E_N^0[f], \quad P - \text{a.s.}$$

These two results are essential for queueing theory in that they provide an easy interpretation of the *cross formulas* of the Little type (linking P_N^0 means and P- means of operational quantities such as the P_N^0-mean waiting time and the P-mean number of customers, see § 1 of Chapter 3).

7.4 Palm Theory in Discrete Time

The Palm theory in continuous time has a counterpart in discrete time which can be developed in very elementary terms. In the present subsection, we shall briefly sketch the discrete time Palm theory, leaving the details to the reader. For this, we shall first adapt the notations and definitions used in continuous time to the discrete time situation.

In discrete time, a *simple point process* on $\mathbb{Z}$ is just a sequence $\{U_n\}, n \in \mathbb{Z}$, where $U_n = 0$ or 1. It is called stationary if the sequence $\{U_n\}$ is strictly stationary, and its *intensity* is then defined by

$$(7.4.1) \quad \lambda_U = E[U_0].$$

Observe that $0 \le \lambda_U \le 1$.

The *canonical framework* in discrete time is the following: $(\Omega, \mathcal{F})$ is a measurable space endowed with an invertible measurable map $\theta_1 : (\Omega, \mathcal{F}) \to (\Omega, \mathcal{F})$ such that θ_1^{-1} is measurable (we can think of θ_1 as the shift to the left although this is not necessary). Define $\theta_n = \theta_1^n$ for all $n \in \mathbb{Z}$. A probability P on $(\Omega, \mathcal{F})$ such that

$$(7.4.2) \quad P \circ \theta_1^{-1} = P$$

(P is θ_1-invariant) is called a stationary probability.

A sequence $\{Z_n\}, n \in \mathbb{Z}$, of random elements with values in an arbitrary measurable space $(E, \mathcal{E})$ is said to be *compatible* with $\{\theta_n\}$ if

$$(7.4.3) \quad Z_n(\omega) = Z_0(\theta_n\omega),$$

for all $n \in \mathbb{Z}$ (with the convention that θ_1^0 is the identity). The sequence $\{Z_n\}$ is then strictly stationary (with respect to P). Thus, if the point process $\{U_n\}$ is compatible with $\{\theta_n\}$, it is stationary. We shall assume it is so. The *Palm probability* P_U associated with $\{U_n\}$ is defined by the formula

$$(7.4.4) \quad E_U^0[Z] = \frac{1}{\lambda_U M} E\left[\sum_{n=1}^{M} (Z \circ \theta_n) 1_{U_n=1}\right] \quad (M = 1, 2, \dots).$$

The theory in discrete time is analogous to the one in continuous time, and we shall therefore omit the details and only state the main formulas. Let $\{T_n\}, n \in \mathbb{Z}$, be the sequence of points of $\{U_n\}$, i.e. the time at which $U_n = 1$ with the same convention as the continuous time case $\dots < T_{-1} < T_0 \leq 0 < T_1 < T_2 < \dots$. We have

$$(7.4.5) \quad P_U^0(T_0 = 0) = 1 \text{ (i.e } P_U^0(U_0 = 1) = 1)$$

and moreover P_U^0 is θ-invariant where $\theta = \theta_{T_1}$.

The *inversion formula* reads

$$(7.4.6) \quad E[f] = \lambda_U E_U^0\left[\sum_{n=1}^{T_1} f \circ \theta_n\right].$$

In discrete time, the Campbell-Little-Mecke formula takes the form

$$(7.4.7) \quad E\left[\sum_{n \in \mathbb{Z}} f(T_n, Z_n)\right] = \lambda_U \sum_{n \in \mathbb{Z}} \int_K f(n, z) P_U^0(Z_0 \in dz),$$

where $f \geq 0$ and $\{Z_n\}$ is a process compatible with $\{\theta_n\}$.

Also, in complete analogy with the continuous time case

$$(7.4.8) \quad (P, \theta_1) \text{ ergodic} \iff (P_U^0, \theta_{T_1}) \text{ ergodic}$$

and in the ergodic case (i.e. when either condition of (7.4.8) holds true)

$$(7.4.9) \quad E_N^0[f] = \lim_{n \uparrow \infty} \frac{1}{n} \sum_{k=1}^{n} f \circ \theta_{T_k}, \quad P-\text{a.s.}$$

The local interpretation of Palm probability is very simple; just observe that in (7.4.4) M can be taken equal to 1, and therefore, in view of the θ_1-invariance of P and of the definition of λU,

(7.4.10) $E_U^0[Z] = \dfrac{E(Z 1_{U_0=1})}{P(U_0 = 1)} = E[Z \mid U_0 = 1].$

Therefore, in discrete time, the Palm probability is just a conditional probability. The ergodic theorem applied to $f = X_0$ where $\{X_n\}$ is compatible with $\{\theta_n\}$ becomes the usual ergodic theorem

(7.4.11) $E[X_0 \mid U_0 = 1] = \dfrac{E[X_0 U_0]}{E[U_0]} = \lim_{M \uparrow \infty} \dfrac{\sum_{n=1}^{N} X_n U_n}{\sum_{n=1}^{N} U_n}.$

Therefore the discrete time theory of Palm probabilities is just a restatement of well known results.

8 Stochastic Intensity

Roughly speaking, Palm probability tells us what happens when there is a point at time t. The concept of stochastic intensity introduced in the present section represents in some way a complementary point of view: it is concerned with the expectation of seeing a point at time t (in a small interval after t) knowing the past history of the point process.

The connection between the two points of view will be formalized in § 9. Before giving the definition of stochastic intensity, we must spend some time introducing notation and a few definitions from the theory of stochastic processes. For all the statements announced without proof in the following sections, the reader is referred to the monograph: Brémaud (1981) *Point Processes and Queues*, Springer-Verlag New York.

8.1 Predictable Processes

A family $\{\mathcal{F}_t\}, t \in \mathbb{R}$, of sub-$\sigma$-fields of $\mathcal{F}$ such that $\mathcal{F}_s \subset \mathcal{F}_t$ whenever $s \leq t$ is called a *history*. If the stochastic process $\{Z(t)\}, t \in \mathbb{R}$, is such that for all t, $Z(t)$ is $\mathcal{F}_t$-measurable, $\{\mathcal{F}_t\}$ is called a *history* of $\{Z(t)\}$ and $\{Z(t)\}$ is said to be $\mathcal{F}_t$-adapted. The smallest history of $\{Z(t)\}$ is $\{\mathcal{F}_t^Z\} = \{\sigma(\{Z(s), s \leq t\})\}$ and is called the *internal history* of $\{Z(t)\}$.

A point process N is said to be *adapted* to the history $\{\mathcal{F}_t\}$ if $N(C)$ is $\{\mathcal{F}_t\}$-measurable whenever $C \subset (-\infty, t]$. The *internal history of N*, $\{\mathcal{F}_t^N\}$, is defined by $\mathcal{F}_t^N = \sigma(\{N(C), C \subset (-\infty, t]\})$. Let N be a point process compatible with the flow $\{\theta_t\}$, and let $Z = \{Z_n\}, n \in \mathbb{Z}$, be a sequence of marks of N. The *internal history of the marked point process (N,Z)* is the history $\{\mathcal{F}_t^{N,Z}\}$ defined by $\mathcal{F}_t^{N,Z} = \mathcal{F}_t^N \vee \mathcal{F}_t^Z$ where $\{\mathcal{F}_t^Z\}$ is the internal history of $\{Z(t)\}$ defined by $Z(t) = Z_n$ if $t \in [T_n, T_{n+1})$. If the history $\{\mathcal{F}_t\}$ verifies $\mathcal{F}_t \supset \mathcal{F}_t^{N,Z}$ for all t, (N, Z) is said to be adapted to $\{\mathcal{F}_t\}$.

Let $\{\mathcal{F}_t\}$ be a history. A process $\{Z(t)\}$ is called $\{\mathcal{F}_t\}$-*progressively* measurable if for each $t \in \mathbb{R}$, the function $(s, \omega) \to Z(s, \omega)$ defined on $(-\infty, t] \times \Omega$ is $\mathcal{B}((-\infty, t]) \otimes \mathcal{F}_t$-measurable. A right-continuous or left-continuous process adapted to $\{\mathcal{F}_t\}$ is $\{\mathcal{F}_t\}$-progressively-measurable.

The σ-field $\mathcal{P}(\mathcal{F}_t)$ defined on $\mathbb{R} \times \Omega$ and generated by the sets of the form $(a, b] \times A$ where $a \leq b$ and $A \in \mathcal{F}_a$ is called the $\mathcal{F}_t$-*predictable* . If the process $\{Z(t)\}, t \in \mathbb{R}$, is such that $(t, \omega) \to Z(t, \omega)$ is $\mathcal{P}(\mathcal{F}_t)$-measurable, it is called $\mathcal{F}_t$-*predictable*.

Example 8.1.1 *Adapted left-continuous process.* Let $\{Z(t)\}$ be adapted to $\{\mathcal{F}_t\}$ and have left-continuous trajectories. Then

$$Z(t, \omega) = \lim_{n \uparrow \infty} Z^{(n)}(t, \omega)$$

where

$$Z^{(n)}(t, \omega) = \sum_{k \in \mathbb{N}} Z\left(\frac{k}{2^n}, \omega\right) 1_{(k/2^n, (k+1)/2^n]}(t) .$$

Since $Z\left(\frac{k}{2^n}\right)$ is $\mathcal{F}_{k/2^n}$ measurable, the function of (t, ω):

$$(t, \omega) \to Z\left(\frac{k}{2^n}, \omega\right) 1_{(k/2^n, (k+1)/2^n]}(t)$$

is $\mathcal{P}(\mathcal{F}_t)$-measurable, and therefore so are the functions $(t, \omega) \to Z^{(n)}(t, \omega)$ and $(t, \omega) \to Z(t, \omega)$.

In particular, if $\{X(t)\}$ is adapted to $\{\mathcal{F}_t\}$ and with left-hand limits $X(t-)$, the process $\{Z(t)\} = \{X(t-)\}$ is $\mathcal{F}_t$-predictable.   □

A random variable T with values in $\overline{\mathbb{R}}$ is called an $\mathcal{F}_t$-stopping-time if $\{T \leq t\} \in \mathcal{F}_t$ for all $t \in \mathbb{R}$. If T is a $\mathcal{F}_t$-stopping time, $Z(t) = 1_{(-\infty, T]}(t)$ defines a $\mathcal{F}_t$-predictable process.

Let T be a $\mathcal{F}_t$-stopping time, where $\{\mathcal{F}_t\}$ is some history. The σ-field $\mathcal{F}_T$ is defined by

$$\mathcal{F}_T = \{A \in \mathcal{F} \mid A \cap \{T \leq t\} \in \mathcal{F}_t \text{ for all } t \in \mathbb{R}\}.$$

As we can readily check, $\mathcal{F}_T$ is a σ-field and T is $\mathcal{F}_T$-measurable; in addition, if $\{X(t)\}$ is $\mathcal{F}_t$-progressively measurable, then $X(T) 1_{\{T < \infty\}}$ is $\mathcal{F}_T$-measurable.

The history $\{\mathcal{F}_t\}$ is said to be *compatible* with the flow $\{\theta_t\}$ if $\theta_t \mathcal{F}_s = \mathcal{F}_{s-t}$ for all $s, t \in \mathbb{R}$. Moreover if any $\{\mathcal{F}_t\}$-predictable process $\{Z(t)\}$ has the form

(8.1.1) $Z(t, \omega) = v(t, \theta_t \omega),$

where $(t, \omega) \to v(t, \omega)$ is $\mathcal{B} \otimes \mathcal{F}$ measurable and for each $t \in \mathbb{R}$, $\omega \to v(t, \omega)$ is $\mathcal{F}_{0-}$-measurable (where $\mathcal{F}_{0-} = \bigvee_{s<0} \mathcal{F}_s$), then $\mathcal{F}_t$ is said to have a *predictable structure* adapted to $\{\theta_t\}$.

The structural result to follow will be the key to a short proof and a generalization of Papangelou's formula in § 9.

(8.1.2) *Let N be a point process compatible with the flow $\{\theta_t\}$ and let $\{Z_n\}$ be a sequence of marks of (N, θ_t). The history $\{\mathcal{F}_t^{N,Z}\}$ has a predictable structure adapted to $\{\theta_t\}$.*

Proof: Call $\tau(\mathcal{F}_t^{N,Z})$ the σ-field on $\mathbb{R} \times \Omega$ generated by the mappings $X : \mathbb{R} \times \Omega \to \mathbb{R}$ of the form

(8.1.3) $X(t, \omega) = v(t, \theta_t \omega),$

where v is $\mathcal{B} \otimes \mathcal{F}$-measurable and such that for each $t \in \mathbb{R}$, $\omega \to v(t, \omega)$ is $\mathcal{F}_{0-}$-measurable. We show that $(\alpha) : \mathcal{P}(\mathcal{F}_t^{N,Z}) \subset \tau(\mathcal{F}_t^{N,Z})$, and $(\beta) : \tau(\mathcal{F}_t^{N,Z}) \subset \mathcal{P}(\mathcal{F}_t^{N,Z})$.

Proof of (α) : It suffices to show that for any $(a, b] \subset \mathbb{R}$ and any random variable H that is $\mathcal{F}_a^{N,Z}$-measurable, the mapping $X(t, \omega) = H(\omega) \, 1_{(a,b]}(t)$ is in $\tau(\mathcal{F}_t^{N,Z})$. To see this, write $X(t, \omega)$ in the form (8.1.3) with $v(t, \omega) = H(\theta_{-t}\omega) \, 1_{(a,b]}(t)$. Clearly v is $\mathcal{B} \otimes \mathcal{F}$-measurable. Also for fixed $t \in \mathbb{R}, \omega \to v(t, \omega)$ is $\mathcal{F}_{0-}^{N,Z}$-measurable. Indeed if $t \notin (a, b]$, $v(t, \omega) \equiv 0$, and if $t \in (a, b], v(t, \omega) = H(\theta_{-t}\omega)$ is $\mathcal{F}_{a-t}^{N,Z}$-measurable (recall that $\mathcal{F}_t^{N,Z}$ is compatible with the flow $\{\theta_t\}$) and therefore since $t > a$, $\mathcal{F}_{0-}^{N,Z}$-measurable.

Proof of (β): It suffices to show that if $W : \Omega \to \mathbb{R}$ is $\mathcal{F}_{0-}$-measurable, then $t, \omega \to W(\theta_t \omega)$ is $\mathcal{P}(\mathcal{F}_t^{N,Z})$-measurable. It is in turn enough to show this for any random variable W of the form $W = \varphi(N([a, b] \times L)), a \leq b \leq 0, L \in \mathcal{K}$. In this case $\{W \circ \theta_t\}$ is a function of a left-continuous process adapted to $\{\mathcal{F}_t^{N,Z}\}$, and therefore $\mathcal{F}_t^{N,Z}$-predictable. $\qquad \square$

8.2 Stochastic Intensity Kernels

Let N be a simple point process, not necessarily stationary, let $\{\mathcal{F}_t\}$ be a history of N, and let $\{\lambda(t)\}$ be a non-negative measurable process adapted to $\{\mathcal{F}_t\}$. The process $\{\lambda(t)\}$ is called an $\mathcal{F}_t$-intensity of N if it is locally integrable (i.e. $\int_C \lambda(s)ds < \infty$ for all bounded Borel sets C) and if

(8.2.1) $E[N((a, b]) \mid \mathcal{F}_a] = E\left[\int_a^b \lambda(s)ds \mid \mathcal{F}_a\right],$

for all $(a, b] \in \mathcal{B}$. Without loss of generality, the stochastic intensity $\{\lambda(t)\}$ can be assumed to be $\mathcal{F}_t$-predictable (cf. Brémaud (1981), Chapter II, T12, p. 31).

Example 8.2.1 *The Poisson process.* Let N be a Poisson process with associated measure

$$E[N(C)] = \int_C \lambda(s)ds,$$

where $\{\lambda(t)\}$ is a deterministic locally integrable function. Then clearly, in view of the independence of the increments of a Poisson process, $\{\lambda(t)\}$ is the $\mathcal{F}_t^N$-intensity of N.   □

Example 8.2.2 *Markov chains.* Let $\{X(t)\}$, $t \in \mathbb{R}_+$, be a Markov chain taking its values in a countable state space E with the discrete topology. Suppose it is continuous on the right and has limits on the left. Then it admits infinitesimal characteristics

$$q_i = \lim_{h \to 0} \frac{1 - p_{ii}(h)}{h} \quad \text{and} \quad q_{ij} = \lim_{h \to 0} \frac{p_{ij}(h)}{h}, \ i \neq j,$$

satisfying the stability and conservation conditions

$$q_i < \infty \quad \text{and} \quad \sum_{\substack{j \in E \\ j \neq i}} q_{ij} = q_i.$$

Let N_{ij} be the point processes counting the transitions from i to j, i.e. for $C \in \mathcal{B}$, $N_{ij}(C) = \sum_{s \in C} 1_{X(s-)=i, X(s)=j}$. It can be shown (this is essentially Lévy's formula for Markov chains; for details see § 10.1) that N_{ij} admits the $\mathcal{F}_t^X$-intensity $\{\lambda_{ij}(t)\} = \{q_{ij} 1_{X(t)=i}\}$.   □

Let N be a point process compatible with the flow $\{\theta_t\}$ and let $\{Z_n\}$ be a sequence of marks of (N, θ_t), $(K, \mathcal{K})$ being the corresponding mark space. Let $\{\mathcal{F}_t\}$ be a history of the marked point process $(N, \{Z_n\})$. Let $\lambda(t, \omega, L), t \in \mathbb{R}, \omega \in \Omega, L \in \mathcal{K}$, be a *stochastic kernel*, that is

- for each t, ω, $\lambda(t, \omega, .)$ is a measure on $(K, \mathcal{K})$.

- for all $L \in \mathcal{K}$, $\{\lambda(t, L)\}$ is adapted to $\{\mathcal{F}_t\}$, where $\lambda(t, L)(\omega) \overset{\text{def}}{=} \lambda(t, \omega, L)$.
- $t \to \{\lambda(t, \omega, K)\}$ is locally integrable.

For each $L \in \mathcal{K}$, let N_L be the point process counting the points T_n with a mark Z_n belonging to the set L:

$$N_L(C) = \sum_{n \in \mathbb{Z}} 1_C(T_n) 1_L(Z_n).$$

If for each $L \in \mathcal{K}, N_L$ admits the $\mathcal{F}_t$-intensity $\{\lambda(t, L)\}$, we say that the marked point process $(N, \{Z_n\})$ admits the $\mathcal{F}_t$-intensity kernel $\lambda(t, dz)$.

Example 8.2.3 *The M/GI input.* Let N be a Poisson process with constant rate λ, and let $\{\sigma_n\}$ be an i.i.d. sequence of non-negative random variables, with common c.d.f. G. Assume that N and $\{\sigma_n\}$ are independent. Define $\mathcal{F}_\infty^\sigma$ to be the σ-field generated by the whole sequence $\{\sigma_n\}$, and for each t, let

$$\mathcal{F}_t \overset{\text{def}}{=} \mathcal{F}_t^N \vee \mathcal{F}_\infty^\sigma \vee \mathcal{G},$$

where $\mathcal{G}$ is an arbitrary σ-field independent of N and $\{\sigma_n\}$. It is not difficult to show that $(N, \{\sigma_n\})$ admits the $\mathcal{F}_t$−intensity kernel $\lambda G(dz)$ (see § 10.2).   □

8.3 Stochastic Intensity Integration Formula and Martingales

Let $(N, \{Z_n\})$ be a point process with mark space $(K, \mathcal{K})$, and admitting a $\mathcal{F}_t$–intensity kernel $\lambda(t, dz)$. By definition, for any $(a, b] \subset \mathbb{R}, A \in \mathcal{F}_a, L \in \mathcal{K}$

$$(8.3.1) \quad E\Big[1_A \sum_{n \in \mathbb{Z}} 1_{(a,b]}(T_n)1_L(Z_n)\Big] = E\Big[1_A \int_{(a,b]} \lambda(t, L)dt\Big].$$

Let us write the last relation under the form

$$(8.3.2) \quad E\Big[\int \int_{\mathbb{R} \times K} H(t, z)N(dt \times dz)\Big] = E\Big[\int \int_{\mathbb{R} \times K} H(t, z)\lambda(t, dz)dt\Big],$$

where $N(C \times L) = N_L(C)$ and $H(t, \omega, z) = 1_A(\omega)1_{(a,b]}(t)1_L(z)$. Since the σ-field $\mathcal{P}(\mathcal{F}_t) \otimes \mathcal{K}$ on $\mathbb{R} \times \Omega \times \mathcal{K}$ is generated by the sets $(a, b] \times A \times L$, where $(a, b] \subset \mathbb{R}, A \in \mathcal{F}_a, L \in \mathcal{K}$, Formula (8.3.2) holds true for any non-negative function $H(t, \omega, z)$ that is $\mathcal{P}(\mathcal{F}_t) \otimes \mathcal{K}$-measurable, by the monotone class theorem. In the special case when there are no marks, it takes the form

$$(8.3.3) \quad E\Big[\int_{\mathbb{R}} H(t)N(dt)\Big] = E\Big[\int_{\mathbb{R}} H(t)\lambda(t)dt\Big].$$

In (8.3.3), N is a point process with $\mathcal{F}_t$–intensity $\{\lambda(t)\}$ and $H(t)$ is a non-negative $\mathcal{F}_t$-predictable process.

Define for all $t \geq 0$

$$(8.3.4) \quad M(t) = N(0, t] - \int_0^t \lambda(s)ds.$$

Let now $\{H(t)\}$ be a $\mathcal{F}_t$-predictable process such that

$$(8.3.5) \quad E[\int_0^t |H(s)|\lambda(s)ds] < \infty, \quad \text{for all} \quad t \geq 0,$$

where $\{\lambda(t)\}$ is an $\mathcal{F}_t$-stochastic intensity of N. Then, by (8.3.3),

$$E[\int_{(0,t]} |H(s)|N(ds)] < \infty, \quad \text{for all} \quad t \geq 0.$$

In particular

$$(8.3.6) \quad m(t) = \int_{(0,t]} H(s)dM(s) \stackrel{\text{def}}{=} \int_{(0,t]} H(s)N(ds) - \int_0^t H(s)\lambda(s)ds$$

is well defined, for all $t \geq 0$. For any $(a, b] \subset (0, \infty)$ and $A \in \mathcal{F}_a$,

$$E[1_A\{m(b) - m(a)\}] = E[1_A \int_{(a,b]} H(s)N(ds)] - E[1_A \int_{(a,b]} H(s)\lambda(s)ds] = 0.$$

To see this, replace $H(t)$ by $H'(t) = 1_A 1_{(a,b]}(t)H(t)$ in (8.3.3) to obtain

$$E[1_A \int_{(a,b]} H(s)N(ds)] = E[1_A \int_{(a,b]} H(s)\lambda(s)ds].$$

Therefore $\{m(t)\}$ is a $\mathcal{F}_t$-martingale in view of the following definition:

(8.3.7) *The real-valued stochastic process $\{m(t)\}$, $t \geq 0$, is called a $\mathcal{F}_t$-martingale if*
$(\alpha)\, m(t)$ *is $\mathcal{F}_t$-measurable for all $t \geq 0$;*
$(\beta)\, E|m(t)| < \infty$ *for all $t \geq 0$;*
$(\gamma)\, E[m(b)|\mathcal{F}_a] = m(a)$, *for all $(a, b] \subset (0, \infty]$.*

A local martingale is defined as follows:

(8.3.8) *The real-valued process $\{m(t)\}$, $t \geq 0$, is called a $\mathcal{F}_t$-local martingale if there exists a non-decreasing sequence of $\mathcal{F}_t$-stopping times $\{S_n\}$, $n \geq 1$, such that*

(8.3.9) $\lim S_n = \infty$, P−a.s.

and $\{m(t \wedge S_n)\}$, $t \geq 0$, is a $\mathcal{F}_t$-martingale. It is called a square integrable local $\mathcal{F}_t$-martingale if moreover

(8.3.10) $E[|m(t \wedge S_n)|^2] < \infty$, *for all $t \geq 0$, all $n \geq 1$* .

The reader is invited to verify that if

(8.3.11) $\displaystyle\int_0^t H(s)\lambda(s)ds < \infty$, P − a.s. for all $t \geq 0$,

then $\{m(t)\}$ given by (8.3.6) is well defined and is a $\mathcal{F}_t$-local martingale.

We now proceed to a characterization of Poisson processes in terms of stochastic intensity. This result plays a role in queueing theory, especially for proving that some streams in a queueing network are or are not Poissonian.

8.4 Watanabe's Characterization of Poisson Processes

(8.4.1) *Let N be a simple point process, and let $\{\mathcal{F}_t\}$ be a history of the form*

(8.4.2) $\mathcal{F}_t = \mathcal{F}_t^N \vee \mathcal{G}$,

for some σ-field $\mathcal{G}$. Let $\{\lambda(t)\}$ be a measurable stochastic process, locally integrable, such that for each t, the random variable $\lambda(t)$ is $\mathcal{G}$- measurable. If N admits the $\mathcal{F}_t$-intensity $\{\lambda(t)\}$, then N is a $\mathcal{G}$-conditional Poisson process with $\mathcal{G}$-conditional associated measure $E[N(C) \mid \mathcal{G}] = \int_C \lambda(t)dt$, that is, by definition: for all $u \in \mathbb{R}$, all $(a, b] \subset \mathbb{R}$,

(8.4.3) $E[e^{iuN(a,b]} \mid \mathcal{G} \vee \mathcal{F}_a^N] = \exp\left\{(e^{iu} - 1) \int_a^b \lambda(t)dt\right\}$.

Proof: Write

$$e^{iuN(a,b]} = 1 + \int_{(a,b]} (e^{iu} - 1)e^{iuN(a,s)} N(ds),$$

and therefore, for any A in $\mathcal{F}_a$

$$(8.4.4) \quad E\big[1_A e^{iuN(a,b]}\big] = P(A) + E\Big[\int_a^b 1_A(e^{iu} - 1)e^{iuN(a,s)}\lambda(s)ds\Big],$$

where we have used Formula (8.3.2) and observed that $\{1_A 1_{(a,b]}(t)e^{iuN(a,t)}\}$ is a $\mathcal{F}_t$-predictable process, left continuous and adapted to $\{\mathcal{F}_t\}$. In the right-hand side of (8.4.4), integration is with respect to the Lebesgue measure and therefore $e^{iu\ N(a,s)}$ can be replaced by $e^{iu\ N(a,s]}$. Having done so, since A is arbitrary in $\mathcal{F}_a$ and since $\lambda(s)$ is $\mathcal{G}$-measurable (and therefore $\mathcal{F}_a$-measurable), we obtain that for all $b > a$,

$$E[e^{iuN(a,b]} \mid \mathcal{F}_a] = 1 + \int_a^b (e^{iu} - 1)E[e^{iuN(a,s]} \mid \mathcal{F}_a]\lambda(s)ds,$$

which gives (8.4.3). $\qquad\square$

Watanabe's theorem is easily generalized to multivariate Poisson processes: let N_j, $1 \leq j \leq K$, be K simple point processes without commun points and let $\mathcal{F}_t$ be of the form (8.4.2) with

$$(8.4.5) \quad \mathcal{F}_t^N = \bigvee_{j=1}^K \mathcal{F}_t^{N_j}$$

(therefore, implicitly, N is the 'vector' $(N_1,\ldots,N_K)$). Let For $1 \leq j \leq K$, let $\{\lambda_j(t)\}$ be a $\mathcal{G}$-measurable locally integrable stochastic process. Then:

$(8.4.6)$ If, for $1 \leq j \leq K$, N_j admits the $\mathcal{F}_t$-intensity $\{\lambda_j(t)\}$, each N_j is a $\mathcal{G}$-conditional Poisson process with $\mathcal{G}$-conditional associated measure $E[N_j(C)|\mathcal{G}] = \int_C \lambda_j(t)dt$, and the N_j's are independent conditionally with respect to $\mathcal{G}$.

The proof is omitted: it analogous to that of the univariate version, and is based on the equation

$$e^{iuN(a,b]} = 1 + \sum_{j=1}^K \int_{(a,b)} (e^{iu_j} - 1)e^{iuN(a,s)} N_j(ds),$$

where

$$e^{iuN(a,b]} \stackrel{\text{def}}{=} e^{i\sum_{j=1}^K u_j N_j(a,b]}.$$

Remark 8.4.1 In (8.4.6), one can take $K = +\infty$, although the proof requires $K < \infty$ (to guarantee finiteness of the involved sums). Indeed, independence of an infinite family of stochastic processes involves only finite subfamilies.

□

The Strong Markov Property of Poisson Processes In the setting of
(8.4.6) with possibly $K = \infty$, let T be a finite $\mathcal{F}_t$-stopping time and define
the histories $\{\mathcal{F}'_t\}$ and the point process N'_j, $1 \le j \le K$, by

(8.4.7) $\mathcal{F}'_t = \mathcal{F}_{T+t}$

and

(8.4.8) $N'_j(a, b] = N_j(a + T, \ b + T]$, $\quad 1 \le j \le K$.

In particular

$$\mathcal{F}'_t = \mathcal{G}' \bigvee \mathcal{F}^{N'}_t,$$

where

$$\mathcal{G}' = \mathcal{G} \vee \mathcal{F}^N_T .$$

Then, for each j, $1 \le j \le K$, N'_j admits the $\mathcal{F}'_t$-intensity $\{\lambda_j(t + T)\}$. To
show this, let $\{H'(t)\}$ be a bounded $\mathcal{F}'_t$-predictable process. Then

$$E[\int_{\mathbb{R}} H'(t) N'_j(dt)] = E[\int_{\mathbb{R}} H'(t - T) N_j(dt)] .$$

Since $\{H(t)\}$ defined by $H(t) = H'(t - T)$ is $\mathcal{F}_t$-predictable,

$$E[\int_{\mathbb{R}} H'(t) N'_j(dt)] = E[\int_{\mathbb{R}} H'(t - T) \lambda_j(t) dt]$$

$$= E[\int_{\mathbb{R}} H'(t) \lambda_j(t + T) dt] .$$

The process $\{\lambda'_j(t)\} = \{\lambda_j(t + T)\}$ is $\mathcal{G}'$-measurable. Applying (8.4.6), we
see that the N'_j's are $\mathcal{G}'$-conditionally independent $\mathcal{G}'$-conditional Poisson
processes with respective $\mathcal{F}'_t$-intensities $\{\lambda'_j(t)\}$.

An interesting special case is when for all j, $1 \le j \le K$

(8.4.9) $\lambda_j(t) \equiv \lambda_j \quad \forall \, t$,

that is the original point processes N_j, $1 \le j \le K$, were Poisson processes
with average intensities λ_j, $1 \le j \le K$, mutually independent and independent of $\mathcal{G}$. In this case, the delayed point processes $S_T N_j$, $1 \le j \le K$, are
independent Poisson processes with intensities λ_j, $1 \le j \le K$, and they are
independent of $\mathcal{G}$ and of $\mathcal{F}^N_T = \vee^K_{j=1} \mathcal{F}^{N_j}_T$. The latter independence property
is the strong Markov property of multivariate Poisson processes.

9 The Connection Between Palm Probability and Stochastic Intensity

9.1 Invariance of Stochastic Intensity

Stochastic intensity provides a detailed description of the dynamics of a point process, and when one knows the underlying physics of the generation of events, one will in most cases be able to provide the stochastic intensity with respect to a history that summarizes the information available at any instant. It is therefore of theoretical importance to know whether or not the stochastic intensity is the same under the stationary probability and the Palm probability. It turns out that, with some provisions to be stated soon, this is the case; therefore the stationary probability and the Palm probability describe the same dynamics. More precisely:

(9.1.1) *Let $\{\mathcal{F}_t\}$ be a history of a point process N, and suppose that both are compatible with the flow $\{\theta_t\}$. Suppose that N has a non-null and finite intensity λ and let P_N^0 be the Palm probability associated with (N, θ_t, P). Suppose that N admits a $(P, \mathcal{F}_t)$ - intensity $\{\lambda(t)\}$ compatible with the flow $\{\theta_t\}$. Then, on $\mathbb{R}_+$, N admits the $(P_N^0, \mathcal{F}_t)$-intensity $\{\lambda(t)\}$.*

Remark 9.1.1 In § 9.2, it will be shown that under the assumptions of (9.1.1), we can always assume that $\{\lambda(t)\}$ is compatible with the flow $\{\theta_t\}$. Also recall that $E[\lambda(0)] = \lambda$. □

Remark 9.1.2 The reader will have noticed that we have been more precise in the terminology (speaking for instance of the $(P, \mathcal{F}_t)$-intensity) because stochastic intensity depends on $\{\mathcal{F}_t\}$ but also, of course, on the underlying probability. This dependence is actually the main concern of (9.1.1). □

Remark 9.1.3 The conclusion of (9.1.1) is that, on $\mathbb{R}_+$, the $(P, \mathcal{F}_t)$-intensity and the $(P_N^0, \mathcal{F}_t)$-intensity coincide, that is, for all $(a, b] \subset \mathbb{R}_+, A \in \mathcal{F}_a$,

$$(9.1.2) \quad E_N^0\Big[N(a, b]1_A\Big] = E_N^0\Big[\int_a^b \lambda(t)dt1_A\Big].$$

□

Proof: By definition of Palm probability, the left-hand side of the above equality is

$$\frac{1}{\lambda}E\Big[\sum_{n\in\mathbb{Z}} 1_{(0,1]}(T_n)(1_A \circ \theta_{T_n})N(a + T_n, b + T_n]\Big].$$

Observe that, if $n \geq 1, T_n$ is a $\mathcal{F}_t$-stopping time : indeed $\{T_n \leq t\} = \{N(0, t] \geq n\} \in \mathcal{F}_t$ (for $n \leq 0, T_n$ is *not* a $\mathcal{F}_t$-stopping time; why ?). Also, since a is non-negative, $1_{(0,1]}(T_n)$ is $\mathcal{F}_{a+T_n}$-measurable. Because $\{\mathcal{F}_t\}$ is compatible with the flow $\{\theta_t\}$, and A is in $\mathcal{F}_a, 1_A \circ \theta_{T_n}$ is $\mathcal{F}_{a+T_n}$-measurable. The process $1_{(0,1]}(T_n)(1_A \circ \theta_{T_n})1_{(a+T_n,b+T_n]}(t)$ is therefore adapted to $\{\mathcal{F}_t\}$, and being left-continuous, it is $\mathcal{F}_t$-predictable. Therefore, for $n \geq 1, a \geq 0$

$$E\Big[1_{(0,1]}(T_n)(1_A \circ \theta_{T_n})N(a+T_n, b+T_n]\Big]$$

$$= \ E\Big[\int_{\mathbb{R}} 1_{(0,1]}(T_n)(1_A \circ \theta_{T_n})1_{(a+T_n,b+T_n]}(t)N(dt)\Big]$$

$$= \ E\Big[\int_{\mathbb{R}} 1_{(0,1]}(T_n)(1_A \circ \theta_{T_n})1_{(a+T_n,b+T_n]}(t)\lambda(t)dt\Big]$$

$$= \ E\Big[1_{(0,1]}(T_n)(1_A \circ \theta_{T_n})\int_{a+T_n}^{b+T_n} \lambda(t)dt\Big].$$

Since $\{\lambda(t)\}$ is compatible with $\{\theta_t\}$,

$$\int_{a+T_n}^{b+T_n} \lambda(t)dt = \Big(\int_a^b \lambda(t)dt\Big) \circ \theta_{T_n},$$

and therefore

$$E\Big[1_{(0,1]}(T_n)(1_A \circ \theta_{T_n})N(a+T_n, b+T_n]\Big]$$

$$= \ E\Big[1_{(0,1]}(T_n)(1_A \circ \theta_{T_n})\Big(\int_a^b \lambda(t)dt\Big) \circ \theta_{T_n}\Big].$$

Summing up the last equality with respect to $n = 1, 2, \ldots$, we obtain the announced result.   □

9.2 Papangelou's Formula

The link between stationary probability, Palm probability and stochastic intensity is provided by the following fundamental result of Papangelou. This result contains most of the PASTA (Poisson Arrivals See Time Averages) and related results of queueing theory (see Chapter 3, § 3).

(9.2.1)   *Let N be a point process and $\{\mathcal{F}_t\}$ be a history of N, both N and $\{\mathcal{F}_t\}$ being compatible with the flow $\{\theta_t\}$. Suppose that the intensity λ of N is finite and non-null, and let P_N^0 be the Palm probability associated with (N, P). Suppose moreover that the $\mathcal{F}_t$-predictable structure is adapted to $\{\theta_t\}$. Then N admits a $(P, \mathcal{F}_t)$-intensity $\{\lambda(t)\}$ if and only if*

(9.2.2) $P_N^0 \ll P$ on $\mathcal{F}_{0-}$,

and in that case $\{\lambda(t)\}$ can be chosen of the form

(9.2.3) $\lambda(t) = (\mu \circ \theta_t)\lambda$,

where μ is the Radon-Nikodým derivative on $\mathcal{F}_{0-}$ of P_N^0 with respect to P:

(9.2.4) $\mu = \dfrac{dP_N^0}{dP} \mid_{\mathcal{F}_{0-}}.$

Remark 9.2.1 The following formula is a compact expression of Papangelou's theorem (9.2.1):

(9.2.5) $E[f(Z(0))\lambda(0)] = \lambda E_N^0[f(Z(0))],$

where $\{Z(t)\}$ is a stochastic process compatible with the flow $\{\theta_t\}$ such that $Z(0)$ is $\mathcal{F}_{0-}$-measurable (and therefore $\{Z(t)\}$ is $\mathcal{F}_t$-predictable in view of the predictable structure of $\{\mathcal{F}_t\}$) and f is a non-negative measurable function from the state space of $\{Z(t)\}$ into $\mathbb{R}$.   □

Proof of (9.2.1). Suppose that (9.2.2) holds, and define μ by (9.2.4). Let now $\{X(t)\}$ be a non-negative $\mathcal{F}_t$-predictable process. Since $\{\mathcal{F}_t\}$ has a predictable structure adapted to $\{\theta_t\}$, $X(t,\omega) = v(t,\theta_t\omega)$ for some function v that is $\mathcal{B} \otimes \mathcal{F}$-measurable and such that for each $t \in \mathbb{R}$, $\omega \to v(t,\omega)$ is $\mathcal{F}_{0-}$-measurable. From the latter property of v and the definition of μ,

$$E_N^0[v(t)] = E[\mu v(t)],$$

and therefore

$$\int_{\mathbb{R}} E_N^0[v(t)]dt = \int_{\mathbb{R}} E[\mu v(t)]dt.$$

Since P is θ_t-invariant

$$\int_{\mathbb{R}} E[\mu v(t)]dt = \int_{\mathbb{R}} E[(\mu \circ \theta_t)(v(t) \circ \theta_t)]dt.$$

On the other hand, the generalized Campbell's formula gives

$$\int_{\mathbb{R}} E_N^0[v(t)]dt = \frac{1}{\lambda}E\left[\int_{\mathbb{R}}(v(t) \circ \theta_t)N(dt)\right] = \frac{1}{\lambda}E\left[\int_{\mathbb{R}} X(t)N(dt)\right].$$

Combining all the above relations, we obtain

$$E\left[\int_{\mathbb{R}} X(t)N(dt)\right] = E\left[\int_{\mathbb{R}}(\lambda\mu \circ \theta_t)X(t)dt\right],$$

where $\{X(t)\}$ is any arbitrary non-negative $\mathcal{F}_t$-predictable process. This shows that $\{\lambda\mu \circ \theta_t\}$ is the $\mathcal{F}_t$-intensity of N.

Before turning to the proof of the converse part, we remark that $\{\lambda\mu \circ \theta_t\}$ is a $\mathcal{F}_t$-predictable process because μ is $\mathcal{F}_{0-}$-measurable and $\{\mathcal{F}_t\}$ is assumed to have a predictable structure adapted to $\{\theta_t\}$.

In order to prove the converse part, we start with the hypothesis that N has the $\mathcal{F}_t$-intensity $\{\lambda(t)\}$. We know that such an intensity can be assumed predictable, that is, in view of the assumption that the predictable structure of $\{\mathcal{F}_t\}$ is adapted to $\{\theta_t\}$,

$$\lambda(t,\omega) = \lambda\widetilde{\mu}(t,\theta_t\omega),$$

where $\widetilde{\mu}$ is $\mathcal{B} \otimes \mathcal{F}$-measurable and for each $t \in \mathbb{R}$, $\omega \to \widetilde{\mu}(t,\omega)$ is $\mathcal{F}_{0-}$-measurable. Let now v be a non-negative $\mathcal{F}_{0-}$-measurable random variable. Since the predictable structure of $\{\mathcal{F}_t\}$ is adapted to $\{\theta_t\}$, $\{X(t)\} = \{v \circ \theta_t\}$ is a $\mathcal{F}_t$-predictable process. Therefore, by the stochastic intensity integration formula, for all $(a,b] \subset \mathbb{R}$,

$$E\left[\int_{(a,b]} (v \circ \theta_t)(\lambda\widetilde{\mu}(t) \circ \theta_t)dt\right] = E\left[\int_{(a,b]} (v \circ \theta_t)N(dt)\right].$$

In view of the θ_t-invariance of P, the left-hand side of this equality is equal to $\lambda E[v \int_{(a,b]} \widetilde{\mu}(t)dt]$, whereas the right-hand side is $\lambda(b-a)E_N^0[v]$. Therefore, for all non-negative random variables v that are $\mathcal{F}_{0-}$-measurable,

$$E_N^0[v] = E\left[v\frac{1}{b-a}\int_a^b \widetilde{\mu}(t)dt\right].$$

This shows that $P_N^0 \ll P$ on $\mathcal{F}_{0-}$ and that $\mu = \frac{1}{b-a}\int_a^b \widetilde{\mu}(t)dt$ is the Radon-Nikodým derivative $\frac{dP_N^0}{dP}|_{\mathcal{F}_{0-}}$

We remark that the proof in the first part can be used to show that $\{\lambda\mu \circ \theta_t\}$ is a predictable $\mathcal{F}_t$-intensity of N. In particular, this intensity is compatible with the shift $\{\theta_t\}$ (we did not start with this as an hypothesis). $\qquad\square$

Mecke's Characterization of Poisson Processes. Let N be a point process and $\{\mathcal{F}_t\}$ be a history of N, both compatible with the flow $\{\theta_t\}$. Suppose that N has a finite intensity λ, and let P_N^0 be the Palm probability associated with (N,θ_t).

(9.2.6) *A necessary and sufficient condition for N to be a Poisson process (i.e. a process such that, for all $(a,b] \subset \mathbb{R}$, the random variable $N(a,b]$ is P-independent of $\mathcal{F}_a$) is*

(9.2.7) $\quad P \equiv P_N^0 \quad$ on $\quad \mathcal{F}_{0-}$.

Proof: In view of (9.2.1), this follows from Watanabe's theorem (8.4.1). $\quad\square$

The result (9.2.1) can be complemented by the following:

(9.2.8) *Let N be a point process and let $\{Z(t)\}$ be a stochastic process with values in the measurable space $(E,\mathcal{E})$, both compatible with the flow $\{\theta_t\}$. Assume that $\lambda = E[N(0,1)]$ is non-null and finite, and that for some history $\{\mathcal{F}_t\}$ of N and $\{Z(t)\}$ with a predictable structure adapted to $\{\theta_t\}$, N admits the $\mathcal{F}_t$-intensity $\{\lambda(t)\}$, of the form $\lambda(t,\omega) = \lambda(0,\theta_t\omega)$, where $\lambda(0)$ is $\mathcal{F}_{0-}$-measurable. Finally, assume that $Z(0)$ has a regular conditional distribution* *w.r.t.* $\mathcal{F}_{0-}$. Then (N, Z), *where* $Z = \{Z_n\} = \{Z(T_n)\}$ *admits the* $\mathcal{F}_t$*-intensity kernel*

$$(9.2.9) \quad \lambda(t, dz) = (\lambda(0)P_N^0(Z(0) \in dz \mid \mathcal{F}_{0-})) \circ \theta_t.$$

Proof: Let $H : \mathbb{R} \times \Omega \times E \to \mathbb{R}_+$ be $\mathcal{P}(\mathcal{F}_t) \otimes \mathcal{E}$-measurable. By the hypothesis made on $\{\mathcal{F}_t\}$,

$$H(t, \omega, z) = v(t, \theta_t \omega, z),$$

for some $v : \mathbb{R} \times \Omega \times E \to \mathbb{R}_+$ that is $\mathcal{B} \otimes \mathcal{F}_{0-} \otimes \mathcal{E}$ measurable.
We have the following sequence of equalities

$$\lambda E_N^0 \left[\int_\mathbb{R} v(t, Z(0)) dt \right] = \lambda E_N^0 \left[\int_\mathbb{R} \int_E v(t, z) P_N^0(Z(0) \in dz \mid \mathcal{F}_{0-}) dt \right]$$

$$= E \left[\int_\mathbb{R} \left[\int_E v(t, z) P_N^0(Z(0) \in dz \mid \mathcal{F}_{0-}) \lambda(0) \right] dt \right]$$

$$= E \left[\int_\mathbb{R} \left[\int_E (v(t, z) \circ \theta_t)(\lambda(0) P_N^0(Z(0)) \in dz \mid \mathcal{F}_{0-})) \circ \theta_t \right] dt \right]$$

$$= E \left[\int_\mathbb{R} \left[\int_E H(t, z)(\lambda(0) P_N^0(Z(0) \in dz \mid \mathcal{F}_{0-})) \circ \theta_t dt \right] \right].$$

On the other hand, by the Campbell- Little-Mecke formula,

$$\lambda E_N^0 \left[\int_\mathbb{R} v(t, Z(0)) dt \right] = E \left[\sum_{n \in \mathbb{Z}} v(T_n, \theta_{T_n}, Z(T_n)) \right]$$

$$= E \left[\sum_{n \in \mathbb{Z}} H(T_n, Z_n) \right]$$

and this concludes the proof. □

9.3 Further Connection with Martingale Theory

In this section, we shall take another look at Papangelou's formula. More precisely, we shall give the equivalent of this formula in the non stationary case when N is a simple point process, not necessarily stationary, but admitting a $(P, \mathcal{F}_t)$-intensity $\{\lambda(t)\}$. Consider a $\mathcal{F}_t$-predictable stochastic process $\{Z(t)\}, t \in \mathbb{R}$, with values in $(E, \mathcal{E})$ and let $f : (E, \mathcal{E}) \to (\mathbb{R}, \mathcal{B})$ be a bounded measurable function. When (P, θ_t) is ergodic, Formula (9.2.5), which was proved in the stationary case, takes the form

$$(9.3.1) \quad \lim_{t \to \infty} \frac{1}{t} \int_0^t f(Z(s)) \lambda(s) ds = \lim_{t \to \infty} \frac{1}{N(0, t]} \int_{(0, t]} f(Z(s)) N(ds).$$

In the non-stationary case, the quantities for which the limit is taken in
(9.3.1) are meaningful. Therefore in the non-stationary case, we shall quite
naturally consider the $(P, \mathcal{F}_t)$-martingale:

$$(9.3.2) \quad M_t = \int_{(0,t]} f(Z(s))(N(ds) - \lambda(s)ds), \ t \geq 0.$$

To be more precise, $\{M_t\}, t \in \mathbb{R}_+$, is a square-integrable local $\mathcal{F}_t$-martingale
and it can be shown that

$$(9.3.3) \quad M_t^2 - <M>_t \text{ is a local } \mathcal{F}_t-\text{martingale},$$

where

$$(9.3.4) \quad <M>_t = \int_0^t f(Z(s))^2 \lambda(s)ds,$$

(for the results stated in this subsection without proof, the reader is re-
ferred to the book by Liptser and Shiryayev, *Theory of Martingales*, Kluwer,
Dordrecht, 1990). An important result of martingale theory, known as the
Martingale Strong Law of Large Numbers (see for instance Dacunha-Castelle
and Duflo, *Probabilités et Statistique*, Masson, Paris, 1982, Theorem 8.2.17,
p. 246) states the following:
(α) On the set $\{<M>_\infty < \infty\}$, $\lim_{t\to\infty} M_t$ exists and is finite.
(β) On the set $\{<M>_\infty = \infty\}$

$$(9.3.5) \quad \lim_{t\to\infty} \frac{M_t}{<M>_t} = 0.$$

Example 9.3.1 Take $f = 1$, that is

$$M_t = N_t - \int_0^t \lambda(s)ds,$$

where $N_t = N((0,t])$. Then $<M>_t = \int_0^t \lambda(s)ds$. By (β), if $\int_0^\infty \lambda(s)ds = \infty$,
then

$$(9.3.6) \quad \lim_{t\to\infty} \frac{N_t}{\int_0^t \lambda(s)ds} = 1$$

and in particular $N_\infty = \infty$. Also we can show that $N_\infty = \infty$ implies
$\int_0^\infty \lambda(s)ds = \infty$, because otherwise, in view of (α), $\lim_{t\to\infty} M_t < \infty$, a contradiction with $\lim_{t\to\infty} M_t = N_\infty - \int_0^\infty \lambda(s)ds = +\infty$.

Note in particular that $\lim_{t\to\infty} \frac{N_t}{t}$ exists if and only if $\lim_{t\to\infty} \frac{\int_0^t \lambda(s)ds}{t}$ exists,
and that the limits are equal when they exist.   □

Example 9.3.2 Consider the martingale $\{M_t\}$ defined by (9.3.2), where f
is bounded. Then on the set

$$(9.3.7) \quad \left\{ \limsup_{t \to \infty} \frac{1}{t} \int_0^t f(Z(s))^2 \lambda(s) ds < \infty \right\},$$

we have

$$(9.3.8) \quad \lim_{t \to \infty} \left\{ \frac{N_t}{t} \frac{1}{N_t} \int_{(0,t]} f(Z(s)) N(ds) - \frac{1}{t} \int_{(0,t]} f(Z(s)) \lambda(s) ds \right\} = 0.$$

Proof: Call B_t the quantity inside the brackets in (9.3.8). By the martingale strong law of large numbers

$$\lim_{t \to \infty} \frac{B_t}{\frac{1}{t} \int_0^t f(Z(s))^2 \lambda(s) ds} = 0$$

and this immediately gives the announced result. □

Clearly the result of Example 9.3.2 can be considered as an avatar of Papangelou's theorem.

10 Poisson Imbedding

Poisson imbedding is a technique of construction of point processes, and more generally of jump processes, using the points of a subjacent Poisson process. It will be used in Chapter 2 for the construction of a general class of stationary point processes with an intensity, the (A, m) point processes. This technique also finds obvious applications in the simulation of point processes.

10.1 Macrostate Models of Markov Chains

All Markov chains occurring in queueing theory can be constructed in the following manner:

Let B be a countable set of *sites* β, and let G be a countable set of *macrostates* g. With each macrostate $g \in G$ is associated a finite set of *active sites* $A(g) \subset B$. With each $g \in G$, $\beta \in A(g)$, is given a probability distribution $(p(\beta, g, g'), g' \in G)$ on G, and a *speed* $c(\beta, g) > 0$. With each $g \in G$, $\beta \in A(g)$ and $g' \in G$ such that $p(\beta, g, g') > 0$ is associated a Poisson processes $N_{\beta, g, g'}$ of intensity $\lambda(\beta) c(\beta, g) p(\beta, g, g')$. The Poisson processes $N_{\beta, g, g'}$ are assumed independent, and independent of a random variable $X(0)$ with values in G, the *initial (macro) state*.

The (macro) state process $\{X(t)\}$, $t \in \mathbb{R}$, is recursively defined as follows:

Suppose that for some t, $X(t)$ is known, equal to g. Then $X(t + s) = X(t) = g$ for all s such that $t + s \leq \tau$, where τ is the first point to the right of t of the following list of Poisson processes:

$$(10.1.1) \quad N_{\beta, X(t), g'}, \ \beta \in A(X(t)), \ g' \ \text{such that} \ p(\beta, X(t), g') > 0 .$$

If β, g' are the site and state corresponding to the Poisson process in the list (10.1.1) with a point at τ (there is only one in view of the independence assumption), then we set $X(\tau) = g'$ and say that the transition $g \to g'$ takes place on site β.

Call $\tau_0 = 0, \tau_1, \tau_2, \ldots$ the successive transition times in this construction. The process $\{X(t)\}$ is defined via this recursive procedure up to time $\tau_\infty = \lim_{n \uparrow \infty} \tau_n$ excluded. If $\tau_\infty = \infty$ almost surely, the process is called *regular*. In most queueing systems, regularity is guaranteed: For instance in a queueing network with a Poisson input, there can be only a finite number of events (departure, transfer from one station to the other) between successive arrivals, and this implies regularity.

From the Markov property of Poisson processes and elementary properties of minimas of exponential times, we see that, when the process is in state g, it stays there for an exponential time of mean q_g^{-1} where

$$(10.1.2) \quad q_g = \sum_{\beta \in A(g)} \lambda(\beta) c(\beta, g)$$

and that the next state is chosen according to the probability distribution $\{q_{g,g'}/q_g, \; g' \in G\}$ where

$$(10.1.3) \quad q_{g,g'} = \sum_{\beta \in A(g)} \lambda(\beta) c(\beta, g) p(g, \beta, g') \; .$$

Also, we can say that being in g, the time which elapses until to the next transition is as explained above, and the site $\beta \in A(g)$ is then chosen with the probability distribution $\{\lambda(\beta) c(s, g)/q_g, \beta \in A(g)\}$ and then the next state is chosen according to the probability distribution $\{p(g, \beta, g'), \; g' \in G\}$.

That $\{X(t)\}$ is a Markov chain satisfying the strong Markov property follows immediately from Watanabe's theorem (8.4.1) and its corollary (8.4.6).

Kolmogorov's and Lévy's Local Martingales. Suppose that $\{X(t)\}$ is regular. For each macrostate $g \in G$, define

$$(10.1.4) \quad Z_g(t) = 1_{\{X(t)=g\}} \; .$$

Call T the collection of triples (g_1, β, g_2) such that $g_1 \in G$, $\beta \in A(g_1)$, and $p(g_1, \beta, g_2) > 0$. For any bounded function $f : G \to \mathbb{R}$, the following equation is easily established

$$f(X(t)) = f(X(0)) + \sum_{(g_1, \beta, g_2) \in T} \int_{(0,t]} f(X(s)) - f(X(s-)) N_{g_1, \beta, g_2}(ds)$$

that is

$$f(X(t)) = f(X(0)) + \sum_{(g_1,\beta,g_2)\in T} f(g_2) \int_{(0,t]} Z_{g_1}(s-)N_{g_1,\beta,g_2}(ds)$$

$$(10.1.5)$$

$$- \sum_{(g_1,\beta,g_2)\in T} f(g_1) \int_{(0,t]} Z_{g_1}(s-)N_{g_1,\beta,g_2}(ds)$$

The assumed regularity of $\{X(t)\}$ implies that there exists only a finite number of discontinuities of $\{X(t)\}$ in a finite interval. Therefore we can find a sequence $\{S_n\}$, $n \geq 1$, of stopping times of $\{X(t)\}$ such that $S_n \uparrow \infty$, and such that the number of discontinuities of $\{X(t)\}$ in $(0, S_n]$ is bounded by n. In particular, for all $n \geq 1$,

$$\sum_{(g_1,\beta,g_2)\in T} f(g) \int_{(0,t\wedge S_n]} Z_{g_1}(s-)N_{g_1,\beta,g_2}(ds) \leq n\|f\| < \infty,$$

where $g = g_1$ or g_2 and $\|f\| = \sup_{g\in G} f(g)$, and in particular, the expectation of this sum is finite. By the stochastic intensity integration formula (8.3.3), using the fact that $H(t,\omega) = 1_{\{0<s\leq t\wedge S_n(\omega)\}} Z_{g_1}(s-)$ is a $\mathcal{F}_t$-predictable process, where $\mathcal{F}_t$ is the past at time t of all the Poisson processes $N_{g,\beta,g'}$, and using the results of § 8.3, it follows that

$$f(X(t)) - f(X(0)) - \sum_{(g_1,\beta,g_2)\in T} f(g_2) \int_{(0,t]} Z_{g_1}(s)\lambda(\beta)c(\beta,g_1)p(g_1,\beta,g_2)ds$$

$$+ \sum_{(g_1,\beta,g_2)\in T} f(g_1) \int_{(0,t]} Z_{g_1}(s)\lambda(\beta)c(\beta,g_1)p(g_1,\beta,g_2)ds$$

is a local martingale w.r.t. $\{\mathcal{F}_t\}$. Using (10.1.2), (10.1.3) and the relation $f(X(s)) = \sum_{g\in G} f(g)Z_g(s)$, we have therefore shown that

$$(10.1.6) \quad f(X(t)) - f(X(0)) + \int_{(0,t]} \{f(X(s))q_{X(s)} - (\sum_{g\in G} f(g))q_{X(s)g}\}ds$$

is a local martingale w.r.t. $\mathcal{F}_t$. In particular, if

$$(10.1.7) \quad q_{X(t)} = \sum_{g\in G} q_{X(t)g} \leq K,$$

for some $K < \infty$, it defines a martingale. The martingale in (10.1.6) is called Kolmogorov's martingale since for the choice $f(g) = 1_{g=g_0}$, it leads to the Kolmogorov differential system.

Let now $f : G \times G \to \mathbb{R}$ be a bounded function such that

$$(10.1.8) \quad f(g,g) = 0 \text{ for all } g \in G .$$

Arguments similar to those given above show that

$$(10.1.9) \quad \int_{s\in(0,t]} f(X(s-),X(s)) - \int_{(0,t]} \left\{ \sum_{g\in G} f(X(s),g) q_{X(s)g} \right\} ds$$

is a local $\mathcal{F}_t$-martingale, and a $\mathcal{F}_t$-martingale if (10.1.7) is verified. The local martingale (10.1.9) is the Lévy-local martingale associated with the Markov chain $\{X(t)\}$.

10.2 Imbedded Thinning

Poisson Processes on Product Spaces as Marked Poisson Processes
Let $(E,\mathcal{E})$ be an arbitrary measurable space and let $\widetilde{N}$ be a Poisson process on $\mathbb{R} \times E$ with the associated σ-finite measure $\widetilde{\mu}$, that is for all $K \geq 1$, all disjoint sets $\widetilde{C_1},\ldots,\widetilde{C_K} \in \mathcal{B}(\mathbb{R})\otimes\mathcal{E}$ with finite $\widetilde{\mu}$-measure, $\widetilde{N}(\widetilde{C_1}),\ldots,\widetilde{N}(\widetilde{C_K})$ are independent Poisson variables with respective means $\widetilde{\mu}(\widetilde{C_1}),\ldots,\widetilde{\mu}(\widetilde{C_K})$.

For each $t \in \mathbb{R}$, let $\mathcal{F}_t$ be the σ-field generated by the random variables $\widetilde{N}(\widetilde{C})$ where $\widetilde{C} \subset \mathcal{B}((-\infty,t]) \otimes \mathcal{E}$.

For $C \in \mathcal{B}(\mathbb{R})$, $F \in \mathcal{E}$, we catch up with previous notation by denoting

$$N(C \times F) = \widetilde{N}(C \times F) \ .$$

Then, for all $a \in \mathbb{R}$, all $C \in \mathcal{B}((a,\infty))$, all $F \in \mathcal{E}$, $N(C \times F)$ is independent of $\mathcal{F}_a$.

In particular for all $a,b \in \mathbb{R}$, $a \leq b$, and all $A \in \mathcal{F}_a$, $C \in \mathcal{B}((a,\infty))$ and all $F \in \mathcal{E}$

$$E[1_A N(C \times F)] = E[1_A \widetilde{\mu}(C \times F)],$$

from which it follows from the monotone class theorem that for any non-negative function $H : \mathbb{R} \times \Omega \times E \to \mathbb{R}$ which is $\mathcal{P}(\mathcal{F}_t) \otimes \mathcal{E}$ measurable

$$(10.2.1) \quad E\left[\int_{\mathbb{R}\times E} H(t,z)N(dt \times dz)\right] = E\left[\int_{\mathbb{R}\times E} H(t,z)\widetilde{\mu}(dt \times dz)\right] \ .$$

Of special interest is the situation where

$$(10.2.2) \quad \widetilde{\mu}(dt \times dz) = dt\,\mu(dz),$$

where μ is a σ-finite measure on $(E,\mathcal{E})$. Then (10.2.1) reads:

$$(10.2.3) \quad E\left[\int_{\mathbb{R}\times E} H(t,\omega,z)N(dt \times dz)\right] = E\left[\int_{\mathbb{R}} \left\{\int_{E} H(t,z)\mu(dz)\right\} dt\right] \ .$$

Example 10.2.1 *i.i.d. marks of a Poisson process.* Another special case of interest is $(E,\mathcal{E}) = (K,\mathcal{K})$ (just a change in notation in order to be consistent with previous ones), and

(10.2.4) $\tilde{\mu}(dt \times dz) = \lambda \, dt \times Q(dz)$,

where Q is a probability distribution on $(K, \mathcal{K})$. Then calling N the projection of $\tilde{N}$ on $\mathbb{R}$, i.e.

$$N(C) = \tilde{N}(C \times K) = N(C \times K),$$

we immediately obtain that N is a Poisson process with intensity λ since $E[N(C)] = E[N(C \times K)] = \lambda \, l(C) Q(K) = \lambda \, l(C)$. Calling $\{T_n\}$, $n \in \mathbb{Z}$, the sequence of points of N, and Z_n the mark of T_n defined by "(T_n, Z_n) is a point of $\tilde{N}$", we have obtained a marked point process $(N, \{Z_n\})$ with the $\mathcal{F}_t$-intensity kernel $\lambda \, dt \, Q(dz)$ since (10.2.1) then reads

$$E\left[\int_{\mathbb{R} \times K} H(t, z) N(dt \times dz)\right] = E\left[\int_{\mathbb{R} \times K} H(t, z) \lambda \, dt \, Q(dz)\right].$$

The reader is invited to provide a proof for the fact that $\{Z_n\}$ is i.i.d., of distribution Q, and independent of $\{T_n\}$. We are now going to show how the above construction can in turn be used for the construction of more general marked point processes, with dependencies. $\square$

Example 10.2.2 *Imbedded thinning.* Let N be a Poisson process of intensity $\lambda > 0$, and let $\{U_n\}$, $n \geq 1$, be a sequence of independent i.i.d. marks of N, uniformly distributed over $[0, 1]$.

Let $\varphi : (M, \mathcal{M}) \to [0, 1]$ be a measurable functional defined on the canonical space of point processes, that is measurable w.r.t. the σ-field generated by the mappings $m \to m(C)$, $C \subset \mathcal{B}((-\infty, 0))$. Define N_1 recursively by

(10.2.5) $N_1((0, t)) = \sum_{n \geq 1} 1_{T_n \leq t} 1_{U_n \leq \varphi(S_{T_n} N_1)}$.

Then N_1 has the $\mathcal{F}_t^{N_1}$-stochastic intensity

(10.2.6) $\lambda_1(t) = \lambda \varphi(S_t N_1)$.

Proof: With $\mathcal{F}_t = \mathcal{F}_t^{N,U}$, we know that $(N, \{U_n\})$ admits the $\mathcal{F}_t$-intensity kernel $\lambda \, dt \, du$. Moreover $\varphi(S_t N_1)$ is $\mathcal{F}_t$-predictable (for a formal proof of this use T34, Appendix A2 of [26]). Therefore for all $\mathcal{F}_t$-predictable non-negative processes $\{H(t)\}$

$$E\left[\int_{\mathbb{R}} H(s)N_1(ds)\right] = E\left[\sum_{n\geq 1} H(T_n)1_{U_n\leq\varphi(S_{T_n}N_1)}\right]$$

$$= E\left[\int_{\mathbb{R}}\int_{[0,1]} H(t)1_{u\leq\varphi(S_t N_1)}N(dt\times du)\right]$$

$$= E\left[\int_{\mathbb{R}}\int_{[0,1]} H(t)1_{u\leq\varphi(S_t N_1)}\lambda\,dt\,du\right] .$$

That is

$$E\left[\int_{\mathbb{R}} H(t)N_1(dt)\right] = E\left[\int_{\mathbb{R}} H(t)\lambda\,\varphi(S_t N_1)dt\right] .$$

Taking in particular $H(t)$ to be $\mathcal{F}_t^{N_1}$-predictable (therefore it is also $\mathcal{F}_t^{N,U}$-predictable since $\mathcal{F}_t^{N_1}\subset\mathcal{F}_t^{N,U}$ for all $t\geq 0$), we see that N_1 has the $\mathcal{F}_t^{N_1}$-intensity (10.2.6). □

Example 10.2.3 In (10.2.3), take $E = \mathbb{R}$ and $\mu(dz) = dz$. (Thus $\widetilde{N}$ is a homogeneous Poisson Process on $\mathbb{R}^2$ with intensity 1). Let φ be as in Example 10.2.2. Define N_1 by

$$N_1((0,t]) = \int_{\mathbb{R}\times\mathbb{R}}\int 1_{(0,t]}(s)1_{(0,\varphi(S_s N_1)]}(z)N(ds\times dz) .$$

Then, with a proof similar to that of Example 10.2.2, we obtain that N_1 has the $\mathcal{F}_t$-intensity $\varphi(S_t N_1)$. □

Bibliographical Comments

The θ_t framework was first introduced in the theory of Palm probabilities by Totoki [128]. It allows us to work in a single abstract probability space, thus avoiding successive translations from one canonical space to another, which tend to be very cumbersome, and very often make simple facts hard to understand.

The presentation of Palm probability that we have adopted in this book is the one in terms of counting (Equation (3.1.1)), due to Matthes (see [92]). In the case of point processes on the line, this definition is the simplest one available, and it directly leads to the basic formula of Mecke [93], the so-called generalized Campbell's formula (Equation (3.3.1)), which is the root of Palm calculus, and is also known in queueing theory as the $H = \lambda G$ formula, where it is attributed to Brumelle [32] who discovered it independently and more importantly noticed its various applications in queueing theory (see Chapter 3). Neveu's original proof of the exchange formula (Equation (3.4.1)) appeared in [102]. It was given for abstract spaces (locally compact with a denumerable base). The proof of this formula given in the present chapter is elementary because it takes advantage of the real line structure. The conservation principle (Equation (3.5.2)) was first stated in these terms by Miyazawa [98]. This elementary observation has a counterpart in the martingale approach to point processes (see the comments of Chapter 3). In Chapter 3, we shall give a compact formula, the so-called Swiss Army formula of [28], which contains Neveu's exchange formula, the formula of inversion and a few others, as well as other formulas of specific interest to queueing theory. The inversion formula is due to Slivnyak [122] and Ryll-Nardzewski [114]. It is related to Smith's formula of renewal theory [124] which gives the limiting distribution of non-lattice regenerative processes. The inverse construction, from Palm to stationary, of Subsection 4.4 is due to Slivnyak [123]. It is a useful tool, permitting the construction of continuous time stationary processes via discrete time stationary processes. The content of Remark 4.4.1 was pointed out to us by H. Thorisson [127]. The local definition of Palm probability (Equation (6.2.1)) is due to Ryll-Nardzewski [114]. Of course the global definition of Matthes (Equation (3.1.1)) is to be preferred because it gives rise to the Palm calculus, via Mecke's formula (Equation (3.3.1)). The cross-ergodic theorems of § 7 are due to Franken and Streller [46]. Their importance is due to the fact that they allow an interpretation of the formulas of Palm calculus, involving at the same time expectations under the Palm probability and the stationary probability, as relations between time-averages and event-averages. More results on ergodic point processes can be found in the article of Delasnerie [38]. The discrete time Palm theory of § 7.4 shows what it is really all about: conditioning at events (Ryll-Nardzewski's interpretation of § 6) occurring at a fixed time $n \in \mathbb{N}$ or $t \in \mathbb{R}$. Only for the case $t \in \mathbb{R}$, the probability of an event occurring at a fixed time is zero under the stationary probability! For historical comments concerning the notion of stochastic intensity, the reader is referred to the introduction of [26]. The characterization of Poisson processes of § 8.4 is due to Watanabe [130], and the proof given in this chapter together with the extension to general histories follows the fundamental ideas of Kunita and Watanabe [79]. The observation that the stochastic intensity on $\mathbb{R}$ is not changed by passage from the Palm probability to the stationary probability was made in [27]. It is reassuring in that it shows that both probabilities give the same dynamics to the point process. Papangelou's proof of his Radon-Nikodým derivative theorem (9.2.1), [105], is different form that given in § 9.2, which is due to Baccelli and Brémaud [4]. The characterization of Poisson processes of (9.2.6) is due to Mecke [94]. The construction of Markov chains of § 10.1 by means of Poisson processes is equivalent to the GSMP (Generalized Semi-Markov Processes) description, due to Matthes [91]. This construction is repeatedly invented in the literature, and finds applications in simulation. The same is true of the construction by imbedding of point processes of § 10.2. The basic facts and historical comments on the measure theoretic approach to point processes can be found in the books of Daley and Vere-Jones [37], Kallenberg [64], Karr [66], Kerstan, Matthes and Mecke [92], and in Neveu's lecture notes [101]. Concerning the martingale theory of stochastic intensity, we shall quote the books of Brémaud [26], and Liptser and Shiryayev [84] (the last chapters, only in the English edition), the lecture notes of Neveu [101], and the article of Jacod [57].

2 Stationarity and Coupling

Introduction

The θ_t-framework presented in Chapter 1 features point processes, sequences and stochastic processes which are compatible with the flow $\{\theta_t\}$. In the study of stationary queueing systems, the input into the system is a marked point process (the marks being, for instance, the service times required by the arriving customers) which is compatible with $\{\theta_t\}$. This input in turn generates *secondary processes* such as the workload process, the departure point process, the congestion process. The following question arises: can the *initial conditions* (for instance the congestion at the origin of times) be chosen in such a way that the secondary process in consideration is stationary? The underlying probability P being assumed θ_t-invariant for all t, a stronger statement is : is the secondary process compatible with the flow $\{\theta_t\}$ and finite (when finiteness has a meaning)?

Questions of this type constitute the *stability* theory of queueing systems and are the main concern of the present chapter. The basic techniques of this theory are applied to a few queueing systems of interest for which we determine the *stability region* under general statistical assumptions.

The basic result which has motivated the present interest in finding general conditions of stability for queueing systems is due to Loynes (1962) who not only proved the fundamental stability theorem for $G/G/1/\infty$ systems but also stated the stability question in very general terms. This theory is presented in § 2 for the $G/G/1/\infty$ queue and in § 3 for the $G/G/s/\infty$ queue. Section 1 introduces the notations and the problem, and shows how to pass from the Palm probability to the stationary probability as far as stability is concerned, whereupon we shall generally work in the Palm framework.

In this setting, the dynamics of the system are described by a stochastic recurrence, for which one has to prove the existence and uniqueness of a stationary solution.

A fundamental concept is that of *construction points*, for instance the arrival times at which the system is empty, from which one can construct all secondary processes of interest from a single stationary process (here the workload).

In spite of Loynes' results, stability theory is far from being a closed subject. Difficulties arise not only because of explosion phenomena (i.e. for instance there are too many arrivals with large service times) but also because of periodicity phenomena. When explosion is possible, the emphasis is on finding a secondary process which is compatible with the flow $\{\theta_t\}$ and *finite*. On the other hand, for many systems such as $G/G/1/0$, studied in § 5, the problem is equivalent to finding a workload which is compatible with $\{\theta_t\}$, the finiteness obviously not being in question (for instance, there is at most one customer in the $G/G/1/0$ system). The stability theory for queueing networks is currently a very active and open research area. The main techniques are exemplified in § 7-8. Section 9 focuses on a general method for the stability of open queueing networks based on subadditive ergodic theory, which we call the *saturation rule*.

For this type of dynamic system, another important issue is that of the nature of the convergence to the stationary regime when it exists. The two main useful notions in this respect are that of construction points and of coupling. The latter is developed in § 4. Two related problems are also considered in this section: the uniqueness of the stationary regimes and the dependence of the stationary regimes on the initial conditions. A basic tool for addressing these questions is Borovkov's renovating events method, which is presented in § 4.

One of the outcomes of this chapter will be the decoupling of two important tasks of queueing theory: that of showing stability of a given system, and that of deriving formulas. Indeed, in many cases, the formulas derived in the stationary framework involve expectation with respect to the stationary probability and/or the Palm probability, which can be interpreted as limits of the corresponding expectations when the process is not started from a stationary state.

1 Stability of the $G/G/1/\infty$ Queue

1.1 The G/G/1/∞ Queue

Let $(\Omega, \mathcal{F}, P)$ be a probability space with a measurable flow $\{\theta_t\}$, $t \in \mathbb{R}$, such that $(P, \{\theta_t\})$ is ergodic, that is to say : P is θ_t-invariant for all $t \in \mathbb{R}$, and if $B \in \mathcal{F}$ is invariant (i.e. $\theta_t B = B$ for all $t \in \mathbb{R}$), then either $P(B) = 0$ or $P(B) = 1$.

Let A be a point process defined on $(\Omega, \mathcal{F})$. Assume A is simple and compatible with $\{\theta_t\}$. It is called the *arrival* (point) process and its n-th 'point' T_n is interpreted as the arrival time of customer n. Recall the convention $T_n < T_{n+1}(n \in \mathbb{Z})$ and $T_0 \leq 0 < T_1$. The *inter-arrival time* between customers n and $n + 1$ is

(1.1.1) $\tau_n = T_{n+1} - T_n, \quad n \in \mathbb{Z}.$

It will be assumed that the intensity of the arrival process is finite

(1.1.2) $\lambda = E[A((0,1])] < \infty.$

Customer n carries an amount of required service (or service time) denoted by $\sigma_n \geq 0$, where the sequence $\{\sigma_n\}$ is assumed to be a sequence of marks of the arrival process (see Chapter 1, § 1.3).

   Letting P_A^0 be the Palm probability associated with P and A, we define the *traffic intensity* ρ by

(1.1.3) $\rho = \lambda E_A^0[\sigma_0].$

Recall from Chapter 1, § 7.2 that the ergodicity of $(P, \{\theta_t\})$ is equivalent to the ergodicity of (P_A^0, θ), where $\theta = \theta_{T_1}$. In terms of P, the traffic intensity is defined by the relation

(1.1.3') $\displaystyle \rho = \lambda \lim_{N \to \infty} \frac{1}{N} \sum_{k=1}^{N} \sigma_k, \quad P - \text{a.s.}$

In terms of P_A^0, we have

(1.1.3'') $\displaystyle \rho = \frac{E_A^0[\sigma_0]}{E_A^0[\tau_0]},$

since $\lambda^{-1} = E_A^0[T_1] = E_A^0[T_1 - T_0]$ (see Chapter 1, § 4.2).

   The sequence $\{(T_n, \sigma_n)\}$, $n \in \mathbb{Z}$, describes the *input* into some queueing system. Using Kendall's terminology, this is a G/G input. It is stationary in two distinct (but related) senses: under the Palm probability P_A^0, the sequence $\{(\tau_n, \sigma_n)\}$, $n \in \mathbb{Z}$, is stationary, and under the stationary probability P, the marked point process $(A, \{\sigma_n\})$ is stationary. The latter stationarity means that the marked point process $A(dt \times d\sigma)$ defined by

$$A(C \times D) = \sum_{n \in \mathbb{Z}} 1_C(T_n) 1_D(\sigma_n) \quad (C \in \mathcal{B}(\mathbb{R}) \ , \ D \in \mathcal{B}(\mathbb{R}_+))$$

and its shifted version $(S_\tau A)(dt \times d\sigma)$ defined by

$$(S_\tau A)(C \times D) = A(\{C + \tau\} \times D) = \sum_{n \in \mathbb{Z}} 1_C(T_n - \tau) 1_D(\sigma_n),$$

have the same distribution, for any $\tau \in \mathbb{R}$.

   Suppose that the G/G input is the input of a queueing system with just one server providing service at unit rate, and that the server is idle only if there is no customer in the queueing system. Suppose also that the queueing system has a waiting room (where customers stay if they are not yet attended by the server, not to be confused with the 'service booth', where customers stay when their service service has started and has not yet been completed) of infinite capacity. We have just described a '$1/\infty$' *queueing station* (1 server,

∞ capacity). The service mechanism, which includes among other things the discipline of service and the priority rules will not be further described at this stage.

Any queueing system with the above input entering the above queueing station is called a $G/G/1/\infty$ *queue*, again in accordance with Kendall's notational system. It is symbolized by Figure 1.1.1.

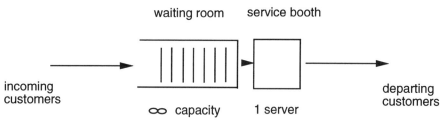

waiting room   **service booth**

incoming
customers

∞ **capacity**   **1 server**

departing
customers

Fig. 1.1.1 $G/G/1/\infty$

1.2 Loynes' Stability Theorem

The Workload in the G/G/1/∞ Queue. For any queueing system, $W(t)$ will denote the amount of service (in time units) remaining to be done by the server(s) at time t. By convention, a *workload process* $\{W(t)\}$, $t \in \mathbb{R}$, will be taken right-continuous with left-hand limits $W(t-)$, so that its evolution between two successive arrivals is described by Lindley's equation:

$$(1.2.1) \quad W(t) = (W(T_n-) + \sigma_n - (t - T_n))^+, \quad t \in [T_n, T_{n+1}),$$

where $a^+ = \max(a, 0)$. In general a workload process $\{W(t)\}$ is defined only for $t \geq 0$, with initial condition $W(0) = Y$, where Y is some non-negative random variable. In this case, we shall use the notation $\{W^Y(t)\}$, $t \geq 0$. For instance, if $T_0 < 0$, the evolution of this process is described by

$$W^Y(t) = \begin{cases} (Y - t)^+, & \text{for } t \in [0, T_1); \\ (W^Y(T_n-) + \sigma_n - (t - T_n))^+, & \text{for } t \in [T_n, T_{n+1}), n \geq 1. \end{cases}$$

Consider the following question : is it possible to choose the initial workload Y in such a way that $\{W^Y(t)\}$, $t \geq 0$, is a stationary process ?

Loynes (1952) posed the problem in the following more ambitious terms:

Can we find a random variable W, which is P-almost surely *finite*, and such that when taking the initial workload Y equal to W in the preceding construction, then $\{W^W(t)\}$, $t \in \mathbb{R}$ satisfies the relation

$$(1.2.2) \quad W^W(t, \omega) = W(\theta_t \omega).$$

Observe that if (1.2.2) holds true, $\{W(t)\}$ is compatible with the flow $\{\theta_t\}$, and therefore P-stationary because P is θ_t-invariant. $\{W(t)\}$, $t \in \mathbb{R}$, is then called a P-stationary workload process.

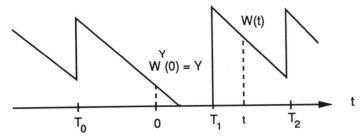

Fig. 1.2.1 A workload process for $G/G/1/\infty$

The Fundamental Result of Stability. Loynes established the following theorem, which will be proved in § 2:

(1.2.3) *Under the stability condition*

(1.2.4) $\rho < 1$,

there exists a unique finite workload process $\{W(t)\}$, $t \in \mathbb{R}$, compatible with the flow $\{\theta_t\}$, and satisfying Equation (1.2.1) for all $n \in \mathbb{Z}$. Moreover, there are an infinite number of negative indices n and an infinite number of positive indices n such that

(1.2.5) $W(T_n-) = 0$.

If the traffic intensity ρ is strictly larger than 1, there exists no finite P-stationary workload process $\{W(t)\}$, $t \in \mathbb{R}$.

(1.2.7) *In the critical case $\rho = 1$, there may or may not exist a finite P-stationary workload process $\{W(t)\}$, $t \in \mathbb{R}$, compatible with the flow $\{\theta_t\}$.*

1.3 Construction Points and Cycles

Let us assume stability (i.e. $\rho < 1$) and let $\{W(t)\}$, $t \in \mathbb{R}$, be the unique P-stationary workload. The point process R defined by

(1.3.1) $$R(C) = \sum_{n \in \mathbb{Z}} 1_C(T_n) 1_{\{0\}}(W(T_n-)),$$

counts the construction points T_n at which an arriving customer finds an empty queue. Clearly R is compatible with $\{\theta_t\}$. Let $\{U_n\}$, $n \in \mathbb{Z}$, be the sequence of 'points' of R, with the usual convention

$U_0 \le 0 < U_1$.

For each $n \in \mathbb{Z}$, let V_{n+1} be the first time t after U_n at which $W(t) = 0$ (see Figure 1.3.1)

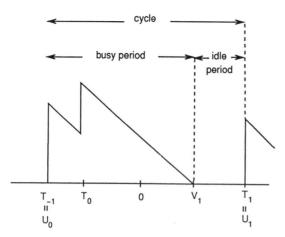

Fig. 1.3.1 Busy period, idle period

The interval $[U_n, U_{n+1})$ is called the n-th *cycle*, $[U_n, V_{n+1})$ is the n-th *busy period* and $[V_{n+1}, U_{n+1})$ is the n-th *idle period*.

Our goal is to construct a *right-continuous congestion process* $\{X(t)\}$, $t \in \mathbb{R}$, where $X(t)$ is the number of customers in the queueing station at time t, being either in the waiting room or at the service booth. We call $\{X(t)\}$ the *system congestion process*, to distinguish it from the *waiting room congestion process* $\{Q(t)\}$ counting the customers in the waiting room. In a $G/G/1/\infty$ queue, $X(t)$ and $Q(t)$ are related by

(1.3.2) $Q(t) = (X(t) - 1)^+.$

In order to construct $\{X(t)\}$ or $\{Q(t)\}$, we must be given the priority rules and the service discipline. Here we shall suppose that there exists only one class of customers so that no question of priority arises. The service discipline is embodied in a rule deciding which of the customers present at time t should be served. Popular disciplines are:

FIFO (First-In-First-Out). When the server completes the service of customer n, he immediately begins to attend customer $n + 1$ if the latter has yet arrived. If the queue is empty, he waits for customer $n + 1$ to arrive and then attends him immediately upon arrival.

LIFO (Last-In-First-Out). This is an apparently unfair service discipline, where an arriving customer places himself at the head of the line. In the *non-preemptive* case, the service of a customer cannot be interrupted once started, whereas in the *preemptive* case, the newly arrived customer is immediately served upon arrival and the customer whose service is interrupted joins the first position in the waiting line. In the *preemptive resume* discipline, he retains the acquired service. Let us mention at this point that LIFO preemptive resume is only apparently unfair, and that it has good properties in certain situations. For instance, if the input is M/GI (Poisson arrival process, independent of the i.i.d. service sequence), the mean sojourn time in the system given that the required service is x is proportional to x, which is quite fair.

RANDOM. When the server finishes the service of a customer, he takes a new customer at random in the waiting room.

SPT (Shortest Processing Time). The server takes the customer in line with the shortest required service time.

SRPT (Shortest Remaining Processing Time). This is a preemptive resume discipline, where at each instant t the server attends the customer with the shortest remaining processing time. A preemption therefore occurs if and only if the newly arrived customer has a required service smaller than the remaining service time of the customer being served.

All the above service disciplines belong to the class of *reasonable* disciplines. By this we mean that if $t \in [U_n, U_{n+1})$, the n-th cycle, the choice of the customer being served at time t depends upon the history of the system only through what happened in the time interval $[U_n, t]$.

Similarly, we can distinguish between those disciplines which depend upon the service times (like SPT or SRPT), and those which do not (like FIFO, LIFO or RANDOM).

Clearly, for any reasonable service discipline, the congestion process $\{X(t)\}$, $t \in [U_n, V_{n+1})$, can be constructed from $\{W(t)\}$, $t \in [U_n, V_{n+1})$, and from the knowledge of the service discipline (maybe together with the help of a random experiment, as in the RANDOM discipline). Moreover this construction results in a congestion process $\{X(t)\}$, $t \in \mathbb{R}$, that is compatible with $\{\theta_t\}$.

Example 1.3.1 *FIFO*. The construction of $\{X(t)\}$ is explained in Figure 1.3.2. More formally, we have

$$X(t) = \sum_{n \in \mathbb{Z}} 1_{T_n \leq t} 1_{T_n + W(T_n -) + \sigma_n > t},$$

and therefore

$$X(0) \circ \theta_t = \sum_{n \in \mathbb{Z}} 1_{T_n \circ \theta_t \leq 0} 1_{T_n \circ \theta_t + W(T_n \circ \theta_t -) + \sigma_n \circ \theta_t > 0}$$

$$= \sum_{n \in \mathbb{Z}} 1_{T_n \leq t} 1_{T_n - t + W(T_n -) + \sigma_n > 0}$$

$$= X(t).$$

$\square$

Example 1.3.2 *RANDOM*. Here the basic input process must be augmented with an i.i.d. sequence $\{Z_n\}$, $n \in \mathbb{Z}$, of $[0,1]^{\mathbb{N}}$-valued random variables, independent of $\{(T_n, \sigma_n)\}$, $n \in \mathbb{Z}$. The coordinates $Z_n^1, Z_n^2, \ldots$ of Z_n,

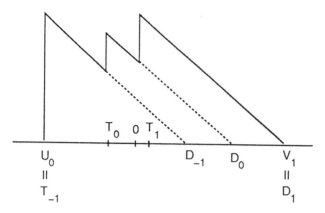

Fig. 1.3.2 Departure process in the FIFO discipline. Here $D_n = T_n + W_n + \sigma_n$ is the departure time of the n-th customer.

are i.i.d. and uniformly distributed in the interval $[0, 1]$. When the n-th service is just completed, if there are k, customers (with indices $(n_1, \ldots, n_k)$) waiting in the queue, the server chooses customer n_i if $Z_n^i < Z_n^j$, for all $1 \leq j \leq k$, $j \neq i$. The knowledge of $\{(T_n, \sigma_n, Z_n)\}$, $n \in \mathbb{Z}$, and of the sequence of construction points $\{U_n\}$, $n \in \mathbb{Z}$, allows us to construct the congestion processes.   □

Remark 1.3.1 The reader will verify by means of examples that for the same sequence $\{(T_n, \sigma_n\}$, $n \in \mathbb{Z}$, different service disciplines give different congestion processes, whereas the workload process remains the same.   □

2 Proof of Loynes' Theorem

2.1 Reduction to the Palm Setting

The proof will be given in the Palm setting. This means that we are looking for a random variable Z that is P_A^0-a.s. finite and verifies the functional equation, called the stationary Lindley equation

$$(2.1.1) \quad Z \circ \theta = (Z + \sigma - \tau)^+, \qquad P_A^0\text{-a.s.},$$

where $\theta = \theta_{T_1}$, $\sigma = \sigma_0$, $\tau = \tau_0$.

If there exists such a random variable, we define a workload sequence $\{W_n\}$ by

$$(2.1.2) \quad W_n = Z \circ \theta^n, \quad n \in \mathbb{Z},$$

and the workload process $\{W(t)\}$ by

$$(2.1.3) \quad \begin{cases} W(T_n-)(\omega) = Z(\theta_{T_n}\omega) \\ W(t) = (W(T_n-) + \sigma_n - (t - T_n))^+, \quad t \in [T_n, T_{n+1}). \end{cases}$$

The first equality defines the sequence $\{W(T_n-)\}$ indeed (since Z is defined on $\Omega_0 = \{T_0 = 0\}$ and $\theta_{T_n}\omega \in \Omega_0$ for all $n \in \mathbb{Z}$). The second equality defines $\{W(t)\}$. However we must check consistency, i.e. that $W(T_n-)$ is indeed the limit as $t \to T_n$, $t < T_n$, of $W(t)$, that is

$$W(T_{n+1}-) = (W(T_n-) + \sigma_n - \tau_n)^+, \quad P-\text{a.s.}, \ \forall n \in \mathbb{Z}.$$

But this follows from (2.1.1) and (2.1.2) which imply that

$$P_A^0 \left[W(T_{n+1}-) = (W(T_n-) + \sigma_n - \tau_n)^+, \ \forall n \in \mathbb{Z} \right] = 1$$

and from the fact that the event in the left-hand side of the latter equality is θ_{T_1}-invariant (see Chapter 1, § 7.1).

Finally, let us check that $W(t)$ defined in (2.1.3) satisfies (1.2.2). We have here $W = W(0) = (Z \circ \theta_{T_0} + \sigma_0 + T_0)^+$. By definition, for $t \in [T_n, T_{n+1})$, $Z \circ \theta_{T_0} \circ \theta_t = W(T_n-)$, $\sigma_0 \circ \theta_t = \sigma_n$ and $T_0 \circ \theta_t = T_n - t$, and therefore $W \circ \theta_t = W(t)$ for all t.

We now come back to the study of (2.1.1). For the sake of notational simplicity, P_A^0 will be denoted P^0.

We recall the basic hypotheses

$$(2.1.4) \quad \tau > 0, \ \sigma \geq 0, \ P^0-\text{a.s.}, \ E^0[\tau] < \infty, \ E^0[\sigma] < \infty$$

and

$$(2.1.5) \quad (P^0, \theta) \text{ is ergodic.}$$

2.2 Construction of the Workload Sequence

Define M_n $(n \geq 0)$ to be the workload found by customer 0 supposing that customer $-n$ found an empty queue upon arrival, that is,

$$M_n = W_n^0 \circ \theta^{-n}, \quad n \geq 0.$$

It is easily checked by induction that

$$(2.2.1) \quad M_n = \left(\max_{1 \leq m \leq n} \sum_{i=1}^{m} (\sigma_{-i} - \tau_{-i}) \right)^+,$$

with the convention that the maximum over an empty set is 0. In particular, M_n is integrable for all $n \in \mathbb{N}$. The sequence $\{M_n\}$ verifies the recurrence relation

$$(2.2.2) \quad M_{n+1} \circ \theta = (M_n + \sigma - \tau)^+$$

and (2.2.1) shows that it is non-decreasing. Denoting by M_∞ the limit

$$(2.2.3) \quad M_\infty = \lim_{n\to\infty} \uparrow M_n = \left(\sup_n \sum_{i=1}^{n}(\sigma_{-i} - \tau_{-i})\right)^+$$

and letting n go to ∞ in (2.2.2), we see that M_∞ is a non-negative random variable satisfying

$$(2.2.4) \quad M_\infty \circ \theta = (M_\infty + \sigma - \tau)^+.$$

The random variable M_∞ is often referred to as Loynes' variable, while the sequence $\{M_n\}$ is called Loynes' sequence. The random variable M_∞ can take infinite values. When using the identity $(a - b)^+ = a - a \wedge b$, equality (2.2.2) becomes

$$(2.2.5) \quad M_{n+1} \circ \theta = M_n - M_n \wedge (\tau - \sigma)$$

and therefore, since P^0 is θ-invariant, and $\{M_n\}$ is increasing and integrable, $E^0[M_n \wedge (\tau - \sigma)] \leq 0$. By monotone convergence

$$(2.2.6) \quad E^0[M_\infty \wedge (\tau - \sigma)] \leq 0.$$

Equality (2.2.4) shows that the event $\{M_\infty = \infty\}$ is θ-invariant. Therefore, in view of the ergodic assumption (2.1.5), $P^0(M_\infty = \infty)$ is either 0 or 1. In view of (2.2.6), $P^0(M_\infty = \infty) = 1$ implies $E^0[\tau - \sigma] \leq 0$. Therefore

$(2.2.7)$ $E^0[\sigma] < E^0[\tau]$ *implies that* $M_\infty < \infty$, P^0-*a.s.*

A partial converse of the above stability result is the following:

$(2.2.8)$ *If* $E^0[\sigma] > E^0[\tau]$, *then no* P^0-*a.s. finite solution of (2.1.1) exists.*

Proof: To prove this, it is enough to show that $M_\infty = \infty$, P^0-a.s., and that M_∞ is the minimal non-negative solution of (2.1.1). The latter is proved by induction. Starting with a non-negative solution Z of (2.1.1), it is easily checked that $Z \geq M_n$ implies $Z \geq M_{n+1}$ (this is true because $M_{n+1} \circ \theta = (M_n + \sigma - \tau)^+ \leq (Z + \sigma - \tau)^+ = Z \circ \theta$). The first term of the induction is $Z \geq 0 = M_0$.

The proof of the property $M_\infty = \infty$, P^0-a.s., follows from

$$\lim_{n\to\infty} \frac{1}{n} \sum_{i=1}^{n}(\sigma_{-i} - \tau_{-i}) = E^0[\sigma - \tau] > 0,$$

since this in turn implies

$$M_\infty = \left(\sup_n \sum_{i=1}^{n}(\sigma_{-i} - \tau_{-i})\right)^+ = \infty.$$

□

In summary, if we exclude the *critical value* $\rho = 1$, the condition $\rho < 1$ is necessary and sufficient for the existence of a finite stationary workload. This condition determines the so-called *stability region* of the $G/G/1/\infty$ queue.

Remark 2.2.1 In the critical case, stability depends on the distribution of the service and inter-arrival sequences. From (2.2.3), we see that $M_\infty = \infty$ P^0-a.s. if and only if

$$(2.2.9) \quad \limsup_{n \to \infty} \sum_{i=1}^{n} (\sigma_{-i} - \tau_{-i}) = \infty \quad P^0 - \text{a.s.}$$

For instance, if the random variables $\sigma_n - \tau_n$ are centered, i.i.d. with a positive finite variance, the central limit theorem and the Borel-Cantelli lemma give (2.2.9), so that the queue is unstable. On the other hand, if $\tau = \sigma = \text{Constant}$, the queue is stable.   □

Remark 2.2.2 The stability issue is often addressed in terms of the convergence in distribution of the transient distribution of W_n to a proper limit distribution. In the stable case, we immediately obtain from the preceding construction that W_n^0 converges in distribution to M_∞ indeed: for all bounded continuous functions f

$$\lim_{n \to \infty} E^0[f(W_n^0)] = \lim_{n \to \infty} E^0[f(W_n^0 \circ \theta^{-n})] = \lim_{n \to \infty} E^0[f(M_n)] = E^0[f(M_\infty)].$$

We will see later on that the following stronger result holds: for all initial conditions Y and for all $m \geq 0$, $(W_n^Y, \ldots, W_{n+m}^Y)$ tends to $(M_\infty, \ldots, M_\infty \circ \theta^m)$ in variation (see § 4.1).   □

2.3 Uniqueness of the Stationary Workload

We shall need the following lemma:

(2.3.1) *Let Z be non-negative, P^0-a.s. finite, and such that $Z - Z \circ \theta \in L^1(P^0)$. Then $E^0[Z - Z \circ \theta] = 0$.*

Proof: For any $C > 0$, $| Z \wedge C - (Z \wedge C) \circ \theta | \leq | Z - Z \circ \theta |$. The conclusion follows from $E[Z \wedge C - (Z \wedge C) \circ \theta] = 0$ and dominated convergence.   □

Remark 2.3.1 The last result admits the following corollary: If the event A is such that $A \subset \theta^{-1} A$ (we will then say that A is θ-contracting), then $A = \theta^{-1} A$ P^0-a.s. Indeed, take $f = 1_A$, and apply Lemma 2.3.1 to obtain $E^0[f - f \circ \theta] = 0$. But $f - f \circ \theta \leq 0$ and therefore $f = f \circ \theta$ P^0-a.s.   □

Remark 2.3.2 When $\rho < 1$, the random variable M_∞ is not always integrable (see for instance the Pollaczek-Kinchine mean value formulas of Chapter 3). Nevertheless, we always have

$$\lim_{n} \frac{1}{n} M_\infty \circ \theta^n = 0 \quad P^0 - \text{a.s.}$$

This follows from $M_\infty - M_\infty \circ \theta \in L^1(P^0)$, Lemma (2.3.1) and the ergodic theorem since

$$\frac{M_\infty \circ \theta^n}{n} = \frac{M_\infty}{n} + \frac{1}{n} \sum_{i=1}^{n}(M_\infty \circ \theta^i - M_\infty \circ \theta^{i-1}).$$

□

We now show that if $\rho < 1$, then $Z = M_\infty$ is the unique non-negative finite solution of (2.1.1). It was shown in the last subsection that M_∞ is the minimal solution. Therefore for any non-negative solution Z, $\{Z = 0\} \subset \{Z = M_\infty\}$. The latter event is θ-contracting and therefore invariant by Remark 2.3.1, since both Z and M_∞ satisfy (2.1.1). Since (P^0, θ) is ergodic, we must then have $P^\theta(Z = M_\infty) = 0$ or 1. It therefore suffices to show that $P^0(Z = 0) > 0$ to obtain $P^0(Z = M_\infty) = 1$, that is, uniqueness. In view of (2.1.1), if $P^0(Z = 0) = 0$, we must have $Z \circ \theta = Z + \sigma - \tau$. If $E^0[Z \circ \theta - Z] = 0$, this implies $E^0[\sigma] = E^0[\tau]$, a contradiction with $\rho < 1$. The proof of uniqueness is then complete in view of Lemma 2.3.1.

At this stage, we have proved: for $\rho > 1$ there is no finite non-negative solution of (2.1.1), and for $\rho < 1$, M_∞ is the unique non-negative finite solution of (2.1.1). It therefore remains to study uniqueness in the critical case $\rho = 1$. The simple example $\sigma = \tau =$ Constant, where there is an infinite number of solutions, that is, $W = M_\infty + c$, where $c > 0$ is arbitrary, is a special case of the following result:

(2.3.2) *If $\rho = 1$, and if there is a finite solution, then for any $c \geq 0$, $Z = M_\infty + c$ is also a finite solution of (2.1.1).*

Proof: Assume that Z is a finite non-negative solution of (2.1.1). Since M_∞ is the minimal solution, then necessarily $M_\infty < \infty$, P^0-a.s. From (2.2.4) and Lemma (2.3.1), we obtain

(2.3.3) $E^0[M_\infty \wedge (\tau - \sigma)] = E^0[M_\infty \circ \theta - M_\infty] = 0.$

Thus

$$E^0[M_\infty \wedge (\tau - \sigma)] = E^0[1_{\{M_\infty \geq \tau - \sigma\}}(\tau - \sigma)] + E^0[1_{\{M_\infty < \tau - \sigma\}}M_\infty] = 0 .$$

In view of $E^0[\tau - \sigma] = 0$,

$$E^0[1_{\{M_\infty \geq \tau - \sigma\}}(\tau - \sigma)] + E^0[1_{\{M_\infty < \tau - \sigma\}}(\tau - \sigma)] = 0,$$

so that

$$E^0[1_{\{M_\infty < \tau - \sigma\}}(M_\infty + \sigma - \tau)] = 0$$

and therefore $M_\infty \geq \tau - \sigma$, P^0-a.s. This in turn implies

$$M_\infty \circ \theta = M_\infty + \sigma - \tau$$

and therefore, for any constant $c \geq 0$,

$$(M_\infty + c) \circ \theta = (M_\infty + c) + \sigma - \tau = ((M_\infty + c) + \sigma - \tau)^+.$$

$\square$

2.4 Construction Points

In this subsection, the stability condition ($\rho < 1$) is assumed to hold. It will be proved that there exists an infinity of negative (resp. positive) indices n such that $Z \circ \theta^n = 0$, where $Z = M_\infty$ is the unique non-negative solution of Lindley's equation (2.1.1). In view of the ergodicity of (P^0, θ) it suffices to show that

(2.4.1) $P^0 [M_\infty = 0] > 0.$

We showed in the previous subsection that if Z is a finite solution of (2.1.1) such that $P^0[Z = 0] = 0$, then $\rho = 1$. Therefore, we cannot have $P^0[M_\infty = 0] = 0$ if $\rho < 1$.

The interest of construction points (i.e. arrival times T_n such that $W(T_n-) = 0$) was explained in § 1.3. They also play a central role in the study of the asymptotic behavior of non-stationary workloads in the stable case (§ 5).

2.5 A Queueing Proof of the Ergodic Theorem

Formula (2.2.6)

$$E^0[M_\infty \wedge (\tau - \sigma)] \leq 0$$

is essentially Hopf's maximal lemma. Indeed, since $M_\infty \geq 0$,

$$E^0[M_\infty \wedge (\tau - \sigma)] \geq \int_{\{M_\infty > \tau - \sigma\}} (\tau - \sigma) dP^0 = \int_{\{M_\infty \circ \theta > 0\}} (\tau - \sigma) dP^0.$$

In addition

$$\{M_\infty \circ \theta > 0\} = \bigcup_{k \geq 0} \left\{ \sum_{i=0}^{k} \tau \circ \theta^{-i} < \sum_{i=0}^{k} \sigma \circ \theta^{-i} \right\}.$$

Therefore (Hopf's Lemma):

(2.5.1) $\displaystyle\int_{\bigcup_{k \geq 0} \{\sum_{i=0}^{k} \tau \circ \theta^{-i} < \sum_{i=0}^{k} \sigma \circ \theta^{-i}\}} (\tau - \sigma) dP^0 \leq 0.$

This lemma allows a direct proof of the ergodic theorem:

(2.5.2) *Whenever (P^0, θ) is ergodic and both σ and τ are non-negative, non identically null and integrable*

$$\lim_{n \to \infty} \frac{\sum_{i=0}^{n} \sigma \circ \theta^{-i}}{\sum_{i=0}^{n} \tau \circ \theta^{-i}} = \frac{E^0[\sigma]}{E^0[\tau]}, \quad P^0\text{-a.s.,}$$

Proof: According to the definition of M_n,

$$\sum_{i=1}^{n} \sigma \circ \theta^{-i} \le \sum_{i=1}^{n} \tau \circ \theta^{-i} + M_n.$$

We know that if $E^0[\sigma] > E^0[\tau]$, $M_n \uparrow M_\infty < \infty$ P^0-a.s. It follows in particular that if $E^0[\tau] > 0$,

$$\lim_{n \to \infty} \sum_{i=1}^{n} \tau \circ \theta^{-i} = \infty, \quad P^0\text{-a.s.}$$

(just take $\sigma = E^0[\tau]/2$ in the last inequality).

Therefore, whenever $E^0[\tau] > 0$ and $E^0[\sigma] < E^0[\tau]$,

$$\limsup_{n \to \infty} \frac{\sum_{i=0}^{n} \sigma \circ \theta^{-i}}{\sum_{i=0}^{n} \tau \circ \theta^{-i}} \le \lim_{n \to \infty} \lim_{n \to \infty} \frac{M_n}{\sum_{i=0}^{n} \tau \circ \theta^{-i}} + 1 = 1.$$

If $E^0[\tau] > 0$, for arbitrary integrable σ, take any a such that $aE^0[\sigma] < E^0[\tau]$ to obtain from the previous inequality

$$\limsup_{n \to \infty} a \frac{\sum_{i=0}^{n} \sigma \circ \theta^{-i}}{\sum_{i=0}^{n} \tau \circ \theta^{-i}} \le 1$$

and therefore

$$\limsup_{n \to \infty} \frac{\sum_{i=0}^{n} \sigma \circ \theta^{-i}}{\sum_{i=0}^{n} \tau \circ \theta^{-i}} \le \inf\{\frac{1}{a} \mid aE^0[\sigma] < E^0[\tau]\}$$

$$= \frac{E^0[\sigma]}{E^0[\tau]}.$$

Interchanging the roles of σ and τ, we obtain similarly

$$\limsup_{n \to \infty} \frac{\sum_{i=0}^{n} \sigma \circ \theta^{-i}}{\sum_{i=0}^{n} \tau \circ \theta^{-i}} \ge \frac{E^0[\sigma]}{E^0[\tau]}.$$

Hence the result.   □

3 The $G/G/s/\infty$ Queue

3.1 The Ordered Workload Vector

The input process is defined on the Palm space of a stationary point process as for $G/G/1/\infty$ queues. There are $s \geq 1$ servers attending customers and the allocation rule is that an arriving customer is assigned to the server with the smallest workload. Once assigned, this customer will wait and then be served at unit rate until completion.

We will construct the stationary workload process $\{W_n\}, n \in \mathbb{Z}$, where $W_n \stackrel{\text{def}}{=} (W_n^1, ..., W_n^s)$ is a permutation in increasing order of the workload found in each server by the nth customer upon arrival: $W_n^1 \leq W_n^2 \leq ... \leq W_n^s$, for all $n \in \mathbb{Z}$.

This ordered vector satisfies the recurrence relation

$$(3.1.1) \quad W_{n+1} = \mathcal{R}(W_n + \sigma_n e - \tau_n i)^+,$$

where $e = (1, 0, ..., 0), i = (1, ..., 1)$, $\mathcal{R}$ is the operator arranging vectors of $\mathbb{R}^s$ in increasing order, and $(x_1, ..., x_s)^+ = (x_1^+, ..., x_s^+)$. Therefore, the equation to be solved on this Palm space reads

$$(3.1.2) \quad Z \circ \theta = \mathcal{R}(Z + \sigma e - \tau i)^+.$$

We denote $(W_n^Y, n \geq 0)$ the solution of (3.1.1) with initial workload $Y \in \mathbb{R}_+^s$. Let M_n be the ordered workload vector found by customer 0 if customer $-n$ finds an empty system.

$$(3.1.3) \quad M_n = W_n^0 \circ \theta^{-n}.$$

In view of (3.1.1)

$$(3.1.4) \quad M_{n+1} \circ \theta = \mathcal{R}(M_n + \sigma e - \tau i)^+, \quad \forall n \geq 0.$$

It is clear that M_n increases (coordinatewise) to a limit M_∞ when $n \to \infty$ and that

$$(3.1.5) \quad M_\infty \circ \theta = \mathcal{R}(M_\infty + \sigma e - \tau i)^+.$$

Notice that M_∞ has possibly infinite coordinates.

3.2 Existence of a Finite Stationary Workload

Let M_n^j, $1 \le j \le s$, be the jth coordinate of M_n. By definition

$$(3.2.1) \quad M_n^1 \le M_n^2 \le \ldots \le M_n^s, \quad \forall\, n \in \mathbb{N}.$$

Using the identity $(a - b)^+ = a - a \wedge b$ in (3.1.4), we obtain

$$
\sum_{j=0}^{s} M_{n+1}^j \circ \theta = (M_n^1 + \sigma - \tau)^+ + \sum_{j=2}^{s} (M_n^j - \tau)^+
$$

$$(3.2.2)$$

$$
= \sum_{j=1}^{s} M_n^j - \left\{ M_n^1 \wedge (\tau - \sigma) + \sum_{j=2}^{s} M_n^j \wedge \tau \right\}.
$$

Therefore in view of the increasingness and the integrability of M_n

$$
E^0\!\left[M_n^1 \wedge (\tau - \sigma) + \sum_{j=2}^{s} M_n^j \wedge \tau \right] \le 0,
$$

so that, letting $n \to \infty$,

$$(3.2.3) \quad E^0\!\left[M_\infty^1 \wedge (\tau - \sigma) + \sum_{j=2}^{s} M_\infty^j \wedge \tau \right] \le 0.$$

Since M_∞ satisfies (3.1.2), we have :

$$(3.2.4) \quad M_\infty^1 \circ \theta = (M_\infty^1 + \sigma - \tau)^+ \wedge (M_\infty^2 - \tau)^+$$

and

$$(3.2.5) \quad M_\infty^s \circ \theta = (M_\infty^1 + \sigma - \tau)^+ \vee (M_\infty^s - \tau)^+.$$

Therefore, both $\{M_\infty^1 = \infty\}$ and $\{M_\infty^s = \infty\}$ are θ-contracting events. In particular, either $M_\infty^1 = +\infty$ P^0-a.s., or $M_\infty^1 < \infty$ P^0-a.s. In the first case, (3.2.3) implies that $E^0[\sigma] \ge sE^0[\tau]$. Hence we have proved that if $E^0[\sigma] < sE^0[\tau]$, then $M_\infty^1 < \infty$ P^0-a.s. Actually, the following stronger result holds:

(3.2.6) If $E^0[\sigma] < sE^0[\tau]$, then $M_\infty < \infty$ P^0-a.s.

Proof: Define $Z_n = (M_n^1 + \sigma - \tau)^+$, so that, from (3.1.4)

$$
M_{n+1}^s \circ \theta = Z_n \vee (M_n^s - \tau)^+ = M_n^s - (M_n^s - Z_n) \wedge \tau.
$$

Since $Z_n \uparrow Z_\infty = (M_\infty^1 + \sigma - \tau)^+$,

$$
M_{n+1}^s \circ \theta \le M_n^s - (M_n^s - Z_\infty) \wedge \tau.
$$

Therefore, $E^0[(M_n^s - Z_\infty) \wedge \tau] \le 0$, which in turn implies

$$
E^0[(M_\infty^s - Z_\infty) \wedge \tau] \le 0.
$$

We now see that if $M_\infty^s = \infty$ a.s. and $M_\infty^1 < \infty$ a.s., then $E^0[\tau] \leq 0$, a contradiction.   □

Notice that we have not used the assumption $E^0[\sigma] < sE^0[\tau]$ to get the latter result. Therefore, the only way for M_∞ to be infinite with non-zero probability is that $M_\infty^j = \infty$, $1 \leq j \leq s$, P^0-a.s. In this case, (3.2.3) implies that $E^0[\sigma] \geq sE^0[\tau]$. Finally

(3.2.7) *If M_∞ is not P^0-a.s. finite, then $M_\infty^j = \infty$ a.s. $\forall j$ and $E^0[\sigma] \geq sE^0[\tau]$.*

Construction Points. Following the lines of § 1.3, we see that it is possible to construct the queue length process provided there exists an infinite number of construction points where $M_\infty^1 \circ \theta^n = 0$ (indeed, if $M_\infty^1 \circ \theta^n = 0$, the number of customers in the system at time T_n- is known exactly; it is the number of components of $M_\infty \circ \theta^n$ which are different from 0). Let us prove that

(3.2.8) *If $E^0[\sigma] < sE^0[\tau]$, for P^0-a.s. all ω, there are infinitely many positive and negative construction points.*

Proof: Assume that $M_\infty^1 > \tau - \sigma$ and $M_\infty^j > \tau$, $j = 2, ..., s$ P^0-a.s. Then, (3.2.3) implies $E^0[\sigma] \geq sE^0[\tau]$. Hence, under the stability condition $E^0[\sigma] < sE^0[\tau]$

(3.2.9) $P^0[M_\infty^1 < \tau - \sigma \text{ or } M_\infty^j < \tau \text{ for some } j \geq 2] > 0$.

In view of (3.1.5), this implies $P^0[M_\infty^1 \circ \theta = 0] > 0$, which concludes the proof, in view of the ergodicity of (P^0, θ).   □

Remark 3.2.1 The stronger property $P^0[M_\infty^s = 0] > 0$ does not hold for all stable $G/G/s/\infty$ queues, as can be checked directly in the following counter example: $s = 3$ and both σ and τ are deterministic random variables : $\sigma = 2$ and $\tau = 1$.   □

3.3 The Maximal Solution

The basic equation (3.1.2) may have several finite solutions, as the following example shows: $s = 2$,

$$\Omega = \{\omega_1, \omega_2\}, \; \theta\omega_1 = \omega_2, \; \theta\omega_2 = \omega_1, \; P^0(\{\omega_1\}) = P^0(\{\omega_2\}) = \frac{1}{2}$$

$$\tau(\omega_1) = \tau(\omega_2) = 1, \; \sigma(\omega_1) = \frac{3}{2}, \; \sigma(\omega_2) = 2.$$

Then for any real number $x \in [1, \frac{3}{2}]$,

$$Z(\omega_1) = (0, x), \; Z(\omega_2) = (x - 1, \frac{1}{2}),$$

defines a finite solution of (3.1.2).

In order to study the structure of the set of finite solutions of (3.1.2), first observe that M_∞ is the minimal one. Indeed $Z \geq 0 = M_0$, and if $Z \geq M_n$, then $Z \circ \theta = \mathcal{R}(Z + \sigma e - \tau i)^+ \geq \mathcal{R}(M_n + \sigma e - \tau i)^+ = M_{n+1} \circ \theta$, that is $Z \geq M_{n+1}$. Therefore, for all $n \geq 0$, $Z \geq M_n$, and in the limit $Z \geq M_\infty$.

Let us now consider the following family of finite solutions of (3.1.2), indexed by $x \in \mathbb{R}_+$, that is,

(3.3.1) $V_\infty^x \overset{\text{def}}{=} \lim_{n\to\infty} V_n^x,$

where $V_0^x = M_\infty + xi$ and

(3.3.2) $V_{n+1}^x \circ \theta = \mathcal{R}(V_n^x + \sigma e - \tau i)^+.$

The existence and the finiteness of the limit in (3.3.1) are guaranteed by the fact that the sequence $\{V_n^x\}$, $n \geq 1$, is non-increasing in n. Indeed

$$V_1^x \circ \theta = \mathcal{R}(V_0^x + \sigma e - \tau i)^+ = \mathcal{R}(M_\infty + xi + \sigma e - \tau i)^+$$
$$\leq \mathcal{R}(M_\infty + \sigma e - \tau i)^+ + xi = M_\infty \circ \theta + xi$$
$$= V_0^x \circ \theta,$$

where we have used the inequality $(a+xi)^+ \leq a^+ + xi$ for all $a \in \mathbb{R}^s$, $x \in \mathbb{R}_+$. Also, if $V_n^x \leq V_{n-1}^x$, then $V_{n+1}^x \circ \theta = \mathcal{R}(V_n^x + \sigma e - \tau i)^+ \leq \mathcal{R}(V_{n-1}^x + \sigma e - \tau i)^+ = V_n^x \circ \theta$, that is $V_{n+1}^x \leq V_n^x$. Hence $V_\infty^x \leq M_\infty + xi$. From (3.3.1) and (3.3.2), the random variable V_∞^x is a solution of (3.1.2).

Similarly, we can show that V_n^x is non-decreasing in x. Indeed if $y \geq x \geq 0$,

$$V_0^y = M_\infty + yi \geq M_\infty + xi = V_0^x$$

and if $V_n^y \geq V_n^x$, then $V_{n+1}^y \circ \theta = \mathcal{R}(V_n^y + \sigma e - \tau i)^+ \geq \mathcal{R}(V_n^x + \sigma e - \tau i)^+ = V_n^x \circ \theta$, i.e. $V_n^y \geq V_n^x$.

From this it follows that

(3.3.3) $V_\infty^\infty = \lim_{x\uparrow\infty} V_\infty^x,$

is well defined and is a solution of the basic equation (3.1.2).

(3.3.4) V_∞^∞ is finite, and is the largest finite solution of (3.1.2).

Proof: We first prove that V_∞^∞ is the largest solution, when assuming for the moment that it is finite. For this, it suffices to prove that for any given finite solution Z of (3.1.2), there exists a constant $x_0 \geq 0$ such that

(3.3.5) $Z \leq M_\infty + x_0 i,$

since (3.1.4) gives by induction $Z \leq V_n^{x_0}$ and therefore $Z \leq V_\infty^{x_0} \leq V_\infty^\infty$. The proof of (3.3.4) goes as follows. Define U to be the smallest non-negative random variable such that

$$Z \leq M_\infty + Ui.$$

Then

$$Z \circ \theta = \mathcal{R}(Z + \sigma e - \tau i)^+$$
$$\leq \mathcal{R}(M_\infty + Ui + \sigma e - \tau i)^+$$
$$\leq \mathcal{R}(M_\infty + \sigma e - \tau i)^+ + Ui$$
$$= M_\infty \circ \theta + Ui.$$

Since $U \circ \theta$ is the smallest non-negative random variable such that $Z \circ \theta \leq M_\infty \circ \theta + (U \circ \theta)i$, we have

$$U \geq U \circ \theta.$$

In view of the ergodicity of (P^0, θ), U must be a constant. Moreover it must be finite since Z and M_∞ are finite.   □

The remaining task is the proof of the finiteness of V_∞^∞. We start with a couple of technical lemmas which will be useful in the proof. Denote by $||z||$ the Euclidian norm of the vector $z \in \mathbb{R}^s$. In what follows, we say that u and $v \in \mathbb{R}^s$ are ordered in the same way if there exists a permutation p of $(1, \ldots, s)$ such that $\mathcal{R}(u) = (u^{p(1)}, \ldots, u^{p(s)})$ and $\mathcal{R}(v) = (v^{p(1)}, \ldots, v^{p(s)})$.

(3.3.6) *For all u and v in $\mathbb{R}^s$, $||u^+ - v^+|| \leq ||u - v||$. If $u \neq u^+$ whereas $v = v^+$, then $||u^+ - v^+|| < ||u - v||$.*

In addition,

(3.3.7) *For all u and v in $\mathbb{R}^s$, $||\mathcal{R}(u) - \mathcal{R}(v)|| \leq ||u - v||$, and $||\mathcal{R}(u) - \mathcal{R}(v)|| = ||u - v||$ if and only if u and v are ordered in the same way.*

Proof: Let $u = u^+ + u^-$, $v = v^+ + v^-$. The properties in (3.3.6) follow from the relation

$$||u - v||^2 - ||u^+ - v^+||^2 = ||u^- - v^-||^2 + 2(u^+ - v^+) \cdot (u^- - v^-)$$
$$= ||u^- - v^-||^2 - 2u^+ \cdot v^- - 2v^+ \cdot u^- \geq 0$$

(use the facts that $u^+.u^- = v^+.v^- = 0$, $u^+ \cdot v^- \leq 0$ and $v^+ \cdot u^- \leq 0$).

We now prove (3.3.7). Let $x = \mathcal{R}(u)$, $y = \mathcal{R}(v)$ and let p (resp. q) be a permutation such that $u = x^p$ (resp. $v = y^q$). We have

$$||x - y||^2 - ||u - v||^2 = 2\left(\sum_{i=1}^s u^i v^i - \sum_{i=1}^s x^i y^i\right)$$
$$= 2\left(\sum_{i=1}^s x^i(y^{r(i)} - y^i)\right),$$

where $r = q \circ p^{-1}$. In order to prove that $||x - y||^2 - ||u - v||^2 \geq 0$, it is thus enough to prove that that if r is such that $r(l) > r(k)$ for some $l < k$, then the permutation r' which coincides with r on all points different from l and k and which permutes $r(l)$ and $r(k)$ is such that

$$\sum_{i=1}^{s} x^i y^{r(i)} \leq \sum_{i=1}^{s} x^i y^{r'(i)}.$$

But this inequality reduces to

$$x^l y^{r(l)} + x^k y^{r(k)} - x_l y^{r(k)} - x^k y^{r(l)} = (x^l - x^k)(y^{r(l)} - y^{r(k)}) \leq 0.$$

□

These lemmas have the following corollaries

(3.3.8) *For all u, v $\in (\mathbb{R}_+)^s$ and c, t $\in \mathbb{R}_+$, $\|\mathcal{R}(u + ce - ti)^+ - \mathcal{R}(v + ce - ti)^+\| \leq \|u - v\|$.*

(3.3.9) *If $(u + ce - ti)^+ \neq (u + ce - ti)$ and $(v + ce - ti)^+ = (v + ce - ti)$, then $\|\mathcal{R}(u + ce - ti)^+ - \mathcal{R}(v + ce - ti)^+\| < \|u - v\|$.*

Proof: In order to obtain (3.3.8), use (3.3.6) and (3.3.7) as follows:

$$\begin{aligned}
\|\mathcal{R}(u + ce - ti)^+ - \mathcal{R}(v + ce - ti)^+\| &\leq \|\mathcal{R}(u + ce - ti) - \mathcal{R}(v + ce - ti)\| \\
&\leq \|(u + ce - ti) - (v + ce - ti)\| \\
&= \|u - v\|.
\end{aligned}$$

Under the hypothesis of (3.3.9), $V \overset{\text{def}}{=} \mathcal{R}(v + ce - ti) = V^+$, whereas $U \overset{\text{def}}{=} \mathcal{R}(u + ce - ti) \neq U^+$. The relation $\|U^+ - V^+\| < \|U - V\| \leq \|u - v\|$ then follows from (3.3.6)-(3.3.7).   □

Proof of the Finiteness of V_∞^∞. Let Z be a finite solution of (3.1.2). By (3.3.8), $\|Z \circ \theta - M_\infty \circ \theta\| = \|\mathcal{R}(Z + \sigma e - \tau i)^+ - \mathcal{R}(M_\infty + \sigma e - \tau i)\| \leq \|Z - M_\infty\|$, and therefore in view of the ergodicity of (P^0, θ), $\|Z - M_\infty\|$ is a constant which must be finite since Z and M_∞ are finite. Therefore, for all $x \geq 0$,

(3.3.10) $\|V_\infty^x - M_\infty\| = C < \infty.$

In § 3.2, We have shown that under the stability condition $\rho < s$, the event $\{M_\infty + \sigma e - \tau i)^+ \neq (M_\infty + \sigma e - \tau i)\}$ is of positive probability. This event is included in $\{(V_\infty^x + \sigma e - \tau i)^+ \neq (V_\infty^x + \sigma e - \tau i)\}$, because if it were not so, by (3.3.9), $P(\|V_\infty^x \circ \theta - M_\infty \circ \theta\| < \|V_\infty^x - M_\infty\|)$ would be of positive probability, a contradiction with (3.3.10). Thus, for all $x > 0$,

$$\{M_\infty^1 = 0\} \subset \{(V_\infty^x)^1 = 0\}.$$

Therefore

$$\{M_\infty^1 = 0\} \subset \{(V_\infty^\infty)^1 = 0\},$$

which implies that

(3.3.11) $P^0((V_\infty^\infty)^1 = 0) > 0.$

Since

$$(V_\infty^\infty)^1 \circ \theta = ((V_\infty^\infty)^1 + \sigma - \tau)^+ \wedge ((V_\infty^\infty)^2 - \tau)^+,$$

the event $\{(V_\infty^\infty)^1 = \infty\}$ is θ invariant. Therefore $P^0((V_\infty^\infty)^1 < \infty) = 1$.

We now conclude the proof by showing that $(V_\infty^\infty)^s < \infty$ P^0-a.s. Observe first that since

$$(V_\infty^\infty)^s \circ \theta = ((V_\infty^\infty)^1 + \sigma - \tau)^+ \vee ((V_\infty^\infty)^s - \tau)^+,$$

the event $(V_\infty^\infty)^s = \infty$ is θ invariant. In addition, for all finite x, we have

$$(3.3.12) \quad (V_\infty^x)^s \circ \theta = (V_\infty^x)^s - ((V_\infty^x)^s - Z^x) \wedge \tau,$$

where

$$Z^x \stackrel{\text{def}}{=} ((V_\infty^x)^1 + \sigma - \tau)^+.$$

From the increasingness of V_∞^x in x, we then obtain

$$(V_\infty^x)^s \circ \theta \leq (V_\infty^x)^s - ((V_\infty^x)^s - Z^\infty) \wedge \tau,$$

where

$$Z^\infty \stackrel{\text{def}}{=} ((V_\infty^\infty)^1 + \sigma - \tau)^+ < \infty \quad \text{a.s.}$$

The random variable $(V_\infty^x)^s \circ \theta - (V_\infty^x)^s$ being integrable (check from (3.3.12) that $-\tau \leq (V_\infty^x)^s \circ \theta - (V_\infty^x)^s \leq (\sigma - \tau)^+$), it follows from Lemma 2.3.1 that

$$E^0[((V_\infty^x)^s - Z^\infty) \wedge \tau] \leq 0.$$

Therefore, by the monotone convergence theorem,

$$E^0[((V_\infty^\infty)^s - Z^\infty) \wedge \tau] \leq 0,$$

which shows that we cannot have $(V_\infty^\infty)^s = \infty$ a.s. and $Z^\infty < \infty$ a.s., since this would imply $E^0[\tau] \leq 0$, a contradiction. $\qquad\square$

4 Coupling

4.1 Coupling and Convergence in Variation

Two stochastic processes $\{X_n\}_{n\geq0}$ and $\{Z_n\}_{n\geq0}$, defined on the same probability space are said to *couple* if there exists a finite random variable N, also defined on this space, such that $X_n = Z_n$ for all $n \geq N$. In this definition, n may take its values in $\mathbb{R}_+$ or in $\mathbb{N}$. The random variable N is the coupling time of the two processes.

(4.1.1) *If $\{X_n\}$ couples with a θ-compatible sequence $\{Z \circ \theta^n\}$, then the sequence $\{X_{n+k}\}_{n\geq0}$ converges in variation to $\{Z \circ \theta^n\}$ as k tends to ∞.*

This follows from the more general result below: let $(E, \mathcal{E})$ be some Polish space with its Borel field, and let $\{W_n\}$ and $\{Z_n\}$ be two E-valued stochastic processes. Denote by $(E^\infty, \mathcal{E}^\infty)$ the infinite product $(\prod_{i=0}^\infty E_i, \prod_{i=0}^\infty \mathcal{E}_i)$ of replicas of $(E, \mathcal{E})$. Recall that $\mathcal{E}^\infty$ is also the Borel field associated with the distance d_∞ on E^∞ defined by:

$$d_\infty(x, y) = \sum_{i=0}^\infty 2^{-i} \frac{d_i(x_i, y_i)}{1 + d_i(x_i, y_i)},$$

where $x = (x_i, i \geq 0)$, $y = (y_i, i \geq 0)$ and d_i is any distance on $(E_i, \mathcal{E}_i)$ generating its topology. In particular, for each k

$$\widetilde{X}_k = (X_k, X_{k+1}, \ldots), \quad \widetilde{Z}_k = (Z_k, Z_{k+1}, \ldots)$$

are random variables of $(E^\infty, \mathcal{E}^\infty)$. Denote by $\widetilde{P}_{X,k}$ and $\widetilde{P}_{Z,k}$ their respective probability distributions. Coupling of $\{X_n\}$ and $\{Z_n\}$ is equivalent to coupling of $\{\widetilde{X}_n\}$ and $\{\widetilde{Z}_n\}$. This implies, as we shall see, that

$$\lim_{k \to \infty} |\widetilde{P}_{X,k} - \widetilde{P}_{Z,k}| = 0,$$

where for all probabilities P_1 and P_2 on $(\Omega, \mathcal{F})$, $|P_1 - P_2|$ is the distance in variation:

$$|P_1 - P_2| = \sup_{A \in \mathcal{F}} (P_1(A) - P_2(A)).$$

Indeed, let $\widetilde{N} = \inf\{n \geq 0 \mid \widetilde{X}_n = \widetilde{Z}_n\}$, and let $C \in \mathcal{E}^\infty$. Then

$$
\begin{aligned}
P(\widetilde{X}_k \in C) - P(\widetilde{Z}_k \in C) &= P(\widetilde{X}_k \in C, \ \widetilde{X}_k = \widetilde{Z}_k) + P(\widetilde{X}_k \in C, \ \widetilde{X}_k \neq \widetilde{Z}_k) \\
&\quad - P(\widetilde{Z}_k \in C, \ \widetilde{X}_k = \widetilde{Z}_k) - P(\widetilde{Z}_k \in C, \ \widetilde{X}_k \neq \widetilde{Z}_k) \\
&= P(\widetilde{X}_k \in C, \ \widetilde{X}_k \neq \widetilde{Z}_k) - P(\widetilde{Z}_k \in C, \ \widetilde{X}_k \neq \widetilde{Z}_k) \\
&\leq P(\widetilde{X}_k \neq \widetilde{Z}_k) = P(\widetilde{N} > k).
\end{aligned}
$$

Therefore, since $\widetilde{N}$ is assumed to be finite, we obtain the coupling inequality

$$|\widetilde{P}_{X,k} - \widetilde{P}_{Z,k}| \leq P(\widetilde{N} > k) \to 0 \quad \text{as } k \to \infty.$$

In particular, if $\{Z_n\}$ is θ-stationary,

$$(4.1.2) \quad |\widetilde{P}_{X,k} - \widetilde{P}_Z| \leq P(\widetilde{N} > k) \to 0 \quad \text{as } k \to \infty,$$

where $\widetilde{P}_Z$ is $\widetilde{P}_{Z,1}$.

Remark 4.1.1 Convergence in variation implies convergence in distribution.

$\square$

Remark 4.1.2 The rate of convergence of $\widetilde{P}_{W,k}$ towards $\widetilde{P}_Z$ can be obtained in some cases. In particular, if it is known that

$$E[\phi(\widetilde{N})] < \infty,$$

for some increasing non-negative mapping $\phi : \mathbb{N} \to \mathbb{R}$, then

$$|\widetilde{P}_{W,k} - \widetilde{P}_Z| = o\left(\frac{1}{\phi(k)}\right),$$

where $o(.)$ is a function such that $\lim_{x \downarrow 0} o(x)/x = 0$. Indeed, from the monotonicity of ϕ, $\phi(n)1_{\widetilde{N}>n} \leq \phi(\widetilde{N})1_{\widetilde{N}>n}$ and therefore $\phi(n)P(\widetilde{N} > n) \leq E[\phi(\widetilde{N})1_{\widetilde{N}>n}]$. By dominated convergence, $E[\phi(\widetilde{N})1_{\widetilde{N}>n}]$ goes to 0 as n goes to ∞, and therefore $\lim_{n\to\infty} \phi(n)P(\widetilde{N} > n) = 0$. This and (4.1.2) give the announced result.   □

We shall need later the notion of coupling of point processes. The two point processes on the real line, M and N, defined on the probability space $(\Omega, \mathcal{F}, P)$, are said to couple if there exists a finite random variable T such that $M(A \cap [T, \infty)) = N(A \cap [T, \infty))$, for all Borel sets A.

This definition is easily extended to marked point processes by requiring that $M(A \cap [T, \infty) \times B) = N(A \cap [T, \infty) \times B)$ for all Borel sets A on the line and all measurable sets B of the mark space.

The reader interested in coupling is advised to read the book by T. Lindvall (1992) *Lectures on the Coupling Method*, Wiley.

4.2 Coupling of Stochastic Recurrent Sequences

The following framework contains all the systems considered so far. Consider a dynamical system where the quantities of interest are described by an E-valued sequence $\{W_n^Y\}$, $n \geq 0$, generated by the *stochastic recurrence*

$$(4.2.1) \quad W_{n+1}^Y = h(W_n^Y, \xi_n), \quad n = 0, 1, \ldots$$

where h is some measurable function. The driving sequence $\{\xi_n\}$, $n \in \mathbb{Z}$, is F-valued (E and F are two Polish spaces) and Y is the initial condition ($W_0^Y = Y$). All these random variables are defined on the same probability space.

Observe that if two solutions $\{W_n^X\}$ and $\{W_n^Y\}$ of (4.2.1) couple, they couple at the first epoch when they meet; a necessary and sufficient condition for coupling is therefore that

$$(4.2.2) \quad N' = \inf\{n \geq 0 \mid W_n^X = W_n^Y\}$$

be a.s. finite.

Consider the case when the reference probability space is $(\Omega, \mathcal{F}, P^0, \theta)$, where (P^0, θ) is ergodic, and assume that the sequence $\{\xi_n\}$ is compatible with the shift θ. The basic questions concerning the solutions of (4.2.1) are then the existence of a stationary solution which is compatible with the shift, the uniqueness of the stationary regimes, and the nature of the convergence of the non-stationary process $\{W_n^Y\}$ towards the stationary regime(s).

Remark 4.2.1 Consider the case when E is $(\mathbb{R}_+)^K$ and the mapping h is non-negative, non-decreasing and continuous in its first argument. The method which was used in § 2 and § 3 leads to simple answers to the first of these questions. Indeed, we can then find a stationary solution $M_\infty \circ \theta^n$ to (4.2.1), where $M_\infty \in \mathbb{R}^K$ is defined by

$$(4.2.3) \quad M_n = W_n^0 \circ \theta^{-n}, \quad n \geq 0,$$

and

$$(4.2.4) \quad M_\infty = \lim_{n \to \infty} \uparrow M_n.$$

It is natural to call M_∞ the Loynes' variable associated with the stochastic recurrence. This solution can be finite or infinite. In case it is a.s. finite, it is the smallest stationary solution of (4.2.1). However, there may be several other finite solutions compatible with θ (e.g. the $G/G/s/\infty$ queue). □

Coupling can then be used to answer the second type of question and to show that the distribution under P^0 of a given solution $\{W_{n+k}^Y\}_{n \geq 0}$ converges in variation to a stationary limit distribution, for instance that of $\{M_\infty \circ \theta^n\}_{n \geq 0}$ under P^0.

Coupling in the $G/G/1/\infty$ Queue. In this subsection, besides the ergodicity of (P^0, θ), the stability condition $\rho < 1$ is assumed to hold. Then, there exists an infinity of negative (resp. positive) indices n such that $Z \circ \theta^n = 0$, where $Z = M_\infty$ is the unique non-negative solution of (2.1.1).

(4.2.5) *For any finite initial condition Y, $\{W_n^Y\}$ couples with the θ-compatible workload process $\{M_\infty \circ \theta^n\}$. Therefore, the process $\{W_{n+k}^Y\}_{n \geq 0}$ under P^0 converges in variation to $\{M_\infty \circ \theta^n\}_{n \geq 0}$ under P^0 when k tends to ∞.*

Proof: Since $W_0^Y = Y \geq 0 = W_0^0$, $W_n^Y \geq W_n^0$ for all $n \geq 0$. In addition, $\{W_n^Y\}$ eventually becomes null. Indeed, $W_n^Y > 0$ for all $n \geq 0$, implies $Y + \sum_{k=0}^n (\sigma_k - \tau_k) \geq 0$, for all $n \geq 0$, which implies that

$$\limsup \frac{1}{n} \sum_{k=0}^n (\sigma_k - \tau_k) \geq 0 \quad \text{a.s.} \quad \text{for all } n \geq 0.$$

This contradicts the fact that $\lim_{n \to \infty} \frac{1}{n} \sum_{k=0}^n (\sigma_k - \tau_k) = E^0[\sigma] - E^0[\tau] < 0$, P^0-a.s.. Thus, for any finite initial condition Y, there exists a finite N such that $W_N^Y = W_N^0 = 0$, and therefore since a recurrence equation of the type (4.2.1) holds for both $\{W_n^Y\}$ and $\{W_n^0\}$ with the same driving sequence, the processes $\{W_n^Y\}$ and $\{W_n^0\}$ couple. So do the processes $\{W_n^{M_\infty}\} = \{M_\infty \circ \theta^n\}$ and $\{W_n^0\}$ by specializing Y to M_∞. This in turn implies that $\{W_n^{M_\infty}\}$ and $\{W_n^Y\}$ couple. $\qquad\square$

The associated non-stationary inter-departure sequence also couples with a compatible sequence, at least for *reasonable* service disciplines. For instance, in the FIFO case, let D_n denote the n-th departure time. The coupling property of $\{D_{n+1} - D_n\}$ with a sequence compatible with the shift is immediate from the relation

$$D_{n+1} - D_n = \tau_n + W_{n+1} - W_n + \sigma_{n+1} - \sigma_n$$

and from the coupling property of $\{W_n\}$. Note that in this case, the stationary inter-departure times are integrable. This follows from the relation

$$\tau + M_\infty \circ \theta - M_\infty + \sigma \circ \theta - \sigma = \sigma \circ \theta + (\tau - M_\infty - \sigma)^+.$$

Similar constructions are possible for other secondary processes like for instance the congestion processes using the construction points (see § 1).

Remark 4.2.2 The coupling properties of the $G/G/1/\infty$ queue can be slightly extended as follows: consider a queue with arrival times $0 = T_0 < T_1, \ldots$ and service times $\sigma_0, \sigma_1, \ldots$, all defined on the probability space $(\Omega, \mathcal{F}^0, P^0, \theta)$, where θ is a shift which is P^0-stationary and ergodic. Here, the sequences $\{\sigma_n\}$ and $\{\tau_n \stackrel{\text{def}}{=} T_{n+1} - T_n\}$ are not assumed to be θ compatible, and in particular $(\Omega, \mathcal{F}^0, P^0, \theta)$ is *not* assumed to be the Palm space of the arrival process. Denote W_n^Y the workload sequence in this queue for an initial workload Y.

(4.2.6) *Assume that the sequences $\{\tau_n\}$ and $\{\sigma_n\}$ couple with θ-compatible sequences $\{\tau \circ \theta^n\}$ and $\{\sigma \circ \theta^n\}$, respectively, where τ and σ are P^0-integrable. If $E^0[\sigma] < E^0[\tau]$, then W_n^Y couples with the stationary sequence $\{M_\infty \circ \theta^n\}$, where M_∞ is the Loynes' variable associated with the sequences $\{\sigma \circ \theta^n\}$ and $\{\tau \circ \theta^n\}$ (see § 2.2).*

Proof: Let N denote the coupling time of the inter-arrival and service times with the stationary sequences. On $\{W_N^Y \geq M_\infty \circ \theta^N\}$ (resp. $\{W_N^Y < M_\infty \circ \theta^N\}$), $W_{N+n}^Y \geq M_\infty \circ \theta^{N+n}$ (resp. $\{W_{N+n}^Y \leq M_\infty \circ \theta^{N+n}\}$), for all $n \geq 0$. Let K (resp. L) be the first n such that $M_\infty \circ \theta^{N+n} = 0$ (resp. $W_{N+n}^Y = 0$). The random variables K and L are finite (provided Y is finite). This implies that

$$W_n^Y = M_\infty \circ \theta^n,$$

for $n \geq N + K \vee L$. $\qquad\square$

A typical example is studied in § 7.1, where we use the property that the output process of a FIFO queue couples with a θ-compatible sequence, where θ is the (discrete) shift associated with the input process of this queue.

Convergence in Variation of the Continuous-Time Workload in $G/G/1/\infty$ Queues. It was shown above that for a $G/G/1/\infty$ queue with $\rho < 1$, for all finite initial conditions, the sequence describing workload at arrival times couples with the unique customer stationary workload sequence. This coupling was established under P^0.

A similar coupling property holds in continuous time, under P.

(4.2.7) *For any finite initial condition Y, the stochastic process $\{W^Y(t)\}$, defined in § 1.2, couples P-almost surely to the stochastic process $\{W \circ \theta_t\}$, defined in (2.1.3). Therefore,*

$$(4.2.8) \quad \lim_{T \uparrow \infty} \sup_A \left| P\left(\{W^Y(t+T)\}_{t \geq 0} \in A\right) - P\left(\{W \circ \theta_t\}_{t \geq 0} \in A\right) \right| = 0,$$

where the supremum is over all Borel sets with respect to the Skorokhod's topology for instance.

Proof: The proof is similar to that of (4.2.5). □

Example 4.2.1 *Coupling in the $G/G/1/\infty$ queue with priority classes.* Let N_1 and N_2 be two θ_t-compatible $\mathbb{R}_+$-marked point processes defined on the same space $(\Omega, \mathcal{F}, P, \theta_t)$, where $\{\theta_t\}$ is ergodic. It is assumed that the superposition of N_1 and N_2 is simple. Let ρ_i, $i = 1, 2$, denote the traffic intensity of N_i, and assume that $\rho_1 + \rho_2 < 1$. Consider this superposition of point processes to be the input of a $G/G/1/\infty$ queue with the following discipline: customers of class 1 (corresponding to N_1) have preemptive priority over those of class 2; within each class, customers are served on a FIFO basis. Then the workload processes $\{W_1(t)\}$ and $\{W_2(t)\}$, representing the workload of customers of class 1 and 2 respectively, couple P-a.s. with uniquely defined θ_t-compatible workload processes, regardless of the initial conditions. Indeed, the total workload $W(t) \overset{\text{def}}{=} W_1(t) + W_2(t)$ couples with a uniquely defined stationary process, in view of (4.2.7) (this discipline leads to the same total workload as global FIFO for instance). The same holds for $W_1(t)$, since customers of class 1 are not affected by those of class 2. Therefore, $\{W_2(t)\} = \{W(t) - W_1(t)\}$ couples with a uniquely defined stochastic process too. □

We now look at the case when the arrival point process is not in its stationary state. To state the problem in simple terms, consider a $GI/GI/1/\infty$ queue with $\rho < 1$, where the arrival process is arbitrarily delayed (and therefore a delayed renewal process, however not assumed stationary) and where the workload at time 0 is also arbitrary. The distribution of the sequence $\{W_{k+n}\}_{n \geq 0}$, where $W_n = W(T_n-)$, converges in variation, as $k \to \infty$, to the distribution under P^0 of $\{Z \circ \theta^n\} = \{M_\infty \circ \theta^n\}$. This is because of the coupling occurring, under P^0, when we start with an arbitrary workload, and because in the delayed renewal case, the sequence $\{\tau_n, \sigma_n\}_{n \geq 1}$ has the same distribution as if the governing probability were P^0, and so (4.2.1) can be used. Thus, if $\widetilde{P}$ denotes the probability associated with the delayed renewal arrival process

$$(4.2.9) \quad \lim_{k \uparrow \infty} \sup_A \left| \widetilde{P}\left(\{W_{n+k}\}_{n \geq 0} \in A \right) - P^0\left(\{Z \circ \theta^n\}_{n \geq 0} \in A \right) \right| = 0.$$

Can we say something similar concerning the continuous time workload process? That is, does the relation

$$(4.2.10) \quad \lim_{T \uparrow \infty} \sup_A \left| \widetilde{P}\left(\{W(t+T)\}_{t \geq 0} \in A \right) - P\left(\{Z \circ \theta_t\}_{t \geq 0} \in A \right) \right|$$

hold, where P is the stationary probability corresponding to a stationary delayed renewal arrival process?

This is obviously possible if the renewal process, arbitrarily delayed, couples with the stationary delayed renewal process, that is if we can construct on the same probability space two renewal processes with the same given inter-arrival distribution and arbitrary distribution of the first point after the origin of times, such that after a finite random time, their points coincide. A necessary and sufficient condition for this is that the inter-arrival probability distribution be spread–out. In the general non–lattice case, convergence in variation is not available, only convergence in distribution is true (for a study of these aspects concerning $GI/GI/1/\infty$ queues, the reference is section 3 of chapter VIII of the book of S. Asmussen, *Applied Probability and Queues*, Wiley, NY, 1987).

The question stated in (4.2.10) has not yet received a complete answer for the $G/G/1/\infty$ queue. In this case, (4.2.10) may well not be true. However, in the case when coupling exists, convergence in variation does hold. More precisely, let M and N be two arrival marked point processes defined on the same probability space $(\Omega, \mathcal{F}, P, \theta_t)$, where θ_t is ergodic. Assume that N is θ_t-compatible. Let P^0 the Palm probability of N and let σ and τ denote the service time and the inter-arrival time associated with point T_0 of N, respectively. Let $W_Q^Y(t)$ denote the workload at time t, for the arrival point process Q (either N or M) and the initial condition Y.

(4.2.11) *If M and N couple and if $E^0[\sigma] < E^0[\tau]$, then the workload process $\{W_M^Y(t)\}$ couples with the stationary workload process $\{W \circ \theta_t\}$ associated with N (see (1.2.3) and (2.1.3)).*

Proof: Let $T \geq 0$ be the coupling time between N and M. By the same arguments as in the proof of (4.2.5), it follows that any solution finite at time T couples with the workload process starting with the value 0 at time T (all what is needed to carry on the argument is that

$$\lim_{N \to \infty} \frac{1}{N - N(T)} \sum_{k=N(T)}^{N} (\sigma_n - \tau_n) = E^0[\sigma] - E^0[\tau]$$

and this is true for any finite random variable T). $\qquad\qquad \square$

Example 4.2.2 *Example 4.2.1. continued.* If we replace the assumption that N_1 and N_2 are θ_t-compatible by the assumption that N_i couples with a θ_t-compatible point process, $i = 1, 2$, the conclusion of Example 4.2.1 remains unchanged in view of (4.2.11). □

We now give an example of non-renewal point process for which the coupling property assumed in (4.2.11) holds.

Example 4.2.3 *Construction and Coupling of Lindvall's (A, m)–Point Processes.* The present example is devoted to the construction of a simple point process N, which is stationary and admits a $(P, \mathcal{F}_t^N)$–intensity $\{\lambda(t)\}$, $t \in \mathbb{R}$, of the form:

$$\lambda(t) = \varphi(S_t N),$$

where φ is a given functional on the canonical space of point processes $(M, \mathcal{M})$, measurable w.r.t. the σ–field generated by the random variables $m \to m(C)$, C Borelian of $(-\infty, 0)$ (recall that m is the notation for generic elements of $(M, \mathcal{M})$, not to be confused with the integer of the (A, m) process).

This construction is not always possible, or if possible, it may not be unique for two main reasons: there could be explosions, or there could be extinctions. The explosive case (forbidding existence) occurs for instance for a functional φ of the form

$$\varphi(N) = \psi(N((-T, 0))),$$

where $\psi : \mathbb{N} \to \mathbb{R}$ is strictly positive and increases to ∞ sufficiently fast. The extinction case (forbidding uniqueness), would occur for instance for a functional of the same form with

$$\psi(0) = 0 \text{ and } \sup_{n \geq 0} \psi(n) < \infty .$$

One must therefore impose conditions on the functional φ in order to make a construction based on regenerative events possible.

The (A, m)–assumption, which allows us to limit the memory of the point process, is as follows:

(A, m)–**assumption:** There exists an integer $m \geq 0$ and a real number $A > 0$ such that $\varphi(N) = \varphi(N')$ whenever both conditions below hold

(a) $N(C \cap (-A, 0]) = N'(C \cap (-A, 0])$ for all Borelians C of $\mathbb{R}$.

(b) $T_{-j}(N) = T_{-j}(N')$ for $j = 0, 1, \ldots, m - 1$, where $\{T_n(N)\}$ is the sequence of points of N with a similar definition for $T_n(N')$.

This assumption tells us that at a given time t, the future probabilistic behavior of the point process only depends on the last m points and/or on the past at depth A (the points in $(t - A, t]$).

We shall now prove uniqueness of the point processes defined there in the sense of coupling. More precisely: given an arbitrary "initial distribution", that is to say a probability distribution P^- on $(M^-, \mathcal{M}^-)$, the restriction of $(M, \mathcal{M})$ to $(-\infty, 0]$, then we can construct two point processes, N and N', on the same probability space $(\Omega, \mathcal{F}, P)$ such that

(α) N is stationary with the $(P, \mathcal{F}_t^N)$–intensity $\varphi(S_t N)$.

(β) The restriction of N' to M^- has the distribution P^-.

(γ) On $\mathbb{R}_+$, N' admits the $(P, \mathcal{F}_t^{N'})$–intensity $\varphi(S_t N')$,

and moreover, there exist two non-negative times U and V with $P(U < \infty) = 1$, $P(V < \infty) = 1$, such that

(δ) $N(C \cap [U, \infty)) = N'(C \cap [U, \infty))$ for all Borelians C of $\mathbb{R}$.

(ε) $\varphi(S_t N) = \varphi(S_t N')$ for all $t \geq V$.

Besides the (A, m) assumption, we shall impose that

$$(4.2.12) \quad 0 < \lambda_1 \leq \varphi(N) \leq \lambda_2 < \infty$$

for some λ_1, λ_2, and for all N (see the bibliographical comments for less restrictive assumptions).

For our construction, we need a stationary framework $(\Omega, \mathcal{F}, P, \theta_t)$ on which are defined two Poisson processes N_1 and $N_{1,2}$ compatible with the shift $\{\theta_t\}$, independent, and of respective intensities λ_1 and $\lambda_{1,2} = \lambda_2 - \lambda_1$. For each $n \in \mathbb{Z}$, define

$$(4.2.13) \quad \tau_n = \min(T_{1,n} - A, T_{1,n-m})$$

and call τ_n a regeneration point if

$$(4.2.14) \quad N_{1,2}((\tau_n, T_{1,n}]) = 0 \ .$$

It is easy to see that, with probability 1, there are an infinite number of such regeneration points, both to the right and to the left of the time origin. We shall denote $\{R_n\}$, $n \in \mathbb{Z}$, the ordered sequence of regeneration points, with $R_0 \leq 0 < R_1$ as usual.

The process N is constructed between R_k and R_{k+1} as follows: in any case, *all* the points of N_1 will be counted as points of N. Now a point $T_{1,2,n}$ of $N_{1,2}$ will be accepted as a point of N with the probability

$$(4.2.15) \quad \frac{\lambda(T_{1,2,n}) - \lambda_1}{\lambda_2 - \lambda_1} \ .$$

The only problem is whether we can compute $\lambda(T_{1,2,n})$ for a given $T_{1,2,n}$. This is indeed possible if we start from R_k (for any k) because there will be no point of $N_{1,2}$ for some time, and when we meet one, all the points of N_1 provide all the past history necessary to compute $\lambda(T_{1,2,n})$ (see the (A, m)–assumption, and use (4.2.14)).

The random acceptance rule (take $T_{1,2,n}$ with acceptation probability given by (4.2.15)) can be translated inside the $(\Omega, \mathcal{F}, P, \theta_t)$ framework if we slightly modify it as follows:

We are given a marked point process N_2 with marks $\{Y_n\}$, compatible with θ_t, N_2 being Poisson with intensity λ_2 and $\{Y_n\}$ being i.i.d., independent of N_2, uniformly distributed on $[0, \lambda_2]$. Define N_1 and $N_{1,2}$ by

(4.2.16)
$$N_1(C) = \sum_{n \in \mathbb{Z}} 1_C(T_{2,n}) 1_{(0,\lambda_1]}(Y_n),$$
$$N_{1,2}(C) = \sum_{n \in \mathbb{Z}} 1_C(T_{2,n}) 1_{(\lambda_1,\lambda_2]}(Y_n),$$

with the obvious meaning for $T_{2,n}$.

Here, for a given $T_{1,2,n}$, the acceptance rule reads: accept if the corresponding mark falls in $(\lambda_1, \lambda(T_{1,2,n})]$.

With this framework, it is obvious that N constructed above is compatible with the shift $\{\theta_t\}$, and therefore stationary. Also it has the required stochastic intensity: indeed

$$N((a,b]) = \sum_{n \in \mathbb{Z}} 1_{(a,b]}(T_{2,n}) 1_{(0,\lambda(T_{2,n})]}(Y_n)$$

and therefore since the marked point process $(N_2, \{Y_n\})$ has the $\mathcal{F}_t^{N_2,Y}$-intensity kernel (see Chapter 1, § 8.2)

$$\lambda_2 dt \frac{1}{\lambda_2} 1_{(0,\lambda_2]}(y) dy = 1_{(0,\lambda_2]}(y) dt\, dy,$$

for any $A \in \mathcal{F}_a^{N_2,Y}$

$$E[1_A N((a,b])] = E\left[1_A \int_a^b \int_0^{\lambda(t)} dy\, dt\right] = E\left[1_A \int_a^b \lambda(t) dt\right],$$

where we have used the fact that $(\omega, t, y) \to 1_A(\omega) 1_{(a,b]}(t) 1_{(0,\lambda(t,\omega))}(y)$ is $\mathcal{P}(\mathcal{F}_t^{N_2,Y}) \otimes \mathcal{B}$ measurable (observe that $\lambda(t,\omega) = \lambda(0, \theta_t \omega)$ where $\lambda(0,\omega)$ is $\mathcal{F}_{0-}^{N_2,Y}$-measurable). Therefore $\{\lambda(t)\}$ is the $\mathcal{F}_t^{N_2,Y}$-intensity of N. But $\mathcal{F}_t^N \subset \mathcal{F}_t^{N_2,Y}$ and $\lambda(t)$ is $\mathcal{F}_t^N$-measurable, therefore $\{\lambda(t)\}$ is the $\mathcal{F}_t^N$-intensity of N.

As for the announced coupling construction, it uses the same $(\Omega, \mathcal{F}, P, \theta_t)$ framework, with N defined as above, and N' defined in a similar way, using the *same* marked point process $(N_2, \{Y_n\})$, only starting the construction from time 0 on, with a fixed history of N' at time 0. At the first regeneration point R_1, N and N' will share the same points up to a time where they have a common history which makes their intensities equal $(\varphi(S_t N) = \varphi(S_t N'))$. From that time on they will have the same points and the same intensity.

Suppose the arrival process of a $G/GI/1/\infty$ queue is of the type described above, and suppose that the stability condition $\rho < 1$ holds true. Let $\tilde{P}$ be the probability corresponding to a version of the point process with arbitrary distribution of the past at time 0. Then (4.2.9) and (4.2.10) are true, where P^0 and P represent the Palm and the stationary version, respectively, of the point process. This is due to the coupling of all versions of the point process with the same intensity, and to the fact that the Palm version has the same stochastic intensity on $\mathbb{R}_+$ as the stationary version (see Chapter 1, § 9.1).

$\square$

4.3 Strong Coupling and Borovkov's Theory of Renovating Events

Strong coupling is said to occur between the stochastic recurrent sequence $\{W_n\} = \{W_n^Y\}$ and the stationary sequence $\{Z \circ \theta^n\}$, where $Z \circ \theta = h(Z, \xi)$, if the random variable

$$(4.3.1) \quad N^o \overset{\text{def}}{=} \inf\{n \geq 0 \mid W_{n+k} \circ \theta^{-n-k} = Z, \ \forall k \geq 0\}$$

is P^0-a.s. finite. For $k \geq 0$, let

$$(4.3.2) \quad W_n(k) = W_{n+k} \circ \theta^{-k}, \quad n \geq -k$$

and let

$$N(k) = \{\inf n \geq -k \mid W_n(k) = Z \circ \theta^n\}.$$

Strong coupling admits the following equivalent definition:

$(4.3.3)$ *Let* $N^* \overset{\text{def}}{=} \sup_{k \geq 0} N(k)$. *Strong coupling occurs between* $\{W_n\}$ *and* $\{Z \circ \theta^n\}$ *if and only if* N^* *is* P^0-*a.s. finite.*

Proof: The random variables N^o and N^* have the same P^0-distribution. Indeed

$$
\begin{aligned}
P^0(N^* \leq n) &= P^0(W_n(k) = Z \circ \theta^n, \text{ for all } k \geq 0) \\
&= P^0(W_{n+k}(0) = Z, \text{ for all } k \geq 0) \\
&= P^0(W_{n+k} \circ \theta^{-n-k} = Z, \text{ for all } k \geq 0) = P^0(N^o \leq n).
\end{aligned}
$$

$\square$

$(4.3.4)$ *Strong coupling of* $\{W_n\}$ *and* $\{Z \circ \theta^n\}$ *implies their coupling.*

Proof: If strong coupling holds, then

$$P^0\left[N < \infty\right] = \lim_n P^0\left[N \le n\right] = \lim_n P^0\left[\{W_n = Z \circ \theta^n\}\right]$$
$$= \lim_n P^0\left[\{W_n \circ \theta^{-n} = Z\}\right]$$
$$\ge \lim_n P^0\left[\bigcap_{k \ge 0}\{W_{n+k} \circ \theta^{-n-k} = Z\}\right]$$
$$= P^0\left[\bigcup_{n \ge 0}\bigcap_{k \ge 0}\{W_{n+k} \circ \theta^{-n-k} = Z\}\right]$$
$$= P^0[N^o < \infty] = 1.$$

□

Remark 4.3.1 *Coupling does not imply strong coupling.* Consider the integer-valued stochastic recurrence associated with the function:

$$h(w, \xi) = \begin{cases} \xi & \text{for } w = 0; \\ w - 1 & \text{for } w \ge 2; \\ w & \text{for } w = 1, \end{cases}$$

with initial condition $W_0 = 0$ and with associated sequence $\{\xi_n\}$ i.i.d. and such that $\xi \in \{1, 2, 3, \ldots\}$, $E^0[\xi] = \infty$. It is easily checked that $\{W_n\}$ couples with the constant sequence equal to 1. However, strong coupling does not hold.

□

Remark 4.3.2 For stable stochastic recurrent sequences with associated function h increasing in its first argument, coupling and strong coupling are equivalent. More precisely, under the assumptions of Remark 4.2.1, whenever the Loynes' variable M_∞ is finite, then $\{W_n^0\}$ and $\{M_\infty \circ \theta^n\}$ couple if and only if they strongly couple. Indeed, in this case

$$0 \le M_1 \le \ldots \le M_\infty$$

Thus, when denoting N the coupling time of $\{W_n\}$ and $\{M_\infty \circ \theta^n\}$, we obtain

$$P^0(N \le n) = P^0(W_n = M_\infty \circ \theta^n) = P^0(W_n \circ \theta^{-n} = M_\infty)$$
$$= P^0(W_{k+n} \circ \theta^{-n-k} = M_\infty, \text{ for all } k \ge 0) = P^0(N^o \le n).$$

Since $N \le N^o$ a.s., the last relation implies that $N = N^o$ a.s. Thus, in this case, not only coupling and strong coupling are equivalent, but in addition the coupling and strong coupling times coincide.

□

We are now in a position to present the theory of renovating events for stochastic recurrences.

Let m be a positive integer and Φ be a measurable function, $\Phi : F^m \to E$ (E and F are the spaces in which W_n and ξ_n take their values respectively). The event A_n is said to be a *renovating event* of length m and associated function Φ, for the stochastic recurrent sequence $\{W_n\}$, if on A_n

(4.3.5) $W_{n+m} = \Phi(\xi_n, \ldots, \xi_{n+m-1})$.

For instance, events of the type $A_n = \{W_n = 0\}$ are renovating events of length 1 since, on A_n, $W_{n+1} = h(0, \xi_n)$.

Borovkov's result gives a sufficient condition for a finite stationary regime of (4.2.1) to exist and for strong coupling to occur:

(4.3.6) *If the stochastic recurrent sequence $\{W_n\}$ admits a sequence of renovating events $\{A_n\}$, $n \geq 0$, all with the same length $m \geq 1$ and the same associated function Φ, and if*

$$(4.3.7) \quad \lim_{n \to \infty} P^0 \left[\bigcap_{k=0}^{\infty} \bigcup_{l=0}^{n} A_l \cap \theta^k A_{l+k} \right] = 1,$$

then $W_n \circ \theta^{-n}$ converges a.s. to a finite limit Z as n tends to ∞. The sequence $\{Z \circ \theta^n\}$ satisfies (4.2.1), and $\{W_n\}$ strongly couples with $\{Z \circ \theta^n\}$.

Proof: We first prove that for all $n \geq l \geq m$, and $k \geq 0$, we have the inclusion

$$(4.3.8) \quad \theta^n A_{n-l} \cap \theta^{n+k} A_{n+k-l} \subset \{W_n \circ \theta^{-n} = W_{n+k} \circ \theta^{-n-k}\}.$$

Indeed, on $\theta^n A_{n-l}$

$$W_{n-l+m} \circ \theta^{-n} = \Phi(\xi_{n-l} \circ \theta^{-n}, \ldots, \xi_{n-l+m-1} \circ \theta^{-n})$$
$$= \Phi(\xi \circ \theta^{-l}, \ldots, \xi \circ \theta^{m-l-1}),$$

and similarly, on $\theta^{n+k} A_{n+k-l}$

$$W_{n+k-l+m} \circ \theta^{-n-k} = \Phi(\xi \circ \theta^{-l}, \ldots, \xi \circ \theta^{m-l-1}).$$

Therefore, on the intersection of these events, $W_{n-l+m} \circ \theta^{-n} = W_{n+k-l+m} \circ \theta^{-n-k}$. In view of the recurrence defining W_n, this implies

$$W_{n-l+m+1} \circ \theta^{-n} = h(W_{n-l+m} \circ \theta^{-n}, \xi_{n-l+m} \circ \theta^{-n})$$
$$= h(W_{n-l+m} \circ \theta^{-n}, \xi \circ \theta^{-l+m})$$
$$= h(W_{n+k-l+m} \circ \theta^{-n-k}, \xi_{n+k-l+m} \circ \theta^{-n-k})$$
$$= W_{n+k-l+m+1} \circ \theta^{-n-k},$$

and by iterating the above calculation, we see that

$$W_{n-l+m+j} \circ \theta^{-n} = W_{n+k-l+m+j} \circ \theta^{-n-k},$$

for all $j \geq 0$. Taking $j = l - m \geq 0$, gives (4.3.8).

The inclusion (4.3.8) implies

$$B_{n,k} \stackrel{\text{def}}{=} \bigcup_{l=m}^{n} \{\theta^n A_{n-l} \cap \theta^{n+k} A_{n+k-l}\} \subset \{W_n \circ \theta^{-n} = W_{n+k} \circ \theta^{-n-k}\}$$

and

(4.3.9) $\displaystyle\bigcap_{k=0}^{\infty} B_{n,k} \subset \{W_n \circ \theta^{-n} = W_{n+k} \circ \theta^{-n-k}, \ \forall k \geq 0\}.$

From (4.3.7), the quantity

$$P^0\left[\bigcap_{k=0}^{\infty} B_{n,k}\right] = P^0\left[\bigcap_{k=0}^{\infty} \theta^{-n} B_{n,k}\right] = P^0\left[\bigcap_{k=0}^{\infty} \bigcup_{l=0}^{n-m} A_l \cap \theta^k A_{l+k}\right]$$

tends to 1 when n goes to ∞, and therefore, by (4.3.9), the increasing sequence of events $\{W_n \circ \theta^{-n} = W_{n+k} \circ \theta^{-n-k}, \ \forall k \geq 0\}$ tends to an event of probability 1 when n goes to ∞. That is

(4.3.10) $P^0[\exists n \text{ s.t. } \forall k \geq 0, W_n \circ \theta^{-n} = W_{n+k} \circ \theta^{-n-k}] = 1.$

We see that with probability one, the sequence $W_q \circ \theta^{-q}$ is eventually constant in q. In other words, there exists a finite random variable Z such that

(4.3.11) $\displaystyle\lim_{n \to \infty} W_n \circ \theta^{-n} = Z \quad P^0\text{-a.s.}$

and

(4.3.12) $P^0[\exists n \text{ s.t. } \forall k \geq 0, W_{n+k} \circ \theta^{-n-k} = Z] = 1.$

By letting n go to ∞ in

$$W_{n+1} \circ \theta^{-n} = h(W_n \circ \theta^{-n}, \xi),$$

and by using (4.3.11) gives

(4.3.13) $Z \circ \theta = h(Z, \xi),$

since h is continuous in its first argument. This concludes the proof that $\{Z \circ \theta^n\}$ is a finite solution of (4.2.1). This solution is reached with strong coupling in view of (4.3.12). $\square$

A sequence of events is said to be compatible with the shift if $A_n = \theta^{-n} A$ for all $n \geq 0$.

(4.3.14) *If the sequence of events $\{A_n\}$ is compatible with the shift, the condition (4.3.7) is equivalent to $P^0(A) > 0$.*

Proof: Since $\theta^k A_{l+k} = A_l$,

$$\bigcap_{k=0}^{\infty} \bigcup_{l=0}^{n} A_l \cap \theta^k A_{l+k} = \bigcup_{l=0}^{n} A_l,$$

and therefore (4.3.7) implies $P^0(A) > 0$. Conversely, let B be the event

$$B = \bigcup_{l=0}^{\infty} \theta^{-l} A.$$

We have $B \subset \theta B$, so that B is of probability zero or one (recall the assumption that (P^0, θ) is ergodic). Since $P^0(B) > P^0(A)$, we must have $P^0(B) = 1$. $\quad\square$

Let $\mathcal{Y}$ be a set of random variables, and consider the sequences $\{W_n^Y\}$, for all possible initial conditions Y in $\mathcal{Y}$.

(4.3.15) *If there exists a sequence of events $\{A_n\}$ compatible with the shift and satisfying the condition $P^0(A_0) > 0$, a function Φ and an integer m, such that, on A_n, $W_n^Y = \Phi(\xi_n, \dots, \xi_{n+m-1})$, for all $Y \in \mathcal{Y}$, then there exists a stationary sequence $\{Z \circ \theta^n\}$, solution of (4.2.1), and such that for all $Y \in \mathcal{Y}$, the sequence $\{W_n^Y\}$ converges with strong coupling to $\{Z \circ \theta^n\}$.*

Proof: Following the same lines as in the proof of (4.3.6), under the preceding assumptions, we obtain that (4.3.9) can be replaced by the stronger statement that

$$(4.3.16) \quad \bigcap_{k=0}^{\infty} B_{n,k} \subset \{W_n^{Y^*} \circ \theta^{-n} = W_{n+k}^Y \circ \theta^{-n-k}, \ \forall k \geq 0, \ \forall Y \in \mathcal{Y}\},$$

where Y^* is an arbitrary element of $\mathcal{Y}$. The conclusion that

$$\lim_{n \to \infty} W_n^Y \circ \theta^{-n} = Z \quad P^0\text{-a.s.,}$$

where Z does not depend on Y, follows immediately. The rest of the proof is as in that of (4.3.6). $\quad\square$

Remark 4.3.3 The last theorem can be used to prove the uniqueness of the solutions of (4.3.13) as follows: if X and X' are two finite solutions such that W_n^X and $W_n^{X'}$ admit the same sequence of renovating events $\{A_n\}$ and the same associated function Φ, then in view of (4.3.15)

$$X = \lim_{n \to \infty} W_n^X \circ \theta^{-n} = \lim_{n \to \infty} W_n^{X'} \circ \theta^{-n} = X'.$$

$\quad\square$

The following converse to (4.3.15) holds:

(4.3.17) *Let $\{W_n^0\}$ be a $(\mathbb{R}_+)^K$-valued stochastic recurrent sequence with constant initial condition. If $\{W_n^0\}$ strongly couples to $\{Z \circ \theta^n\}$, where Z is a finite stationary solution of $Z \circ \theta = h(Z, \xi)$, then $\{W_n^0\}$ admits a θ-compatible sequence of renovating events of positive probability.*

Proof: In view of (4.3.2), N^o P^0-a.s. finite implies that there exists a finite m such that the event $A = A_0 = \{N^* = m + 1\}$ is of positive P^0-measure. On this event, we have

$$W_{m+1}(k) = W_{m+1}^0 = g(\xi_0, \dots, \xi_m), \quad \forall k \geq 0$$

for some deterministic function g obtained by iterating h. More generally, on the set $A_n = \theta^{-n} A$, we have

$$W_{m+1}(k) \circ \theta^n = g(\xi_n, \dots, \xi_{n+m}), \quad \forall k \geq 0.$$

In particular, for $k = n$,

$$W_{m+1}(n) \circ \theta^n = W_{n+m+1}^0 = g(\xi_n, \ldots, \xi_{n+m}).$$

Thus $\{A_n\}$ is a θ-compatible sequence of renovating events.   □

Uniqueness of the $G/G/s/\infty$ Workload Let $W_n = W_n(Y)$ be the solution of (3.1.1) with initial condition Y, and consider the associated events

$$(4.3.18) \quad A_n(Y) = \left\{ W_n^1(Y) = 0, W_n^j(Y) \le \sum_{k=0}^{j-2} \tau_{n+k}, \; j = 2, \ldots, s \right\}.$$

It is clear from (3.1.1) that $A_n(Y)$ is a sequence of renovating events of length $s - 1$, since the workload vector at the arrival time of customer $n + s - 1$ only depends on τ_j, σ_j, $j = n, \ldots, n + s - 2$ (in fact $W_{n+s-1} = \mathcal{R}(\sigma_n - \sum_{k=0,s-2} \tau_{n+k}, \sigma_{n+1} - \sum_{k=1,s-2} \tau_{n+k}, \ldots, \sigma_{n+s-2} - \tau_{n+s-2}, 0)$ - see Figure 4.3.1 for an example).

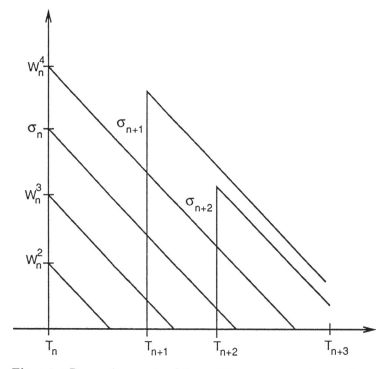

Fig. 4.3.1 Renovating events of the multiserver queue with $s = 4$

Let $A_n(V_\infty^\infty)$ be the renovating events (4.3.18) associated with the maximal solution $W_n = V_\infty^\infty \circ \theta^n$ (see § 3.3).

(4.3.19) *If $E^0[\sigma] < sE^0[\tau]$ and if $P^0[A_0(V_\infty^\infty)]$ is strictly positive, then the sequence $\{M_\infty \circ \theta^n\}$ is the unique stationary solution of (3.1.1) compatible with θ.*

Proof: Let $\mathcal{Z}$ be the set of finite solutions of (3.1.2). For all $Z \in \mathcal{Z}$, $A_n(V_\infty^\infty) \subset A_n(Z)$, since $V_\infty^\infty \geq Z$. Therefore, (4.3.15) can be applied with $A_n = A_n(V_\infty^\infty)$ and $\mathcal{Y} = \mathcal{Z}$. This in turn implies that for all Z, the stationary sequence $\{W_n^Z\}$ couples with the sequence $\{W_n^{M_\infty}\} = \{M_\infty \circ \theta^n\}$, so that $M_\infty = Z$ a.s.   □

In the renewal case, the condition (4.3.18) takes the simpler form:

(4.3.20) *If the stability condition $E^0[\sigma] < sE^0[\tau]$, is satisfied and if the $\mathbb{R}^2$-valued variables (τ_n, σ_n) are i.i.d., then the condition $P^0[A_0(V_\infty^\infty)] > 0$ is satisfied if the random variable τ_0 has an infinite support.*

Proof: From (3.3.11), we know that $P^0[(V_\infty^\infty)^1 = 0] > 0$. This plus the finiteness of V_∞^∞ imply that there exists some finite $x \in \mathbb{R}$ such that $P^0[(V_\infty^\infty)^1 = 0, (V_\infty^\infty)^j \leq x, j = 2, \ldots, s] > 0$. Using the independence assumption, we obtain

$$P^0[(V_\infty^\infty)^1 = 0, (V_\infty^\infty)^j \leq \sum_{k=0}^{j-2} \tau_k, j = 2, \ldots, s]$$

$$\geq P^0[(V_\infty^\infty)^1 = 0, (V_\infty^\infty)^j \leq \sum_{k=0}^{j-2} \tau_k, (V_\infty^\infty)^j \leq x, j = 2, \ldots, s]$$

$$\geq P^0[\tau_0 \geq x] P^0[(V_\infty^\infty)^1 = 0, (V_\infty^\infty)^j \leq x, j = 2, \ldots, s] > 0.$$

□

Observe that if Y is an initial condition satisfying the condition $Y \leq V_\infty^\infty$ a.s. (for instance $Y = 0$), then under the assumptions of (4.3.18), the convergence of the sequence $\{W_n(Y)\}$ to the unique stationary regime $\{M_\infty \circ \theta^n\}$ takes place with coupling. Indeed, denoting by $A_n(Y)$ the renovating events (4.3.17) associated with the sequence $\{W_n(Y)\}$, we obtain by induction that the sequence $\{V_\infty^\infty \circ \theta^n\}$ is a stationary upper bound of $\{W_n(Y)\}$, so that $A_n(V_\infty^\infty) \subset A_n(Y)$. This inclusion in turn implies that the renovating events $A_n(Y)$ satisfy condition (4.3.7). This result extends to more general initial conditions (see the bibliographical notes), using the same method, though with more elaborate stationary upper bounds.

5 Stability of the $G/G/1/0$ Queue

5.1 Counterexamples

The setting for the $G/G/1/0$ queue is that of § 1.1 (the $G/G/1/\infty$ queue) except that there is no waiting room, and therefore any customer who finds a busy server upon arrival is lost (i.e. he is rejected and disappear). Therefore there is at most one customer in the system, and the equation for the workload process is

$$(5.1.1) \quad W(t) = (W(T_n-) + \sigma_n 1_{W(T_n-)=0} - (t - T_n))^+ \ , \ t \in [T_n, T_{n+1}),$$

whereas the workload sequence satisfies the equation

$$(5.1.2) \quad W_{n+1} = (W_n + \sigma_n 1_{W_n=0} - \tau_n)^+.$$

Within the Palm framework, Loynes' problem consists in finding a P^0-a.s. finite non-negative random variable Z such that

$$(5.1.3) \quad Z \circ \theta = (Z + \sigma 1_{Z=0} - \tau)^+,$$

where $P^0 = P_A^0$ and $\theta = \theta_{T_1}$. A typical trajectory of the workload process is illustrated in Figure 5.1.1, where the tagged arrivals are not accepted in the system.

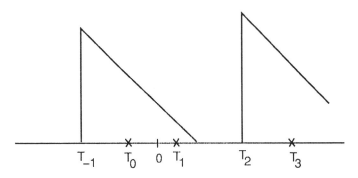

Fig. 5.1.1 A typical trajectory of the $G/G/1/0$ workload

It is intuitively clear that no problem should arise for proving the finiteness of Z. However a new problem arises, as demonstrated by the following examples. We have situations where $(\alpha) : Z$ does not exist, and $(\beta) : Z$ is not unique. These examples are constructed on the following space

$$\Omega = \{\omega_1, \omega_2\} \ , \ P^0(\{\omega_1\}) = P^0(\{\omega_2\}) = \frac{1}{2},$$

with the shift

$$\theta\omega_1 = \omega_2 \ , \quad \theta\omega_2 = \omega_1.$$

We immediately check that (P^0, θ) is ergodic, and that P^0 is θ-invariant. Define the random variable σ and τ by

$$\sigma(\omega_1) = \sigma_1 \ , \ \sigma(\omega_2) = \sigma_2 \ , \ \tau(\omega_1) = \tau(\omega_2) = 1,$$

so that, when adopting the notation

$$Z(\omega_1) = Z_1 \ , \ Z(\omega_2) = Z_2 \ ,$$

the basic equation (5.1.3) reads

$$(5.1.4) \quad \begin{aligned} Z_1 &= (Z_2 + \sigma_2 1_{Z_2=0} - 1)^+, \quad &(a) \\ Z_2 &= (Z_1 + \sigma_1 1_{Z_1=0} - 1)^+. \quad &(b) \end{aligned}$$

Example 5.1.1 Take $\sigma_1 = 1$, $\sigma_2 > 2$. There is no solution of (5.1.4). Indeed if $Z_1 = 0$, then from (5.1.4b), $Z_2 = (\sigma_1 - 1)^+ = 0$, and therefore, going back to (5.1.4a), $Z_1 = (\sigma_2 - 1)^+ > 0$, a contradiction. If $Z_2 = 0$, (5.1.4a) gives $Z_1 = (\sigma_2 - 1)^+ = \sigma_2 - 1$, therefore, from (5.1.4b), $Z_2 = (\sigma_2 - 1)^+ > 0$, another contradiction. Thus, necessarily $Z_1 > 0$ and $Z_2 > 0$ (This means that all customers are rejected). But then, from (5.1.4.b), $Z_2 = (Z_1 - 1)^+$, and taking the latter expression in (5.1.4a), $Z_1 = ((Z_1 - 1)^+ - 1)^+$ which is not possible if $Z_1 > 0$.   □

Example 5.1.2 Take both σ_1 and σ_2 in the open interval $(1,2)$. Then the system (5.1.4) does not have a unique solution. Indeed

$$Z_1 = 0 \ , \ Z_2 = \sigma_1 - 1$$

and

$$Z_1 = \sigma_2 - 1 \ , \ Z_2 = 0,$$

are both solutions (they correspond to rejecting every even customer and every odd customer respectively).   □

In § 5.2, we simultaneously address the existence and the uniqueness problems, by finding sufficient conditions for renovating events to exist. In § 5.3, we then show that existence is always granted if we accept to work on an enriched sample space containing more than just the input process $\{(\sigma_n, \tau_n)\}$.

5.2 Coupling in the G/G/1/0 Queue

Renovating events of length 1 are provided by sets of the type

(5.2.1) $A_n \subset \{W_n = 0\}$.

(5.2.2) *If the condition*

$$(5.2.3) \quad P^0 \left[\sup_{l \geq 1} (\sigma \circ \theta^{-l} - \sum_{i=1}^{l} \tau \circ \theta^{-i}) \leq 0 \right] > 0,$$

holds, then (5.1.3) admits at most one solution.

Proof: Let

$$(5.2.4) \quad S = \sup_{l \geq 1} (\sigma \circ \theta^{-l} - \sum_{i=1}^{l} \tau \circ \theta^{-i})^+.$$

The random variable S is finite if $E^0[\sigma] < \infty$ and $0 < E^0[\tau] < \infty$ (see § 6.1 below). Let us prove that if Z is a finite stationary solution of (5.1.3), then $Z \leq S$ a.s. For this, we show that the event $\{Z \leq S\}$ is θ-contracting and of positive probability.

To obtain S, we take the largest (for $l \leq -1$) among the workloads left by customer l at time 0. Therefore, clearly $(S - \tau)^+ \leq S \circ \theta$ and since $(\sigma - \tau)^+ \leq S \circ \theta$, we find that on $\{Z \leq S\}$,

$$Z \circ \theta = (\sigma - \tau)^+ 1_{Z=0} + (Z - \tau)^+ 1_{Z>0}$$
$$\leq (\sigma - \tau)^+ 1_{Z=0} + (S - \tau)^+ 1_{Z>0} \leq S \circ \theta,$$

which completes the proof of the θ-contraction. For proving that $P^0[Z \leq S] > 0$, it is enough to show that $P^0[Z = 0] > 0$. Since Z satisfies (5.1.3), the assumption $P^0[Z = 0] = 0$ implies

$$Z \circ \theta = (Z - \tau)^+ = (Z - \tau),$$

which in turn implies $E^0[Z \circ \theta - Z] < 0$, a contradiction with Lemma 2.3.1.

Therefore, for any finite solution Z of (5.1.3), the sequence $\{W_n^Z = Z \circ \theta^n\}$ admits $A_n = \{S \circ \theta^n = 0\}$ as a stationary sequence of renovating events of length 1 (since on A_n, $W_n^Z = 0$). From (4.3.15), it suffices to show that $P^0(S = 0) > 0$, in order to prove the uniqueness property. But this is a direct consequence of (5.2.3). □

(5.2.5) *Under the condition (5.2.3), (5.1.2) admits a unique solution which is compatible with the shift and which is reached with strong coupling by the sequence $\{W_n^0\}$.*

Proof: For all $n \geq 0$,

$W_n^0 \leq S_n = S \circ \theta^n.$

This shows that sequence $\{W_n^0\}$ admits $\{S_n = 0\}$ as renovating events of length 1, where $S_n = S \circ \theta^n$. Therefore, from (4.3.6), $W_n^0 \circ \theta^{-n}$ tends to a finite limit Z, which is a solution of (5.1.3), and $\{W_n^0\}$ couples with $\{Z \circ \theta^n\}$. Uniqueness was obtained in (5.2.2). $\qquad\square$

Remark 5.2.1 Consider the case when the random variables $\{\sigma_n, -\tau_n\}$ are P^0-*associated* (see § 3.1, Chapter 4, for the definition of association). This is for instance the case if each of the sequences $\{\sigma_n\}$ and $\{\tau_n\}$ is i.i.d. and if these two sequences are independent. Under this assumption, the condition (5.2.3) can be further simplified using Property (3.1.5), Chapter 4, which implies that

$$P^0\left[\sup_{l \geq 1}(\sigma \circ \theta^{-l} - \sum_{i=1}^l \tau \circ \theta^{-i}) \leq 0\right] \geq \prod_{l \geq 1} P^0\left[\sigma \circ \theta^{-l} - \sum_{i=1}^l \tau \circ \theta^{-i} \leq 0\right]$$

$$= \prod_{l \geq 1}\left(1 - P^0\left[\sigma \circ \theta^{-l} > \sum_{i=1}^l \tau \circ \theta^{-i}\right]\right).$$

Therefore, in view of classical results on infinite products, (5.2.3) is satisfied if

$$(5.2.6) \quad P^0\left[\sigma > \sum_{i=0}^l \tau \circ \theta^i\right] < 1 \quad \forall l \geq 1$$

and

$$(5.2.7) \quad \sum_{l=1}^\infty P^0\left[\sigma > \sum_{i=0}^l \tau \circ \theta^i\right] < \infty.$$

In the renewal case (i.e. under P^0, the sequences $\{\sigma_n\}$ and $\{\tau_n\}$ are independent and each sequence is i.i.d), the last condition will be satisfied whenever the random variable σ is integrable. Indeed, in this case

$$\sum_{l=1}^\infty P^0\left[\sigma > \sum_{i=0}^l \tau \circ \theta^i\right] = \sum_{l=1}^\infty E^0\left[T_l < \sigma\right] = \int_{[0,\infty)} R(t)dP^0[\sigma \leq t],$$

where $R(t)$ is the renewal function $R(t) = \sum_{l=1}^\infty P^0[T_l < t] = E^0\left[N(0,t)\right]$. We obtain (5.2.7) when using the fact that $R(t)/t$ tends to λ as t goes to ∞ (Renewal Theorem). Therefore, under the above stated renewal and integrability assumptions, if $P^0[\sigma \leq \tau] > 0$, then (5.2.6) is satisfied and (5.2.3) holds. $\qquad\square$

5.3 Construction of an Enriched Probability Space

The results of this section will not be used later and they may be skipped on the first reading. We shall now consider situations where existence is not granted, at least on the probability space where the random sequences $\{\sigma_n\}$ and $\{\tau_n\}$ are defined. We start by defining the positive, integer-valued random variable

$$(5.3.1) \quad \nu = \inf\left\{n \mid n \geq 1, \ \sum_{k=0}^{n-1} \tau_k \geq \sigma\right\},$$

with the convention that $\nu = \infty$ if $\sum_{k=0}^{n=1} \tau_k < \sigma$ for all $n \geq 1$. However this latter case P^0-almost surely never occurs because $\lim_{n \to \infty} \sum_{k=0}^{n} \tau \circ \theta^k = +\infty$, P^0-a.s. since (P^0, θ) is ergodic and $E_0 \tau > 0$.

The random variable ν is the index of the first customer after customer 0 to be accepted if customer 0 is accepted.

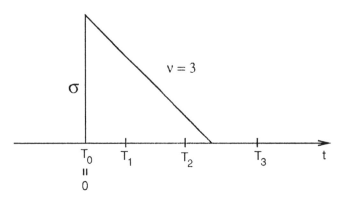

Fig. 5.3.1 The random variable ν

Define

$$(5.3.2) \quad B_n = \{\omega \in \Omega \mid (\nu \circ \theta^{-m})(\omega) \leq m \text{ for all } m \geq n\},$$

that is the set of samples such that for all $m \geq n$, customer $-m$, whenever he is accepted, completes his service before customer 0 arrives. We first show that

$$(5.3.3) \quad \bigcup_{n=1}^{\infty} B_n = \Omega, \ P^0\text{-a.s.}$$

that is, for (almost) all samples, there is an index $n \geq 0$ depending upon the sample, and such that any customer arrived before customer n, whenever accepted, would leave the system before customer 0 arrives.

Indeed $\sum_{k=0}^{\nu-2} \tau_k < \sigma$, and therefore

$$E^0\left[\sum_{k=0}^{\infty} \tau_k 1_{\nu>k+1}\right] < E^0[\sigma] < \infty.$$

Using the θ-invariance of P^0, this reads

$$E^0\left[(\tau \circ \theta^{-1})(\sum_{l=1}^{\infty} 1_{\nu \circ \theta^{-l} > l})\right] < \infty.$$

Since $\tau > 0$, P^0-a.s., this implies $\sum_{l=1}^{\infty} 1_{\nu \circ \theta^{-l} > l} < \infty$, P^0-a.s., which is the announced result.   □

For $\omega \in \Omega$, let $\mathcal{L}_\omega : \mathbb{N} \to \mathbb{N}$ be the mapping

$$(5.3.4) \quad \mathcal{L}_\omega(i) = \begin{cases} i+1 & \text{if } \nu \circ \theta^{-i} > i+1, \\ 0 & \text{otherwise.} \end{cases}$$

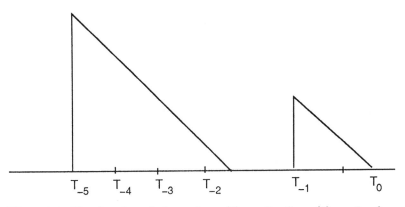

Fig. 5.3.2 The function $\mathcal{L}$: here $\mathcal{L}_{\theta^{-4}\omega}(1) = 2$, $\mathcal{L}_{\theta^{-3}\omega}(2) = 3$, $\mathcal{L}_{\theta^{-2}\omega}(3) = 0$, $\mathcal{L}_{\theta^{-1}\omega}(0) = 1$

Let $L_\omega^m : \mathbb{N} \to \mathbb{N}, m \geq 1$ be defined by

$$(5.3.5) \quad L_\omega^m(i) = \mathcal{L}_{\theta^{-1}}(\omega) \circ \mathcal{L}_{\theta^{-2}\omega} \circ \ldots \circ \mathcal{L}_{\theta^{-m}\omega}(i).$$

In words, $L_\omega^m(i)$ is the (absolute) value of the index of the customer present in the server at time 0, when considering only customer $-(m+i)$ and customers $n > -m$ (see Figure 5.3.2).

Define the subset $H_m(\omega)$ of $\mathbb{N}$ by

$$(5.3.6) \quad H_m(\omega) = L_\omega^m(\mathbb{N}), m \geq 1.$$

This is the set of all the indices (up to the sign) of customers present in the server at time 0 when considering only customer $-m - i$ and customers

$n > -m$, and when letting i vary over $\mathbb{N}$. By construction $H_m(\omega) \neq 0$. In addition, $\mathcal{L}_\omega(\mathbb{N}) \in [0, n]$ if $\omega \in B_n$, so that $H_m(\omega)$ is a finite set owing to (5.3.3). Using the relation

$$L_\omega^{m+1}(\mathbb{N}) = L_\omega^m \circ \mathcal{L}_{\theta-m+1\omega}(\mathbb{N}),$$

we also obtain that $H_{m+1}(\omega) \subset H_m(\omega)$. Hence

(5.3.7) $H_n(\omega) \to H(\omega) \neq \emptyset$.

Since $L^{m+1} \circ \theta = \mathcal{L} \circ L^m$, $H_{m+1} \circ \theta = \mathcal{L}(H_m)$, and therefore $card\,(H_{m+1} \circ \theta) \leq card\,(H_m)$. Letting $m \uparrow \infty$, we see that $card\,(H \circ \theta) \leq card\,(H)$. Therefore, since (P^0, θ) is ergodic

(5.3.8) $card\quad H(\omega) = $ constant, P^0-a.s.

We are now in a position to construct the enriched space $(\overline{W}, \overline{F}, \overline{P}^0, \overline{\theta})$ defined by

(5.3.9) $\begin{cases} \overline{\Omega} = \{(\omega, i) \in \Omega \times \mathbb{N} \mid i \in H(\omega)\}, \\ \overline{F} = \text{ trace on } \overline{\Omega} \text{ of } F \otimes \mathcal{P}(\mathbb{N}), \end{cases}$

where $\mathcal{P}(\mathbb{N})$ denotes the set of subsets of $\mathbb{N}$, and

(5.3.10) $\begin{cases} \overline{P}^0(A, i) = E^0[1_A \delta_{\{i\}}(H)], \\ \overline{\theta}(\omega, i) = (\theta(\omega), \mathcal{L}_\omega(i)). \end{cases}$

$\overline{P}^0$ is a σ-finite measure. on $(\overline{\Omega}, \overline{F})$. $\overline{\theta}$ is an automorphism on $(\overline{\Omega}, \overline{F})$. To show this, it is enough to prove that $\mathcal{L}_\omega : H(\omega) \to H(\theta(\omega))$ is bijective. $\mathcal{L}_\omega$ is clearly surjective. It is also injective since $card\,(H(\omega)) = card\,H(\theta(\omega))$.

Define the mapping $f : \overline{\Omega} \to \Omega$ by $f(\omega, i) = \omega$. We have $P^0 = \overline{P}^0 \circ f^{-1}$ and $f \circ \overline{\theta} \circ f^{-1} = \theta$. Therefore, $(\overline{\Omega}, \overline{F}, \overline{P}^0, \overline{\theta})$ is an enrichment of (Ω, F, P^0, θ). Let us show that $\overline{P}$ is $\overline{\theta}$ invariant i.e. :

$$\int_{\overline{\Omega}} 1_{A \times \{i\}}(\omega, j) d\overline{P}^0(\omega, j) = \int_{\overline{\Omega}} 1_{A \times \{i\}}(\theta(\omega), \mathcal{L}_\omega(j)) d\overline{P}^0(\omega, j).$$

Indeed, the right-hand side is by definition

$$\sum_{j \in \mathbb{N}} \int_\Omega 1_A(\theta(\omega)) 1_{\{i\}}(\mathcal{L}_\omega(j)) \delta_{\{j\}}(H(\omega)) dP^0(\omega),$$

or, in view of the $\theta-$invariance of P^0 :

$$\sum_{j \in \mathbb{N}} \int_\Omega 1_A(\omega) 1_{\{i\}}(\mathcal{L}_{\theta-1\omega}(j)) \delta_{\{j\}}(H(\theta^{-1}(\omega))) dP^0(\omega).$$

Since $\mathcal{L}_{\theta^{-1}\omega}$ is a bijection from $H(\theta^{-1}(\omega))$ into $H(\omega)$, the event $\{i \in H(\omega)\}$ is equal to the event $\{\exists\, j \in \mathbb{N} \mid \mathcal{L}_{\theta^{-1}\omega}(j) = i,\ j \in H(\theta^{-1}\omega)\}$, which completes the proof of the $\overline{\theta}$ invariance of $\overline{P}^0$.

Construction of a Stationary Solution. Define $\overline{W}$ on $\overline{\Omega}$ by

$$(5.3.11) \quad \overline{W}(\omega, i) = \begin{cases} (\sigma \circ \theta^{-i} - \sum_{k=1}^{i} \tau \circ \theta^{-k})^+, & \text{if } i \neq 0, \\ 0 & \text{otherwise.} \end{cases}$$

Since $\sigma \circ \theta^{-i} - \sum_{k=1}^{i} \tau \circ \theta^{-k} > 0$ when $i \in H(\omega)$, $\quad i \neq 0$,

$$(5.3.11)' \quad \overline{W}(\omega, i) = \begin{cases} \sigma \circ \theta^{-i} - \sum_{k=1}^{i} \tau \circ \theta^{-k}, & \text{if } i \neq 0, \\ 0 & \text{otherwise} \end{cases}$$

Let us check that

$$(5.3.12) \quad \overline{W} \circ \overline{\theta} = (\overline{W} + \sigma 1_{\{\overline{W}=0\}} - \tau)^+.$$

First case : $\mathcal{L}_\omega(i) = i+1, i \neq 0$. Then, $\overline{W} \circ \overline{\theta} = \overline{W}(\theta(\omega), \mathcal{L}_\omega(i)) = \overline{W}(\theta(\omega), i+1) = \sigma \circ \theta^{-i} - \sum_{k=0}^{i} \tau \circ \theta^{-k}$. Since $\mathcal{L}_\omega(i) = i+1, \sigma \circ \theta^{-i} - \sum_{k=0}^{i} \tau \circ \theta^{-k} > 0$ and a fortiori $\sigma \circ \theta^{-i} - \sum_{k=1}^{i} \tau \circ \theta^{-k} > 0$. i.e. $\overline{W}(\omega, i) > 0$. Hence, $\overline{W} + \sigma.1_{\{\overline{W}=0\}} - \tau = \overline{W} - \tau = \sigma \circ \theta^{-i} - \sum_{k=1}^{i} \tau \circ \theta^{-k} - \tau = \overline{W} \circ \overline{\theta}$.

Second case : $\mathcal{L}_\omega(i) = 0, i \neq 0$. Then, $\overline{W} \circ \overline{\theta} = \overline{W}(\theta(\omega), 0)$. Since $\mathcal{L}_\omega(i) = 0, \sigma \circ \theta^{-i} - \sum_{k=0}^{i} \tau \circ \theta^{-k} \leq 0$. Since $i \in H(\omega), \overline{W} = \sigma \circ \theta^{-i} - \sum_{k=1}^{i} \tau \circ \theta^{-k} > 0$. Therefore, $\overline{W} + \sigma.1_{\{\overline{W}=0\}} - \tau = \overline{W} - \tau = \sigma \circ \theta^{-i} - \sum_{k=0}^{i} \theta^{-k} \leq 0$. Thus, $(\overline{W} + \sigma.1_{\overline{W}=0} - \tau)^+ = 0 = \overline{W} \circ \overline{\theta}$.

Third case : $\mathcal{L}_\omega(i) = i + 1, i = 0$. We have $\mathcal{L}_\omega(i) = 1$ and $\overline{W}(\theta(\omega), \mathcal{L}_\omega(i)) = \overline{W}(\theta(\omega), 1) = (\sigma \circ \theta^{-1} - \tau \circ \theta^{-1}) \circ \theta = \sigma - \tau$. Since $i = 0, \overline{W}(\omega, i) = 0$. Therefore $\overline{W} + \sigma.1_{\{\overline{W}=0\}} - \tau = \sigma - \tau$. Now $\mathcal{L}_\omega(0) = 1$ also implies that $\sigma > \tau$, and therefore $(\overline{W} + \sigma.1_{\{\overline{W}=0\}} - \tau)^+ = \overline{W} \circ \overline{\theta}$.

Fourth case : $\mathcal{L}_\omega(i) = 0, i = 0$. Therefore $\overline{W}(\theta(\omega), \mathcal{L}_\omega(i)) = \overline{W}(\theta(\omega), 0) = 0$. But $\mathcal{L}_\omega(0) = 0, \sigma - \tau < 0$ and $\overline{W}(\omega, i) = 0$, so that $\overline{W} + \sigma.1_{\{\overline{W}=0\}} - \tau = \sigma - \tau \leq 0$. $\qquad \square$

6 Other Queueing Systems

This section contains a few important examples. In the first subsection we treat the pure delay system $G/G/\infty$, which is rather atypical in stability theory. In the second one, we show how the 'raw' $G/G/1/\infty$ model can be augmented so as to represent priorities.

6.1 The $G/G/\infty$ Pure Delay System

The input $\{\sigma_n, \tau_n\}$, $n \in \mathbb{Z}$ is defined as in § 1.1. The system has an infinite reservoir of servers, so that any customer is immediately attended. Therefore, customer n arriving at time T_n leaves at time $T_n + \sigma_n$ (service is provided at unit rate).

The state of the system is described by the random element $R_n \in \mathbb{R}^\infty$, where $R_n = (R_n^1, R_n^2, R_n^3, \ldots)$ is an ordering in decreasing order

(6.1.1) $R_n^1 \geq R_n^2 \geq \ldots$

of the residual service times at time T_n. In view of the assumptions on the input, we have

(6.1.2) $R_n = R \circ \theta^n$,

where R has the following entries properly reordered

(6.1.3) $\{(\sigma \circ \theta^i - |T_i|)^+ ; i \leq -1\}$.

The number of non-null coordinates of R is the number X_0 of customers in the system just before the arrival of customer 0 (see Figure 6.1.1).

(6.1.4) *If τ and σ are integrable,*

(6.1.5) $P^0[X_0 < \infty] = 1$

and therefore, in this sense, the $G/G/\infty$ system is 'stable'.

Proof: We prove that

(6.1.6) $P[X(0) < \infty] = 1$,

where P is the θ_t- stationary probability associated to P^0 and where $X(t)$ is the number of customers in the system at time t. Indeed (6.1.6) implies (6.1.5) in view of the results of § 7.1 of Chapter 1.

But

$$X(0) = \sum_{n \in \mathbb{Z}} f(T_n, \sigma_n),$$

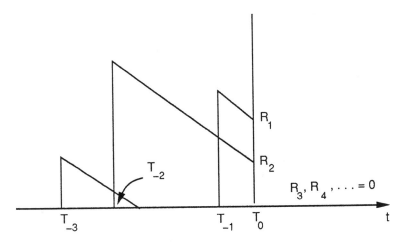

Fig. 6.1.1 The pure delay system

where $f(t,\sigma)$ is 1 if $t < 0$ and $\sigma > -t$, and 0 otherwise. By Campbell's formula ((3.3.2) of Chapter 1), and formula (3.1.4) of Chapter 1,

$$E[X(0)] = \int_{-\infty}^{0} \left(\int_{-t}^{\infty} P^0(\sigma_0 \in dx) \right) \lambda dt = \lambda \int_{0}^{\infty} (1 - P^0(\sigma_0 \le t)) dt,$$

i.e., since $\lambda = 1/E^0[\tau]$,

$$(6.1.7) \quad E[X(0)] = \frac{E^0[\sigma]}{E^0[\tau]} = \rho < \infty,$$

and therefore (6.1.6) holds.

More generally, denoting $X_r(t)$ the number of busy servers at time t with a load larger or equal to $r > 0$, we obtain

$$(6.1.8) \quad E[X_r(0)] = \lambda \int_{r}^{\infty} (1 - P^0(\sigma \le t)) dt.$$

$\square$

6.2 Service Disciplines in $G/G/1/\infty$: the Vector of Residual Services

This section focuses on service disciplines in the general $G/G/1/\infty$ model of § 1. The stability condition $E^0[\sigma] < E^0[\tau]$ is supposed to hold, and therefore there exists a unique finite stationary load W.

We construct a state richer in information than W, which features in particular the service discipline (LIFO, FIFO, SRPT, ...).

Let S be an infinite vector of non-negative numbers, i.e. $S \in \mathbb{R}_+^\mathbb{N}$, and only the I first coordinates of S are non-null, where I is random. S is the vector of residual service times of the I customers present in the system just before time 0. In position I, we find the customer being presently served, in position $I - 1$, the next customer to be served, etc.

When customer 0 arrives, this possibly changes the priorities. The priority vector at time 0+ is S^+, where

$$(6.2.1) \quad S^+(\omega) = \phi(\omega)(S(\omega) + \sigma(\omega)e_{I(\omega)+1}),$$

where e_i is the i-th vector of the canonical base of $\mathbb{R}^\mathbb{N}$, and $\phi(\omega)$ is a permutation on $\mathbb{R}^\mathbb{N}$ involving only the $I(\omega) + 1$ first coordinates. The function ϕ describes service disciplines in a way which is best explained through examples.

First-In-First-Out.

$$(6.2.2) \quad \phi(S^1, S^2, \ldots, S^I, S^{I+1}) = (S^{I+1}, S^1, S^2, \ldots, S^I).$$

Last-In-First-Out without Preemption.

$$(6.2.3) \quad \phi(S^1, S^2, \ldots, S^I, S^{I+1}) = (S^1, S^2, \ldots, S^{I+1}, S^I).$$

There is no preemption i.e. the last customer arriving does not interrupt the service of customer being serviced.

Last-In-First-Out with Preemption.

$$(6.2.4) \quad \phi(S^1, S^2, \ldots, S^I, S^{I+1}) = (S^1, S^2, \ldots, S^I, S^{I+1}) = \text{identity}.$$

Shortest-Remaining-Processing-Time. SRPT is a priority discipline with preemption, where $S = (S^1, S^2, \ldots, S^I, 0, \ldots)$ always satisfies the relation $S^1 \geq S^2 \geq \ldots \geq S^I$. We define SRPT by :

$$(6.2.5) \quad \phi(S + \sigma e_{I+1}) = \begin{cases} (\sigma, S^1, S^2, \ldots, S^I), & \text{if } S^1 \leq \sigma, \\ \text{identity}, & \text{if } S^I > \sigma, \\ (S^1, \ldots, S^{j-1}, \sigma, S^j, \ldots, S^I) & \text{if } S^j \leq \sigma < S^{j-1}, \\ & 2 \leq j \leq I. \end{cases}$$

Shortest-Processing-Time. It is the same discipline as SRPT, but without preemption. The only change with respect to SRPT is in the case $S^I > \sigma$ where, for SPT, $\phi = (S^1, S^2, \ldots, S^{I-1}, \sigma, S^I)$.

A discipline is said to use no information on the service times if the permutation ϕ does not depend on the actual value of the coordinates of S, as it is the case for the first three disciplines.

For all the above disciplines, the permutation ϕ is 'deterministic'. The RANDOM discipline provides an example where ϕ is a function of both S and ω.

In the general case, the random permutation ϕ_n is used at time T_n, and for all $S \in \mathbb{R}_+^\mathbb{N}$, $\phi_n(\omega, S) = \phi_0(\theta^n \omega, S)$.

For the last two disciplines, the arrival of a new customer creates a modification of the order of service which depends at most upon σ and S. There exist more complex disciplines for which ϕ depends upon the whole sequence $(\sigma \circ \theta^{-n}, S \circ \theta^{-n}, n \geq 0)$. We shall only consider disciplines which depend upon

$$(6.2.6) \quad (\sigma \circ \theta^{-n}, S \circ \theta^{-n}; 0 \leq n \leq \nu),$$

where

$$(6.2.7) \quad \nu = \inf\{n \geq 0 | W \circ \theta^{-n} = 0\}.$$

Such disciplines will be said to be *admissible*. For each admissible discipline ϕ, there corresponds a unique stationary state $S = S_\phi$. The actual construction uses the construction points as follows :

$(6.2.8a) \quad S_{\phi,n} = 0$, if n is a construction point $(W \circ \theta^{-n} = 0)$,

$(6.2.8b) \quad S_{\phi,n}^+ = \phi(S_{\phi,n} + \sigma_n e_{I_n+1})$,

$$(6.2.8c) \quad S_{\phi,n+1}^j = \left(\sum_{k=j}^\infty (S_{\phi,n}^+)^k - \tau_n\right)^+ - \left(\sum_{k=j+1}^\infty (S_{\phi,n}^+)^k - \tau_n\right)^+.$$

The last equality expresses that the residual service times are consumed at unity rate, in the order of the customers (see Figure 6.2.2).

We are now in a position to construct the time-stationary state. Let P be the stationary probability associated with P^0. Let ϕ be an admissible service discipline. From the sequence of marks $(S_{\phi,n}, n \in \mathbb{Z})$ and $(S_{\phi,n}^+, n \in \mathbb{Z})$ we can construct the process of residual service times $(S_\phi(t), t \in \mathbb{R})$ by

$$(6.2.9a) \quad S_\phi(T_n) = S_{\phi,n}^+, \quad n \in \mathbb{Z},$$

and for $t \in [T_n, T_{n+1})$, $n \in \mathbb{Z}$

$$(6.2.9b) \quad S_\phi^j(t) = \left(\sum_{k=j}^\infty (S_{\phi,n}^+)^k - (t - T_n)\right)^+ - \left(\sum_{k=j+1}^\infty (S_{\phi,n}^+)^k - (t - T_n)\right)^+.$$

This construction must be shown to be $P-$consistent, i.e. we must show that the evolution dynamics are respected, i.e.

$$(6.2.10) \quad S_\phi(T_n) = \phi(S_\phi(T_n^-) + \sigma_n e_{I_n+1}), \quad n \in \mathbb{Z}, \quad P-\text{a.s.}$$

But $S_\phi(T_n^-) = S_{\phi,n}$ in view of (6.2.9b) and (6.2.8c), and $S_\phi(T_n) = S_{\phi,n}^+$ by definition (6.2.9a) and therefore (6.2.10) can be reduced to

$$S_{\phi,n}^+ = \phi(S_{\phi,n} + \sigma_n e_{I_n+1}), \quad n \in \mathbb{Z}.$$

Since this is P^0-a.s. true, (6.2.10) is verified in view of the invariance results of § 7.1, Chapter 1.

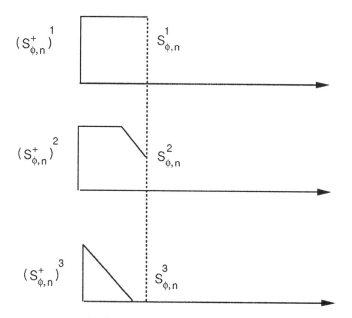

Fig. 6.2.2 $(S_{\phi,n}^+)^j = 0$ for $j = 4, 5, 6, \ldots$; $S_{\phi,n}^j = 0$ for $j = 4, 5, 6, \ldots$

6.3 $G/G/1/\infty$ Queues with Vacations

The corresponding system. is a $G/G/1/\infty$ queue in which the server takes vacations (during which no customers are served) in the following two situations:

(a) the queue just became empty;

(b) upon return from vacation, the server finds the queue still empty.

The sequence of vacation times is assumed to be independent of the input sequence; we denote it $\{V_k\}_{k\geq 1}$; the queue starts with an arbitrary workload at time 0.

Before considering this queue, we shall consider the following abstract construction, which is closely related to the original problem but must be interpreted, as we shall do later.

We suppose that the G/G input is stationary ergodic, with traffic intensity $\rho < 1$, and we let $\{W(t)\}_{t\in\mathbb{R}}$ be the associated stationary workload (constructed for a system with one server and infinite capacity of the waiting room).

Let now $\widetilde{N}$ be a stationary point process with finite intensity $\widetilde{\lambda}$. We shall "distribute the points of $\widetilde{N}$ in the idle periods of the queue" as Figure 6.3.1 shows.

The point process so obtained is now called N_V. Each point of N_V will be taken to be the start of a vacation, the length of the vacation being the

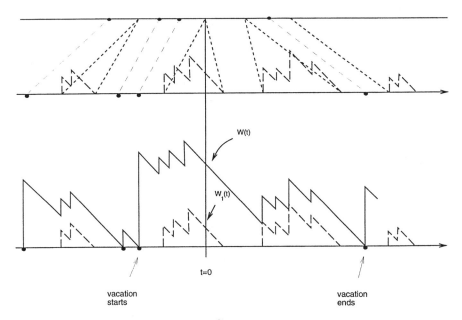

Fig. 6.3.1 Distributing the points of $\widetilde{N}$

time separating this point from the next point minus the length of the busy period in between, if any.

Now, we construct the process $\{W_1(t)\}$, $t \in \mathbb{R}$, as indicated in Figure 6.3.1, by considering that a start of vacation represents the arrival of a virtual customer, with virtual required service equal to the duration of the vacation, and then defining $\{W_1(t)\}$ as the workload process relative to the superposition of the streams of the original customers and of the virtual customers.

The reader is invited to prove formally that $\{W(t)\}$, $\{W_1(t)\}$ and N_V are jointly stationary.

Consider now the case when the input process is not stationary but couples to a stationary ergodic input process, so that, in particular, the non stationary workload process $\{\widetilde{W}(t)\}$ couples after a finite stopping time to the stationary workload $\{W(t)\}$ above (see § 4.2).

If in a addition, the point process with time sequence $\{V_1 + \ldots + V_n\}_{n \geq 1}$ couples strongly to the stationary point process $\widetilde{N}$ above, then clearly, the total workload process $\{\widetilde{W}_1(t)\}$ taking into account the original customers and the virtual customers, couples after a finite time to $\{W_1(t)\}$ above.

In this sense, we can say that this $G/G/1/\infty$ queue with multiple vacations has a unique asymptotic stationary regime.

Remark 6.3.1 The above assumptions of coupling are satisfied in the GI/GI case if the arrival process is a renewal process with spreadout distribution (see S. Asmussen, already quoted), and the vacation sequence also. $\qquad\square$

Remark 6.3.2 For the FIFO discipline, the workload process receives the following interpretation: $\widetilde{W}_1(T_n-)$ is the waiting time of the customer arriving at time T_n. $\qquad\square$

6.4 $G/G/1/\infty$ Queues with Mutual Service

In this system, there are two streams of customers arriving to a single server queue with infinite waiting room. Customers of both classes are served under a global FIFO discipline. An additional rule states that a customer of one class can only be served if there is at least one customer of the other class in the waiting room. If not, he has to wait till the arrival of the next customer of the other class.

Let M and N be two G/G input type marked point processes defined on $(\Omega, \mathcal{F}, P, \theta_t)$, with the usual ergodicity and integrability assumptions. The points of M are denoted $\{T_n\}$ and those of N $\{S_n\}$. Similarly, α will denote the service time of customer T_0 of M and β that of S_0 in N.

Let W_n be the waiting time experienced by customer T_n, that is the total time between its arrival and the time it starts being served. One easily checks that $\{W_n\}$ satisfies the stochastic recurrence

$$(6.4.1) \quad W_{n+1} = \left\{ (W_n + \alpha_n - \tau_n)^+ + \sum_{T_n \leq S_m < T_{n+1}} \beta \circ \theta_{S_m} \right\} \vee \left\{ S_1 \circ \theta_{T_{n+1}} \right\}$$

where $\tau_n = T_{n+1} - T_n$. As it is easily checked, the technique of Remark 4.2.1 applies, when taking the Palm space of M as reference probability space. Let M_n (resp. M_∞) denote the associated Loynes' sequence (resp. variable).

The relation

$$E_M^0 \left[\left\{ (M_n + \alpha - \tau)^+ + \sum_{0 \leq S_m < T_1} \beta \circ \theta_{S_m} \right\} \vee \left\{ S_1 \circ \theta_{T_1} \right\} - M_n \right] \geq 0$$

follows from the non-decreasingness of $\{M_n\}$. Assuming that M_∞ is P_M^0 a.s. infinite (it is necessarily either a.s. finite or a.s. infinite because of the ergodic assumption on the G/G inputs), when letting n go to infinity in this relation, we obtain that

$$(6.4.2) \quad E_M^0 \left[\alpha - \tau + \sum_{0 \leq S_m < T_1} \beta \circ \theta_{S_m} \right] \geq 0,$$

from the dominated convergence theorem. When using Neveu's exchange formula, this condition rewrites:

$$E_M^0(T_1) \le E_M^0(\alpha) + \frac{E_M^0(T_1)}{E_N^0(S_1)} E_N^0(\beta),$$

or equivalently, if $\rho_1 = \lambda E_M^0(\alpha)$ denotes the traffic intensity of the first arrival process and $\rho_2 = \mu E_N^0(\beta) \ge 1$ that of the second one, $\rho_1 + \rho_2 \ge 1$.

Thus the queue is stable if $\rho = \rho_1 + \rho_2 < 1$. One easily checks that it is unstable if $\rho > 1$.

So the stability region is the same at that of a queue with two input streams but where customers do not have to wait for customers of the other class!

7 Stability of Queueing Networks via Coupling

7.1 $G/G/1/\infty$ Queues in Tandem

Consider a network of J $G/G/1/\infty$ FIFO queues in tandem, that is,

- The first queue is fed by some external input stream, which is assumed to form a stationary point process N on the probability space $(\Omega, \mathcal{F}, P^0, \theta_t)$, where (θ_t) is ergodic;
- The output of queue j is the input of queue $j + 1$, $j = 1, J - 1$.

The point process $N = \sum \delta_{T_n}$ is assumed to be simple and to have a finite intensity. The service time of customer 0 in queue j, is a $\mathbb{R}_+$-valued mark σ^j associated with T_0. It is assumed that these marks are all P^0 integrable.

Let $(\Omega, \mathcal{F}^0, P^0, \theta)$ be the Palm space of the external input point process.

Let $W_n = (W_n^1, \ldots, W_n^J)$, where W_n^j is the waiting times of the n-th customer to be served in queues $j \in (1, \ldots, J)$.

(7.1.1) If $E[\sigma_j] < E[\tau]$, $j = 1, \ldots, J$, then $\{W_n\}$ couples with a uniquely defined and finite stationary sequence $\{W \circ \theta^n\}$ which does not depend on the initial condition.

Proof: The proof is by induction on j. The induction hypothesis states that $\{W_n^j\}$ couples with a stationary sequence $\{W^j \circ \theta^n\}$ which does not depend on the initial condition, and that the inter-event times of the output process of queue j couple with a θ-compatible and integrable sequence. The induction assumption holds true for $j = 1$, in view of Remark 4.2.2. The stationary sequence with which $\{W_n^1\}$ couples is merely the Loynes' sequence associated with the external input stream and the marks σ_n^1. Assume the property holds for queue j. Then the inter-event times of the input process to queue $j + 1$ couple with a θ-compatible and integrable sequence, and the hypothesis holds true for queue $j + 1$ in view of Remark 4.2.2. □

7.2 Kelly Type Networks

Consider a network of J single server queues with infinite waiting room capacity. Customers arrive to this network following a stationary point process N, defined on the probability space $(\Omega, \mathcal{F}, P, \theta_t)$, where (θ_t) is ergodic. This point process admits the marks $\{r_n\} = \{r \circ \theta_{T_n}\}$ and $\{\sigma_n\} = \{\sigma \circ \theta_{T_n}\}$, where

- $r = (r^1, r^2, \ldots)$ is a $\{1, \ldots, J\} \cup \{0\}$-valued sequence which describes the route of customer 0 through the network. Each r is of the form $r = (r^1, r^2, \ldots, r^l, 0, 0, \ldots)$, where the l first coordinates belong to $\{1, \ldots, J\}$. This sequence describes the sequence of queues to be visited by customer 0: first r^1 is visited; when customer 0 completes his service there, he is routed to queue r^2 an so on; after he has completed in queue r^l, customer 0 leaves the network. The random variable l, which describes the total number of queues along the route of customer 0, is assumed to be finite.

- $\sigma = (\sigma^1, \sigma^2, \ldots)$ is a $\mathbb{R}_+$-valued sequence which describes the service requirements of customer 0 at the successive queues of his route.

The general question is the following: if we specify the service discipline (for instance FIFO at each queue), under what condition does the network reach a stationary regime? There are no general answers to this question. Known results are relative to specific probabilistic assumptions (e.g. independence) or specific service disciplines. The aim of this section is to study a particular discipline for which coupling arguments can be used under the preceding general statistical assumptions.

This discipline is based on priority classes. A customer who visits the m-th queue of his route is said to be of class $m \geq 1$. The priority rule in each queue is the following:

- Customers of class m have a preemptive priority over customers of class $m + 1, m + 2, \ldots$;

- Within each class, customers are served on a FIFO basis.

We denote ρ_k the mean value of the workload brought to queue k per unit of time, that is, (see Example 3.1.1, Chapter 1)

$$(7.2.1) \quad \rho_k = \lambda E^0 \left[\sum_{i=1}^{\infty} (\sigma^i 1_{r^i = k}) \right],$$

where E^0 denotes expectation with respect to the Palm measure of N, and λ is the intensity of N.

Let $W^{k,m}(t)$ denote the workload of customers of class m in queue k at time t. The main result of this section is the following property:

(7.2.2) If $\rho_k < 1$ for all $k = 1, \ldots, J$, then for all $m \geq 1$, the random process $\{W^m(t)\} = \{(W^{1,m}, \ldots, W^{J,m})\}$ couples with a stationary process $\{W^m \circ \theta_t\}$, and the total workload $\{W(t)\} \overset{\text{def}}{=} \{\sum_{m \geq 1} W^m(t)\}$ admits a finite stationary regime $\{W \circ \theta_t\}$, $W \in \mathbb{R}^J$.

Proof: In the proof, P denotes the stationary probability of N. If A is a θ_t-compatible point process, E^0_A denotes expectation with respect to the Palm probability of A. All point processes to be used are defined on $(\Omega, \mathcal{F}, P, \theta_t)$, and admit marks in $\{\{1, \ldots, J\} \cup \{0\}\}^N \times \{\mathbb{R}_+\}^N$. If A denotes such a marked point process, its points and marks will be denoted $T(A)_n, r(A)_n$ and $\sigma(A)_n$ respectively, or simply T_n, r_n and σ_n when no ambiguity is possible.

Let $A^{k,m}$ (resp. $D^{k,m}$) denote the arrival (resp. departure) point process of customers of class m to queue k. For all k, the marked point process $A^{k,1}$ is defined by

$$A^{k,1} = \sum_{n \in \mathbb{Z}} \delta_{T_n \times (r_n, \sigma_n)} 1_{r_n^1 = k}.$$

This point process is θ_t-compatible. Its intensity is

$$\lambda^{k,1} = \lambda P^0(r^1 = k),$$

and

$$E^0_{A^{k,1}}[\sigma^1] = E^0[\sigma^1 \mid r^1 = k].$$

In view of the preemptive nature of the service discipline, customers of class 1 are not affected by customers of other classes, so that if the traffic intensity

$$\rho^{k,1} \stackrel{\text{def}}{=} \lambda P^0_N(r^1 = k) E^0[\sigma^1 \mid r^1 = k] = \lambda E^0[\sigma^1; \; r^1 = k]$$

is less than 1, then the workload process $\{W^{k,1}(t)\}$ couples with a uniquely defined θ_t-compatible workload process P-a.s. Since the condition $\rho_k < 1$ implies $\rho^{k,1} < 1$, we see that the above coupling property is satisfied, so that the departure process $D^{k,1}$ defined by

$$D^{k,1} = \sum_{n \in \mathbb{Z}} \delta_{(T(A^{k,1})_n + V_n) \times ((A^{k,1})_n, \sigma(A^{k,1})_n)}$$

couples with a uniquely defined θ_t-compatible point process $\widehat{D}^{k,1}$. In this last definition, we take $V_n = W^{k,1}(T(A^{k,1})_n+)$, the workload just after the arrival of the n-th customer of $A^{k,1}$, which coincides with the sojourn time of this customer since the discipline is FIFO within each class. In view of the results of § 5.4, Chapter 1, $\widehat{D}^{k,1}$ has the same intensity as $A^{k,1}$. Similarly, in view of the results on delayed point processes of (5.4.3), Chapter 1,

$$E^0_{\widehat{D}^{k,1}}[\sigma^m] = E^0_{A^{k,1}}[\sigma^m], \quad \forall m \geq 1.$$

The point processes $A^{k,2}$ are then defined as the superposition

$$A^{k,2} = \sum_{j=1,\ldots,J} \sum_{n \in \mathbb{Z}} \delta_{T(D^{j,1})_n \times (r(D^{j,1})_n, \sigma(D^{j,1})_n)} 1_{r(D^{j,1})_n^2 = k}.$$

Thus, $A^{k,2}$ couples with a θ_t-compatible point process $\widehat{A}^{k,2}$ P-a.s. The intensity of $\widehat{A}^{k,2}$ is

$$
\begin{aligned}
\lambda^{k,2} &= \sum_{j=1,\ldots,J} \lambda P_N^0(r^1 = j) P_{\widehat{D}^{j,1}}^0(r^2 = k) \\
&= \sum_{j=1,\ldots,J} \lambda P_N^0(r^1 = j) P_{A^{j,1}}^0(r^2 = k) \\
&= \sum_{j=1,\ldots,J} \lambda P_N^0(r^1 = j) P_N^0(r^2 = k) \\
&= \lambda P_N^0(r^2 = k).
\end{aligned}
$$

In addition, the traffic intensity $\rho^{k,2}$ of this point process is

$$
\begin{aligned}
\rho^{k,2} &= \sum_{j=1}^J \lambda^{j,1} P_{\widehat{D}^{j,1}}^0(r^2 = k) E_{D^{j,1}}^0[\sigma^2 \mid r^2 = k] \\
&= \sum_{j=1}^J \lambda^{j,1} E_{A^{j,1}}^0[\sigma^2;\ r^2 = k] \\
&= \sum_{j=1}^J \lambda^{j,1} E_N^0[\sigma^2; r^2 = k \mid r^1 = j] \\
&= \lambda E_N^0[\sigma^2;\ r^2 = k].
\end{aligned}
$$

The induction assumption is now that for all $k = 1, \ldots, J$, the point processes $A^{k,m}$ couples with a θ_t-compatible point processes $\widehat{A}^{k,m}$, with intensity

$$
\lambda^{k,m} = \lambda P_N^0(r^m = k)
$$

and with traffic intensity brought to queue k equal to

$$
\rho^{k,m} = \lambda E_N^0[\sigma^m;\ r^m = k].
$$

Using the results of Examples 4.2.1 and 4.2.2, together with the fact that

$$
\sum_{p=1}^m \rho^{k,m} \le \rho_k < 1,
$$

we obtain that $W^{k,m}(t)$ couples with a uniquely defined θ_t-compatible workload process. This allows us to construct a θ_t-compatible departure point process $\widehat{D}^{k,m}$, with which $D^{k,m}$ couples. This and the same arguments as above allow us to prove that the property holds for $m + 1$. $\qquad\square$

Remark 7.2.1 In what precedes, we should check that the involved superpositions have no common points so as to get simple input point processes at each step. This property will for instance be satisfied if the service times are independent, i.i.d. and with a distribution that is absolutely continuous with respect to the Lebesgue measure.   □

Remark 7.2.2 Because $\rho_k = \sum_m \rho^{k,m} < 1$, queue k with an arrival process equal to the superposition of the point processes $(\widehat{A}^{k,m})_{m \geq 1}$ admits a stationary regime, which is characterized by the workload process $(W^k \circ \theta_t)$. If the random variable l, defining the maximal number of queues visited by customer 0 is bounded, we easily chek that the total workload process $\{W^k(t)\} = \{\sum_{m \geq 1} W^{k,m}(t)\}$ couples with $\{W^k \circ \theta_t\}$.   □

8 Stability of Queueing Networks via Recurrence Equations

8.1 Finite Capacity Queues in Tandem with Blocking

Consider a network of J FIFO servers in tandem. The first server has a waiting rooms of infinite capacity and is fed by an external arrival stream, which forms a stationary and ergodic point process with the usual properties. The basic probability space is the Palm space of this point process. There are no intermediate waiting rooms between server j and $j+1$, $1 \leq j \leq J-1$, and a customer having completed its service in server j is blocked there as long as server $j+1$ is not empty (this is the so-called manufacturing blocking mechanism). Note that in this finite capacity queueing system, no customers are lost, as it was the case in the system considered in § 5. More generally, finite capacity queues fall into two categories depending on whether a lack of space provokes a loss or a blocking.

The J-dimensional mark $\sigma_n = (\sigma_n^1, \ldots, \sigma_n^J)$ is supposed to be associated with the n-th point, denoted T_n, of the external input process. The mark σ_n^j is the service time of the n-th customer to enter server j (who is also the customer who entered the first queue at time T_n in view of the FIFO assumptions). Let $Y^j \in \mathbb{R}$ denote the time when server j gets free of all its initial workload. For $n \geq 0$ and $1 \leq j, k \leq J$, let

$$\lambda_n^{j,k} = \sum_{i=j}^{k} \sigma_n^i,$$

with the convention that $\lambda_n^{j,k} = 0$ for all $j > k$, and

$$l_n^j = \lambda_n^{1,j} - \lambda_{n+1}^{1,j-1}.$$

Denote by D_n^j the time when customer n leaves server j, and by W_n^j the quantity

$$W_n^j = D_n^j - T_n - \lambda_n^{1,j},$$

which represents the total amount of waiting time of customer n between its arrival time in queue 1 and its departure time from server j.

(8.1.1) *The variables W_n satisfy the recurrence equation*

$$(8.1.2) \quad W_n^k = \begin{cases} \max_{\{1 \le j \le k+1\}} (Y^j - \lambda_0^{1,j-1})^+, & \text{for } n = 0; \\ \max_{\{1 \le j \le k+1\}} (W_{n-1}^j + l_{n-1}^j - \tau_{n-1})^+, & \text{for } n > 0, \end{cases}$$

where $W_n^{J+1} = Y^{J+1} = -\infty$ by convention.

Proof: Since server 1 gets free of customer n, $n \ge 0$ (resp. its initial workload) at $D_n^1 \ge 0$, (resp. $D_{-1}^1 = Y^1$), customer $n + 1$, $n \ge -1$ starts its service in server 1 at time $T_{n+1} \vee D_n^1$ and completes it at time $(T_{n+1} \vee D_n^1) + \sigma_{n+1}^1$. Since server 2 gets free of customer n (resp. its initial workload) at D_n^2 (resp. $D_{-1}^2 = Y^2$), customer $n + 1, n \ge -1$ will hence leave server 1 and start its service in 2 at time

$$D_{n+1}^1 = (T_{n+1} + \sigma_{n+1}^1) \vee (D_n^1 + \sigma_{n+1}^1) \vee D_n^2.$$

More generally, if customer $n + 1$ leaves server $k - 1$, $k < J$ at D_{n+1}^{k-1}, then it will complete its service in server k at $(D_{n+1}^{k-1} + \sigma_{n+1}^k)$ and leave server k at

$$D_{n+1}^k = (D_{n+1}^{k-1} + \sigma_{n+1}^k) \vee D_n^{k+1},$$

whereas for server J,

$$D_{n+1}^J = (D_{n+1}^{J-1} + \sigma_{n+1}^J).$$

Simple substitutions based on the last three relations imply

$$D_{n+1}^k = (T_{n+1} + \lambda_{n+1}^{1,k}) \vee \max_{\{1 \le j \le k+1\}} (D_n^j + \lambda_{n+1}^{j,k}), \ n \ge -1,$$

with the conventions $D_n^{J+1} = -\infty$, $D_{-1}^j = Y^j$. Equation (8.1.2) follows by subtracting $T_{n+1} + \lambda_{n+1}^{1,k}$ from both sides of the last relation.   □

Let

$$l_n^{j,k} = \begin{cases} l_n^j & \text{if } 1 \le j \le k + 1; \\ -\infty & \text{otherwise.} \end{cases}$$

Equation (8.1.2) rewrites

$$(8.1.3) \quad W_{n+1}^k = \max_j (W_n^j + l_n^{j,k} - \tau_n)^+, \ n \ge 0, \ k = 1, \dots, J,$$

where the maximum now bears on all $j = 1, \dots, J$.

8.2 Existence of a Stationary Solution

The stochastic recurrence (8.1.3) falls in the class (4.2.1), i.e. $W_{n+1} = h(W_n, \xi_n)$, where the function h is non-negative, continuous and coordinate-wise non-decreasing in its first argument. Therefore the sequences $\{M_n^k\}$, $1 \leq k \leq J$, defined by

(8.2.1)
$$M_0^k = 0$$
$$M_{n+1}^k \circ \theta = \max_j (M_n^j + l^{j,k} - \tau)^+,$$

are non-decreasing in n, and if we denote by M_∞^k the limiting value (that is, the Loynes' variable associated with (8.1.3)), then $\{M_\infty \circ \theta^n\}$ is a stationary solution of (8.1.3) (see § 4.2). it is easily shown that M_∞ is the minimal stationary solution of

(8.2.2) $\quad Z^k \circ \theta = \max_j (Z^j + l^{j,k} - \tau)^+.$

The derivation of the stability region requires a few technical lemmas.

(8.2.3) *For all $j = 1, \ldots, J$, the event $\{M_\infty^j = \infty\}$ is θ invariant.*

Proof: For all j, we have $j \in \pi^j = \{k \text{ s.t } l^{k,j} \neq -\infty\}$. $\qquad\qquad \square$

(8.2.4) *Either $P^0[\cap_{j=1,\ldots,J}\{M_\infty^j = \infty\}]$ equals 1 or $P^0[\cap_{j=1,\ldots,J}\{M_\infty^j < \infty\}]$ equals 1.*

Proof: Both events are obviously θ-invariant. If $P^0[\cap_{j=1,\ldots,J}\{M_\infty^j < \infty\}]$ is not 1, it is hence 0, so that $P^0[M_\infty^j = \infty] = 1$ for at least one $j = 1, \ldots, J$, in view of (8.2.3). But since $\{j - 1, j, j + 1\} \subset \pi^j$ (at least for $j \neq 1, J$),

$$\{M_\infty^j = \infty\} \subset \{M_\infty^{j+1} \circ \theta = \infty\} \cap \{M_\infty^j \circ \theta = \infty\} \cap \{M_\infty^{j-1} \circ \theta = \infty\},$$

where the undefined events like $\{M_\infty^{J+1} = \infty\}$ are Ω by convention. Therefore $P^0[M_\infty^j = \infty] = 1$ implies $P^0[M_\infty^{j+1} = \infty] = 1$ and $P^0[M_\infty^{j-1} = \infty] = 1$. The property that $P^0[\cap_{j=1,\ldots,J}\{M_\infty^j = \infty\}] = 1$ follows immediately. $\qquad \square$

The following expression of M_n will also be needed later on:

(8.2.5) *For every $n \geq 1$ and $j = 1, \ldots, J$,*

(8.2.6) $\quad M_n^j = \max_{1 \leq m \leq n} \left(H_m^j - \sum_{p=1}^m \tau \circ \theta^{-p} \right)^+,$

where

(8.2.7) $\quad H_m^j = \max_{\{j_0,\ldots,j_m=1,\ldots,J, j_0=j\}} \sum_{p=1}^m l^{j_p,j_{p-1}} \circ \theta^{-p}.$

Proof: The proof is by induction on n. For $n = 1$, (8.2.6) is obvious. Suppose it holds for some $n \geq 1$. Then, we obtain from equation (8.2.1) that

$$M_{n+1}^j = \max_k \left(M_n^k \circ \theta^{-1} + l^{k,j} \circ \theta^{-1} - \tau \circ \theta^{-1} \right)^+ .$$

Using the inductive assumption, we obtain

$$M_{n+1}^j = \left(\max_k \left(\max_{1 \le m \le n} (H_m^k - \sum_{p=1}^m \tau \circ \theta^{-p}) \circ \theta^{-1} \right)^+ + (l^{k,j} - \tau) \circ \theta^{-1} \right)^+$$

$$= \left(\max_{1 \le m \le n} \max_k \max \left(l^{k,j} \circ \theta^{-1} - \tau \circ \theta^{-1}, \right. \right.$$

$$H_m^k \circ \theta^{-1} + l^{k,j} \circ \theta^{-1} - \sum_{p=2}^{m+1} \tau \circ \theta^{-p} - \tau \circ \theta^{-1} \right)^+$$

$$= \max \left(0, H_1^j - \tau \circ \theta^{-1}, \left(\max_{1 \le m \le n} H_{m+1}^j - \sum_{p=1}^{m+1} \tau \circ \theta^{-p} \right) \right)$$

$$= \left(\max_{1 \le m \le n+1} H_m^j - \sum_{p=1}^m \tau \circ \theta^{-p} \right)^+ .$$

Therefore the equation holds for $n + 1$.   □

Let

$$(8.2.8) \quad Q_n = \max_{\{j_0,\ldots,j_n=1,\ldots,J\}} \sum_{p=1}^n l^{j_p,j_{p-1}} \circ \theta^{-p}, \quad n = 1, 2, \ldots$$

(8.2.9) *The sequence $U_{m,m+n} = Q_n \circ \theta^{-m}$, $m \in \mathbb{Z}$, $n \ge 1$, is a positive and integrable sub-additive ergodic process in the sense that for all $n \ge 2$, and all $0 < q < n \in \mathbb{N}$*

$$(8.2.10) \quad U_{m,m+n} \le U_{m,m+q} + U_{m+q,m+n},$$

In addition, there exists a constant $0 < \gamma < \infty$ such that

$$(8.2.11) \quad \lim_{n \to \infty} \frac{Q_n}{n} = \lim_{n \to \infty} \frac{E^0[Q_n]}{n} = \gamma. \qquad a.s.$$

Proof: The positiveness of Q_n follows from

$$Q_n \ge \sum_{p=1}^n l^{1,1} \circ \theta^{-p} \ge \sum_{p=1}^n \sigma^1 \circ \theta^{-p} \ge 0.$$

We obtain by induction that

$$(8.2.12) \quad Q_n \le \sum_{p=1,\ldots,n} \sum_{j_p=1,\ldots,J} \sigma_{j_p} \circ \theta^{-p},$$

so that the integrability of Q_n (and hence $U_{m,m+n}$) follows from the integrability of the service times.

The sub-additive property (8.2.10) follows from the bounds

$$
\begin{aligned}
U_{m,m+n} &= \max_{\{j_0,\ldots,j_n=1,\ldots,J\}} \left(\sum_{p=1}^{n} l^{j_p,j_{p-1}} \circ \theta^{-p} \right) \circ \theta^{-m} \\
&\leq \max_{\{j_0,\ldots,j_q=1,\ldots,J\}} \left(\sum_{p=1}^{q} l^{j_p,j_{p-1}} \circ \theta^{-p} \right) \circ \theta^{-m} \\
&+ \max_{\{j_q,\ldots,j_n=1,\ldots,J\}} \left(\sum_{p=q+1}^{n} l^{j_p,j_{p-1}} \circ \theta^{-p} \right) \circ \theta^{-m} \\
&= \max_{\{j_0,\ldots,j_q=1,\ldots,J\}} \left(\sum_{p=1}^{q} l^{j_p,j_{p-1}} \circ \theta^{-p} \right) \circ \theta^{-m} \\
&+ \max_{\{j_0,\ldots,j_r=1,\ldots,J\}} \left(\sum_{p=1}^{r} l^{j_p,j_{p-1}} \circ \theta^{-p} \right) \circ \theta^{-q} \circ \theta^{-m} \\
&= U_{m,m+q} + U_{m+q,m+q+r},
\end{aligned}
$$

where $r = n - q$. sub-additive ergodic theorem (Kingman (1976) *Sub-additive Processes*, Ecole d'Eté de Probabilité de Saint-Flour) implies that there exists a non-negative constant γ such that

$$
\lim_{n\to\infty} \frac{U_{0,n}}{n} = \lim_{n\to\infty} \frac{E^0[U_{0,n}]}{n} = \gamma \quad \text{a.s.}
$$

The finiteness of γ follows from the bounds (8.2.12).   □

We now state the main result on the stability region.

(8.2.13) If $\gamma < E^0[\tau]$, then $M_\infty < \infty$ a.s. If $\gamma > E^0[\tau]$, then $M_\infty^j = \infty$ a.s. for all $j = 1,\ldots,J$.

Proof: Assume the event $\cap_{j=1,\ldots J}\{M_\infty^k = \infty\}$ is of probability 1. and let H_m^j be defined as in (8.2.7). In view of (8.2.6), $\max_{j=1,\ldots,J} M_n^j \uparrow \infty$ a.s. is equivalent to

$$
\limsup_{n\to\infty} \max_{j=1,\ldots,J} H_n^j - \sum_{m=1}^{n} \tau \circ \theta^{-m} = \infty \quad \text{a.s.}
$$

Using the identity $Q_n = \max_j H_n^j$ in the last relation implies

$$
\limsup_{n\to\infty} \frac{Q_n}{n} - \frac{\sum_{m=1}^{n} \tau \circ \theta^{-m}}{n} \geq 0 \quad \text{a.s.}
$$

From the ergodic assumption and (8.2.9), this implies

$$\gamma \geq E^0[\tau].$$

Therefore $\gamma < E^0[\tau]$ implies $M_\infty^j < \infty$ a.s. for all $j = 1, \ldots, J$, in view of (8.2.4). The first part of the theorem is thus proved.

Assume now that $\gamma > E^0[\tau]$. Then

$$\lim_{n \to \infty} \frac{Q_n}{n} = \gamma > E^0[\tau] \quad \text{a.s.}$$

which implies

$$\lim_{n \to \infty} \max_{j=1,\ldots,J} M_n^j = \lim_{n \to \infty} Q_n - \sum_{m=1}^n \tau \circ \theta^{-m} = \infty \quad \text{a.s.}$$

From (8.2.4), the last fact implies that $M_\infty^j = \infty$ a.s. for all $j = 1, \ldots, J$. $\quad\square$

8.3 Uniqueness of the Stationary Solutions

In what follows, we stress the initial condition by writing $W_n^k(Y)$, where $W_n(Y)$ is given by (8.1.2).

(8.3.1) *Assume that $\gamma < E^0[\tau]$. Then for any $Y \in \mathbb{R}_+^J$, $\{W_n(Y)\}$ and $\{M \circ \theta^n\}$ couple in finite time.*

Proof: It can easily be checked by induction on n that for all $n \geq 0$, $W_n(Y) \geq W_n(0) = M_n \circ \theta^n \geq 0$. Assume that the statement of the theorem does not hold. Then $W_n(Y) > W_n(0)$ for all $n \geq 0$ (in the sense that $W_n(Y) \geq W_n(0)$ with a strict inequality on at least a coordinate). For any fixed $n \geq 1$, let $k_n \in \{1, \ldots, J\}$ be an index such that $W_n^{k_n}(Y) > W_n^{k_n}(0) \geq 0$. In view of (8.2.1), there exists an index k_{n-1} such that

$$W_n^{k_n}(Y) = \max_{\{j\}}(W_{n-1}^j(Y) + L^{j,k_n} \circ \theta^{n-1})^+$$
$$= W_{n-1}^{k_{n-1}}(Y) + L^{k_{n-1},k_n} \circ \theta^{n-1},$$

where $L^{i,j} = l^{i,j} - \tau$. It is easy to see that necessarily $W_{n-1}^{k_{n-1}}(Y) > W_{n-1}^{k_{n-1}}(0) \geq 0$. If this were not true, we would then have

$$W_n^{k_n}(Y) = W_{n-1}^{k_{n-1}}(Y) + L^{k_{n-1},k_n} \circ \theta^{n-1}$$
$$\leq W_{n-1}^{k_{n-1}}(0) + L^{k_{n-1},k_n} \circ \theta^{n-1}$$
$$\leq \max_{\{j\}}(W_{n-1}^j(0) + L^{j,k_n} \circ \theta^{n-1})^+ = W_n^{k_n}(0)$$

and hence, $W_n^{k_n}(Y) \leq W_n^{k_n}(0)$, a contradiction with the definition of k_n.

Similarly, there exists an index k_{n-2} such that

$$W_{n-1}^{k_{n-1}}(Y) = \max_{\{j\}}(W_{n-2}^{j}(Y) + L^{j,k_{n-1}} \circ \theta^{n-2})^{+}$$

$$= W_{n-2}^{k_{n-2}}(Y) + L^{k_{n-2},k_{n-1}} \circ \theta^{n-2}$$

and $W_{n-2}^{k_{n-2}}(Y) > W_{n-2}^{k_{n-2}}(0) \geq 0$. More generally, we can find a series of indices k_{n-i}, $i = 1, 2, \ldots, n$, which satisfy the relations

$$W_{n-i+1}^{k_{n-i+1}}(Y) = W_{n-i}^{k_{n-i}}(Y) + L^{k_{n-i},k_{n-i+1}} \circ \theta^{n-i}.$$

Therefore,

$$W_n^{k_n}(Y) = W_0^{k_0}(Y) + \sum_{i=1}^{n} L^{k_{i-1},k_i} \circ \theta^{n-i}.$$

Obviously $\sum_{i=1}^{n} L^{k_{i-1},k_i} \circ \theta^{n-i} \leq Q_n \circ \theta^n - \sum_{m=0,n-1} \tau \circ \theta^m$, where Q_n is defined by (8.2.8). Hence

$$W_n^{k_n}(Y) \leq Y^{k_0} + Q_n - \sum_{m=0,n-1} \tau \circ \theta^m.$$

Using the same arguments as in (8.2.9), we obtain that $(Q_n \circ \theta^n)/n \to \gamma$, when $n \to \infty$. Therefore, under the assumption $\gamma < E^0[\tau]$, the last relation shows that $W_n^{k_n} \to -\infty$ when $n \to \infty$, where comes the contradiction. □

This coupling result implies the following properties:

(8.3.2) *Let Y be an arbitrary non-negative real vector in $\mathbb{R}_+^J$. If $\gamma < E^0[\tau]$, then the distribution of $\{W_{n+k}(Y)\}_{n\geq 0}$ under P^0 converges in variation to that of the finite process $\{M_\infty \circ \theta^n\})n \geq 0$ when k tends to ∞.*

(8.3.3) *Assume that $\gamma < E^0[\tau]$, then, M_∞ is the unique finite stationary solution of (8.2.1) compatible with the shift.*

Proof: Assume there is another finite solution V. From the coupling property, there exists a finite integer $N(V) > 0$ such that for all $n \geq N(V)$,

$$V \circ \theta^n = W_n(V) = W_n(0) \quad \text{a.s.}$$

Using once more the coupling property, we obtain another finite integer $N(M_\infty) > 0$ such that for all $n \geq N(M_\infty)$,

$$M_\infty \circ \theta^n = W_n(M_\infty) = W_n(0) \quad \text{a.s.}$$

Hence for all $n \geq N = \max(N(V), N(M_\infty))$,

$$M_\infty \circ \theta^n = V \circ \theta^n \quad \text{a.s.}$$

which immediately implies that $V = M_\infty$ a.s. □

9 The Saturation Rule

9.1 The Monotone Separable Framework

In view of the examples of the preceding sections, it seems natural to state that the stability region of an open queueing systems can be obtained as follows: 'saturate' the queues which are fed by the external arrival stream with an infinite customer population; if μ denotes the 'intensity' of the departure stream in this saturated system (for Markovian systems, μ can be obtained by computing the steady state of a Markov chain of smaller dimension than that of the initial non-saturated system), then the system is stable when the intensity of the arrival process, λ, satisfies the condition $\lambda < \mu$.

This 'engineering rule', which we will refer to as the *saturation rule*, does not hold for all systems (see the examples below). The aim of the present section is to set a natural framework, which involves two main properties called *separability* and *external monotonicity* in which this rule can be rigorously proved when dropping the Markovian assumptions and replacing them by standard stationary ergodic assumptions, namely the arrival point process is a stationary ergodic marked point process of finite intensity.

For any queueing system within this framework (to be defined below), we will denote X_n the time of the last activity to take place in the system, whenever one starts with n customers, all arrived at time 0 in an empty system. This notion of *time to inactivity*, turns out to be the adequate way of implementing the saturation idea for non-Markov systems. The main result is then:

(9.1.1) *The sequence $\{X_n\}$ satisfies a SLLN:*

$$(9.1.2) \quad \lim_n \frac{X_n}{n} = \gamma(0) \quad \text{a.s.,}$$

for some non-negative constant $\gamma(0)$; this constant will also be finite if the input marked process satisfies natural integrability conditions. Whenever the intensity of the input process satisfies the condition $\lambda < \gamma^{-1}(0)$, then the system is stable, whereas it is unstable if $\lambda > \gamma^{-1}(0)$.

Stability here means that the time to inactivity when the system is fed by the restriction of the point process on $(-\infty, t)$ admits a finite steady state regime. This usually implies most standard acceptations of stability.

The Framework. Let N be a marked point process with points $\{T_n\}_{n \in \mathbb{Z}}$ and marks $\{\xi_n\}_{n \in \mathbb{Z}}$, where $\xi_n \in (K, \mathcal{K})$. This point process is *not* assumed to be simple (nor to be stationary at this stage). We only assume that $T_n \leq T_{n+1}$, for all n. We shall use the notations τ_n for $T_{n+1} - T_n$, $c + N$ for the point process $\{T_n + c\}$ and cN for the point process $\{cT_n\}$, where $c \in \mathbb{R}$. In what follows, we shall not adopt the usual rule of renumbering, so that the n-th point of $N + c$ will be $T_n + c$ by definition.

For all $m \leq n \in \mathbb{N}$, let $X_{[m,n]}(N)$ be the time of the last activity in the network, when this one starts empty and is fed by the $[m,n]$ restriction of N, namely the point process $\{T_l\}_{m \leq l \leq n}$. We assume to be given a set of functions $\{f_l\}$, $f_l : \mathbb{R}^l \times K^l \to \mathbb{R}$, such that:

(9.1.3) $X_{[m,n]}(N) = f_{n-m+1}\{(T_l, \xi_l), \ m \leq l \leq n\}$,

for all n, m and N. We assume that the functions f_n are such that the following properties hold for all N:

(1) **(causality)**:   For all $m \leq n$,

$$X_{[m,n]}(N) \geq T_n;$$

(2) **(external monotonicity)**:   For all $m \leq n$,

$$X_{[m,n]}(N') \geq X_{[m,n]}(N),$$

whenever $N' \overset{\text{def}}{=} \{T'_n\}$ is such that $T'_n \geq T_n$ for all n;

(3) **(homogeneity)**: $\forall c \in \mathbb{R}, \ \forall m \leq n$

$$X_{[m,n]}(c + N) = X_{[m,n]} + c;$$

(4) **(separability)**:   If, for all $m \leq l < n$, $X_{[m,l]}(N) \leq T_{l+1}$, then

$$X_{[m,n]}(N) = X_{[l+1,n]}(N).$$

In words, property (4) simply states that if the arrival of customer $l + 1$ takes place later than the last activity for the arrival process $[m, l]$, then the evolution of the network after time T_{l+1} is the same as in the network which 'starts empty' at this time.

The Sub-additive Property. Let

(9.1.4) $Z_{[m,n]}(N) \overset{\text{def}}{=} X_{[m,n]}(N) - T_n = X_{[m,n]}(N - T_n)$.

Note that $Z_{[m,n]}(N)$ is a function of $\{\xi_n\}$ and $\{\tau_l\}_{m \leq l \leq n-1}$ only. In particular, $Z_n(N) \overset{\text{def}}{=} Z_{[n,n]}(N)$ is not a function of $\{\tau_n\}$.

(9.1.5) *Under the above conditions, the variables $X_{[m,n]}$ and $Z_{[m,n]}$ satisfy the internal monotonicity property: for all N*

(9.1.6) $X_{[m-1,n]}(N) \geq X_{[m,n]}(N), \quad Z_{[m-1,n]}(N) \geq Z_{[m,n]}(N) \quad (m \leq n).$

Proof: Consider the point process N' with points:

$$T'_j = \begin{cases} T_j - Z_{m-1}(N) & \text{for } j \leq m - 1; \\ T_j & \text{for } j \geq m . \end{cases}$$

Since the $[m, \infty]$ restrictions of N and N' coincide, $X_{[m,n]}(N) = X_{[m,n]}(N')$. The separability assumption implies that $X_{[m-1,n]}(N') = X_{[m,n]}(N')$. Finally, the external monotonicity implies that $X_{[m-1,n]}(N') \leq X_{[m-1,n]}(N)$. □

(9.1.7) *Under the above conditions,* $\{Z_{[m,n]}\}$ *satisfies the following sub-additive property: for all* $m \leq l < n$, *for all* N

(9.1.9) $Z_{[m,n]}(N) \leq Z_{[m,l]}(N) + Z_{[l+1,n]}(N) \leq Z_{[m,l]}(N) + Z_{[l,n]}(N).$

Proof: Introduce two auxiliary point processes $N^1 = \{T_j^1\}$ and $N^2 = \{T_j^2\}$ defined by

$$T_j^1 = \begin{cases} T_j & \text{for } j \leq l; \\ T_j + Z_{[m,l]}(N) & \text{for } j > l . \end{cases}$$

and

$$T_j^2 = \begin{cases} T_j - Z_{[m,l]}(N) & \text{for } j \leq l; \\ T_j & \text{for } j > l . \end{cases}$$

So $T_j^2 = T_j^1 - Z_{[m,l]}(N)$, for all j. Then, using assumptions (1)-(4) of our framework

$$X_{[m,n]}(N) \overset{(2)}{\leq} X_{[m,n]}(N^1) \overset{(4)}{=} X_{[l+1,n]}(N^1)$$
$$\overset{(3)}{=} X_{[l+1,n]}(N^2) + Z_{[m,l]}(N) = X_{[l+1,n]}(N) + Z_{[m,l]}(N).$$

Therefore

$$Z_{[m,n]}(N) = X_{[m,n]}(N) - T_n \leq X_{[l+1,n]}(N) - T_n + Z_{[m,l]}(N)$$
$$= Z_{[l+1,n]}(N) + Z_{[m,l]}(N).$$

□

9.2 Proof of the Saturation Rule

Assume that the point process N is stationary and ergodic, and take its Palm space $(\Omega, \mathcal{F}, P^0, \theta)$ as reference probability space. Assume that:

$$E^0 T_n \overset{\text{def}}{=} \lambda^{-1} < \infty, \quad E^0 Z_n < \infty.$$

Then Kingman's sub-additive ergodic theorem (already quoted) gives:

(9.2.1) *There exists a finite and positive constant* γ *such that the a.s. limits*

(9.2.2) $\lim \dfrac{Z_{[-n,-1]}}{n} = \lim \dfrac{E^0 Z_{[-n,-1]}}{n} = \lim \dfrac{Z_{[1,n]}}{n} = \lim \dfrac{E^0 Z_{[1,n]}}{n} = \gamma$

hold P^0*-a.s.*

Note that we then have

$$\lim_n \frac{X_{[1,n]}}{n} = \gamma + \lambda^{-1}.$$

Let A be the event $A = \{\lim Z_{[-n,0]} = \infty\}$.

(9.2.3) *Under the foregoing assumptions, $P^0(A) \in \{0,1\}$.*

Proof: Note that $\theta A = \{\lim Z_{[-n,-1]} = \infty\}$. But owing to the sub-additive property, $Z_{[-n,-1]} \geq Z_{[-n,0]} - Z_0$. This and the integrability of Z_0 imply that $\theta A \supseteq A$. $\qquad\qquad\square$

For all $0 \leq c < \infty$, the sequences

$$X_{[m,n]}(cN) \overset{\text{def}}{=} f_{n+1-m}\{(c \cdot T_l, \xi_l); m \leq l \leq n\}$$

and

$$Z_{[m,n]}(cN) = X_{[m,n]}(cN) - c \cdot T_n$$

satisfy all the monotonicity and sub-additive properties mentioned above. In addition, for all n

    (a) $Z_{[-n,-1]}(cN)$ is decreasing in c;

    (b) $X_{[1,n]}(cN)$ is increasing in c.

We have

(9.2.4) *For all $c \geq 0$, there exists a non-negative constant $\gamma(c)$ such that*

$$\lim \frac{Z_{[-n,-1]}(cN)}{n} = \gamma(c) \quad \text{a.s.;}$$

$\gamma(c)$ *is decreasing in c while $\gamma(c) + c\lambda^{-1}$ is increasing in c.*

The main result on the stability region is:

(9.2.5) *If $\lim Z_{[-n,0]} \to \infty$ a.s., then $\lambda\gamma(0) \geq 1$. If $\lambda\gamma(0) > 1$, then $\lim Z_{[-n,0]} \to \infty$ a.s.*

Proof: We first prove the second assertion. Let Q be the point process with all its points equal to 0: $T_n(Q) = 0$ for all n. For n fixed, let N^n be the point process with points $T_j^n = T_{-n} - T_0$, for all j. Then

$$Z_{[-n,0]}(N) = X_{[-n,0]}(N) - T_0 \overset{(2)}{\geq} X_{[-n,0]}(N^n)$$

$$\overset{(3)}{=} X_{[-n,0]}(Q) + T_{-n} - T_0 = Z_{[-n,0]}(Q) + T_{-n} - T_0$$

and

$$\liminf \frac{Z_{[-n,0]}(N)}{n} \geq \gamma(0) - \lambda^{-1} > 0,$$

which concludes the proof of the second assertion.

We now prove the first one. For each integer $l \geq 1$, let K_l be the random variable

$$K_l = \min\{n \geq 1 : \quad Z_{[-n,0]}(N) \geq T_l - T_0\},$$

which will be P^0 a.s. finite if $Z_{[-n,0]}$ tends to ∞. From the sub-additive property, for all $n, l \geq 1$

$$Z_{[-n,l]} \leq Z_{[-n,0]} + Z_{[1,l]} \leq Z_{[-n,0]} + \sum_{i=1}^{l} Z_i,$$

where the random variables $Z_i = Z_0 \circ \theta^i$ do not depend on the inter-arrival times and are integrable. For all $n \geq 1$, let $\widehat{N}^n$ be the point process with points

$$\widehat{T}_j^n = \begin{cases} T_j - T_0 & \text{for } j \leq 0; \\ Z_{[-n,0]}(N) & \text{for } j \geq 1 \end{cases}$$

and let $\widetilde{N}^n$ be defined by

$$\widetilde{T}_j^n = Z_{[-n,0]}, \quad \text{for all } j.$$

Then

$$(X_{[-n,l]}(N) - T_0)1_{n \geq K_l} \overset{(2)}{\leq} X_{[-n,l]}(\widehat{N}^n)1_{n \geq K_l}$$
$$\overset{(4)}{=} X_{[1,l]}(\widehat{N}^n)1_{n \geq K_l} = X_{[1,l]}(\widetilde{N}^n)1_{n \geq K_l}$$
$$\overset{(3)}{=} \left(Z_{[-n,0]}(N) + X_{[1,l]}(Q)\right)1_{n \geq K_l}$$
$$= \left(Z_{[-n,0]}(N) + Z_{[1,l]}(Q)\right)1_{n \geq K_l}.$$

Therefore

$$Z_{[-n,l]}(N)1_{n \geq K_l} = \left(X_{[-n,l]}(N) - T_l\right)1_{n \geq K_l}$$
$$\leq (Z_{[-n,0]}(N) + Z_{[1,l]}(Q) - T_l + T_0)1_{n \geq K_l}.$$

Finally,

$$Z_{[-n,l]}(N) - Z_{[-n,0]}(N)$$
$$= \left(Z_{[-n,l]}(N) - Z_{[-n,0]}(N)\right)\left[1_{n < K_l} + 1_{n \geq K_l}\right]$$
$$(9.2.6) \qquad \leq \left(\sum_{i=1}^{l} Z_i\right)1_{n < K_l} + \left(Z_{[1,l]}(Q) - T_l + T_0\right)1_{n \geq K_l}$$
$$= \Psi_l 1_{n < K_l} + Z_{[1,l]}(Q) - T_l + T_0,$$

where

$$\psi_l \stackrel{\text{def}}{=} \sum_{i=1}^{l} Z_i - Z_{[1,l]}(Q) + T_l - T_0$$

is P^0-integrable. By making use of the relations $Z_{[-n,l]} = Z_{[-n-l,0]} \circ \theta^l$, $Z_{[-n-l,0]} \ge Z_{[-n,0]}$ and $E^0 Z_{[-n-l,0]} < \infty$, we obtain from (9.2.6) that

$$0 \le E^0 Z_{[-n,l]} - E^0 Z_{[-n,0]} \le E^0\{\psi_l 1_{n<K_l}\} + E^0 Z_{[1,l]}(Q) - l\lambda^{-1}.$$

If K_l is a.s. finite for all l, the right-hand side of the last equation tends to $E^0 Z_{[1,l]}(Q) - l\lambda^{-1}$ as $n \to \infty$. Therefore

$$\frac{E^0 Z_{[1,l]}(Q)}{l} \ge \lambda^{-1},$$

for all l. Finally, when letting l go to infinity and when making use of (9.2.4), we obtain

$$\gamma(0) = \lim_l \frac{E^0 Z_{[1,l]}(Q)}{l} \ge \lambda^{-1}.$$

$\square$

Thus if $\lambda\gamma(0) < 1$, the random variable

$$Z \stackrel{\text{def}}{=} \lim_n Z_{[-n,0]} \quad \text{a.s.}$$

is P^0-a.s. finite and it provides a minimal stationary regime for the time to inactivity, which is defined as the time to the last activity in the system when subject to the $[-\infty, 0]$ restriction of N.

9.3 Examples

We start with a few examples which all fall within the monotone separable framework.

Example 9.3.1 *The $G/G/1/\infty$ queue.* Here, $X_{[m,n]}$ is the departure time of customer n, when there are $n + 1 - m$ customers with arrival times T_l and service times σ_l, $m \le l \le n$; $Z_{[m,n]}$ is then the sojourn time of customer n. The computation of $\gamma(0)$ is trivial, by the strong law of large numbers. $\square$

Example 9.3.2 *The $G/G/s/\infty$ queue.* Here, $X_{[m,n]}$ is the last departure time from the queue with customers arriving at T_l, $m \le l \le n$, that is

$$(9.3.1) \quad Z_{[m,n]}(N) = \max(W^1_{[m,n]}(N) + \sigma_n, W^s_{[m,n]}(N)),$$

where $W_{[m,n]}(N) = (W^1_{[m,n]}(N), \dots, W^s_{[m,n]}(N))$ is the ordered workload vector (see § 3.1) at time T_n-, for this arrival process (we assume that the queue is initially empty). We have

$$\lim_n \frac{Z_{[1,n]}(Q)}{n} = \gamma(0) \quad \text{a.s.},$$

as a consequence of (9.2.4). The computation of the constant $\gamma(0)$ is immediate from the relation

(9.3.2) $\lim \dfrac{W_{[m,n]}^j(Q)}{n} = \gamma(0) \quad \text{a.s.} \quad (1 \le j \le s).$

Indeed since

$$\sum_{i=1}^n \sigma_n = \sum_{j=1}^s W_{[1,n]}^j(Q),$$

the relation $\gamma(0) = E^0(\sigma)/s$ follows by an immediate limiting argument.

Proof of (9.3.2) The property for $j = s$ follows from the relation $Z_{[1,n]}(Q) = W_{[1,n+1]}^s(Q)$. In order to prove the property for all j, it is enough to show that

$$\Delta_n \stackrel{\text{def}}{=} W_{[m,n]}^s(Q) - W_{[m,n]}^1(Q),$$

is such that Δ_n/n tends to 0 a.s. Let

$$u_n \stackrel{\text{def}}{=} \max(\sigma_n, \ldots, \sigma_{n+s-1}), \quad \text{and} \quad U_n \stackrel{\text{def}}{=} \min(\sigma_n, \ldots, \sigma_{n+s-1}).$$

By comparing the original queue and the queue with workload

$$(W_{[1,n]}^1(Q), \ldots, W_{[1,n]}^1(Q))$$

at time T_n- and with constant service time u_n over the interval $n, n + 1, \ldots, n + s - 1$, we see that

$$W_{[1,n+s]}^1(Q) \ge W_{[1,n]}^1(Q) + u_n, \quad (n \ge 0).$$

Similarly, when considering the queue with workload

$$(W_{[1,n]}^1(Q), W_{[1,n]}^s(Q), \ldots, W_{[1,n]}^s(Q))$$

at time T_n- and with constant service time U_n, we obtain

$$W_{[1,n+s]}^s(Q) \le \max(W_{[1,n]}^s(Q), W_{[1,n]}^1(Q) + sU_n) \quad (n \ge 0).$$

Thus

$$\Delta_{n+s} \le \max(sU_n, \Delta_n - u_n), \quad (n \ge 0).$$

The solution $\{D_k^l\}$ of the equation

$$D_{k+1}^l = \max(sU_{ks+l}, D_k^l - u_{ks+l}), \quad (n \ge 0, \ 0 \le l < s),$$

with initial condition $D_0^l = \Delta_l$, is such that $\Delta_{ks+l} \leq D_k^l$ for all k and l. Posing $C_k^l = D_k^l - sU_{(k-1)s+l}$, we see that $\{C_k\}$ satisfies the Lindley equation

$$C_{k+1}^l = (C_k^l + sU_{(k-1)s+l} - sU_{ks+l} - u_{ks+l})^+,$$

and so C_k^l/k tends to 0 a.s. for all l (use Remark 2.3.2 plus a coupling argument, in the case when θ^s is ergodic).   □

Example 9.3.3 *Finite capacity tandem queues with Blocking.* We take $X_{[m,n]}$ equal to the time to empty the network with the same arrival process as above. The constant $\gamma(0)$ is the same one as obtained in (8.2.11). There is no simple analytical characterization of the stability region in this case.   □

Example 9.3.4 *A queueing system which does neither satisfy the separability condition nor the saturation rule.* Consider an *assembly queue* with two independent Poisson arrival streams with the same intensity $\lambda/2$. The system starts empty. Whenever there are customers of both classes in the queue, service is provided at rate μ. The completion of a service consumes one customer of each class. Whenever the queue has no customers of either class, it is blocked. Let us consider as input stream the superposition of the two Poisson processes properly marked. If one saturates the system with an infinite customer population, the (Markov) departure rate is μ. Similarly, if one takes the viewpoint of letting n customers of this input stream arrive at time 0, the last activity of the system takes place at time $\mu^{-1}n/2 + o(n)$. A rough application of the saturation rule would suggest that if $\lambda < \mu$, the system is stable. However, such queues are always unstable (see the bibliographical notes), whatever the values of λ and μ. Note that this system does not satisfy the separability property.   □

Bibliographical Comments

The historical paper concerning the stability of queueing systems within a stationary ergodic framework is that of Loynes [87]. This basic construction, which is given in § 1-2, is of wide applicability. In particular, it extends to all queueing systems amenable to a representation in terms of a stochastic recurrence with certain monotonicity properties (see § 4.2 and Remark 4.2.1). The interpretation of Garsia's proof of Hopf's lemma ([49]) and the queueing-theoretic proof of the ergodic theorem which are given in § 2.5. are due to Neveu [103]. The proof of the existence of stationary states for $G/G/s/\infty$ and $G/G/1/0$ queues (§ 3. and § 5. respectively) are borrowed from Neveu [103] and from Flipo [44]. The first construction of the steady state of the $G/G/1/0$ loss system in the general case is due to Lisek [85]. The ideas leading to the maximal solution of § 3.3 come from Foss [45] and Brandt [23] (see also the book by Brandt, Franken and Lisek [24] which contains several

other results on the matter) . The coupling method and its relation to convergence in variation (§ 4.1-4.2) are the object of the book [83] by Lindvall.
This book also contains a very complete survey on the applications of this
method. In particular, coupling properties of various classes of processes including renewal processes and Harris Markov chains are analyzed. The study
of coupling of point processes with a stochastic intensity was initiated by
Lindvall [82] who introduced the (A, m) point process. His result is more
general than that of Example 4.2.3, and is obtained by introducing a Harris
chain. A review of imbedding and coupling techniques for point processes
is given in [30], where an extension of the (A, m) process to finite random
memory is considered. The notion of strong coupling and the method of renovating events are due to Borovkov [20], where more other sufficient conditions
for uniqueness of the stationary regimes of $G/G/s/\infty$ and $G/G/1/0$ queues
can be found. This method is also of wide applicability since it applies to
all stochastic recurrences, regardless of their monotonicity properties. More
results on the relationship between coupling and renovating events can be
found in the survey paper [21] by Borovkov and Foss, which also contains
detailed comments on the relation between Harris recurrence and renovating
events. New applications of renovating events theory to the uniqueness of the
stationary regimes of closed queueing networks were recently proposed by
Mairesse [88]. The construction of the stationary regime for acyclic queueing
networks via coupling which is described in § 7.1 was used by several authors. See in particular the paper of Konstantopoulos and Walrand [77], and
the book [63] of Kalashnikov and Rachev. The priority discipline analyzed in
§ 7.2 is borrowed from Dumas [41]. The results on finite capacity blocking
queues considered in § 8 are taken from Baccelli and Liu [9]. The basic reference concerning sub-additive ergodic theory is Kingman [73]. The method
developed in § 8 extends to the class of discrete event systems which can be
represented as a $(\max, +)$-linear stochastic recurrence like Equation (8.1.3)
(for more details on this see [6]). Subadditive ergodic theory is known to be
a key mathematical tool in percolation theory, among others. The saturation
rule of § 9, which was given in Baccelli and Foss [8], suggests that it also provides a central tool for stability issues in queueing theory. We conclude with
a short survey of recent developments on the stability of queueing networks
within the stationary ergodic framework; Bramson [22] has shown that the
condition requiring that the traffic intensity be less than one at each queue
(that is, condition $\rho_k < 1$, for all k, where ρ_k is defined in (7.2.1)) is not sufficient for stability in Kelly-type networks with FIFO discipline (that is, the
networks of § 7.2, but with a FIFO discipline). The counter-example involves
a two-queue Kelly-type network with a single class of customers (that is, all
customers have the same route). FIFO Kelly-type networks do not satisfy
the external monotonicity property of the monotone separable framework of
§ 9. On the other hand, Jackson-type networks, where the service times and
the routing decisions are sequences attached to *nodes* and not to customers,

fall within this framework; in addition the constant $\gamma(0)$ can be computed and it was shown in [7] that the stability region is $\rho_k < 1$ for all k, using the saturation rule. Other networks for which the construction of the stationary regimes is still an open question are polling systems. A construction of a non-Markovian polling system was given in Massoulié [90].

3 Formulas

Introduction

Chapter 1 introduced the θ_t-framework, a convenient formalism for the study of point processes and stochastic processes which are jointly stationary. In Chapter 2, it was shown that the house is not empty but shelters a number of stationary queueing systems. In the stable case, coupling arguments often show convergence in variation of an initially non-stationary state to the stationary state obtained by a construction of Loynes' type. Thanks to the existence of construction points, from which secondary processes (as the congestion process in $G/G/1/\infty$) can be obtained from the stationary state (the workload process in $G/G/1/\infty$), the convergence in variation of the secondary processes is a consequence of the same phenomenon for the stationary state. This state of things allows one to obtain the basic formulas of queueing theory concerning limit processes directly on the stationary system, in the θ_t-framework. This separates the task of obtaining formulas from that of obtaining limit distributions, and enables one to give short and elementary proofs of the classical formulas and results of queueing theory.

In this chapter, some consequences of the main formulas of Chapter 1, namely Mecke's formula, the stochastic intensity integration formula, the rate conservation law and Papangelou's formula, will be harvested. All these formulas are given in terms of the stationary probability and of the Palm probability associated with certain point processes. In the ergodic context, averages under a Palm probability receive an interpretation as empirical averages under the stationary probability, as explained in § 7 of Chapter 1 (cross-ergodic theorems).

The objective of the present chapter is to present in a unified manner a few classical results and formulas of queueing theory. Special systems will be considered only when they are interesting from a pedagogical point of view, and therefore no attempt at exhaustivity should be expected. However, most of the fundamental formulas and results which intervene in the mathematical study of particular systems will be reviewed. This includes Little's formula, the formula of Pollaczek and Khinchin and its consequences, Kleinrock's conservation law, Cobham's priority formulas, the PASTA property, the busy cycle formula, insensitivity properties, etc.

The presentation is made in the θ_t-framework, which is recalled in § 1.1, and the derivations are based on the Palm-martingale calculus, that is to say the combined use of Mecke's formula in its more general form (the function space Campbell–Little–Mecke formula (2.1.1)), of the notion of stochastic intensity kernels and of the associated stochastic intensity integration formula.

1 Little's Formula

1.1 The θ_t-Framework for Stationary Queueing Systems

Let us recall the θ_t-framework of Chapter 1, § 1.3. There is a probability space $(\Omega, \mathcal{F}, P)$, on which a measurable flow $\{\theta_t\}$, $t \in \mathbb{R}$, is defined. Probability P is θ_t-invariant for all $t \in \mathbb{R}$. Also there are a number of point processes and stochastic processes which are compatible with the flow $\{\theta_t\}$. Recall that the point process N and the stochastic process $\{Z(t)\}$ are called compatible with the flow $\{\theta_t\}$ if

$$N(\theta_t\omega, C) = N(\omega, C + t)$$

and

$$Z(t, \omega) = Z(0, \theta_t\omega),$$

for all $t \in \mathbb{R}$, $\omega \in \Omega$ and $C \in \mathcal{B}$. The preceding chapter was partly devoted to the construction of such frameworks in a queueing context.

In the θ_t-framework, a sequence $\{Z_n\}$, $n \in \mathbb{Z}$, of marks of N has the canonical form

$$Z_n = Z(T_n),$$

where $\{Z(t)\}$ is defined by

$$Z(t) = Z_n \quad \text{if } t \in [T_n, T_{n+1}).$$

The stochastic process $\{Z(t)\}$ is therefore compatible with the flow $\{\theta_t\}$. It is called the canonical process associated with the mark sequence $\{Z_n\}$ and the point process N. A sequence with the above property is called θ_t-compatible.

Observe that $\{Z(t)\}$ and N, being compatible with the same flow $\{\theta_t\}$, are jointly stationary, since P is θ_t-invariant.

Example 1.1.1 *G/G input stream.* Let $\{(T_n, \sigma_n)\}$, $n \in \mathbb{Z}$, be a *G/G* input stream, and let A be the arrival point process defined by

$$(1.1.1) \quad A(C) = \sum_{n \in \mathbb{Z}} 1_C(T_n).$$

In the θ_t-framework, this input stream is compatible with a flow $\{\theta_t\}$ in the sense that $A(\omega, C + t) = A(\theta_t\omega, C)$ and $\sigma_n(\omega) = \sigma_0(\theta_{T_n}\omega)$. The canonical process $\{\sigma(t)\}$ associated with the sequence of required services $\{\sigma_n\}$ is defined by $\sigma(t) = \sigma_n$ if $t \in [T_n, T_{n+1})$. □

In the θ_t-framework, stationarity is implied by the θ_t-invariance of the underlying probability P.

Example 1.1.1. (cont'd): $G/G/1/\infty$ *queue.* The arrival rate

(1.1.2) $\lambda = E[A((0, 1])]$,

is assumed positive and finite, in which case the Palm probability P_A^0 associated with (A, P) is well defined. Under the stability condition

(1.1.3) $\rho \overset{\text{def}}{=} \lambda E_A^0[\sigma_0] < 1$,

the existence of a finite $G/G/1/\infty$ workload process $\{W(t)\}$, compatible with the flow $\{\theta_t\}$ and satisfying the evolution equation

(1.1.4) $W(t) = (W(T_n-) + \sigma_n - (t - t_n))^+$, $T_n \le t < T_{n+1}$,

was proved in Chapter 2, § 2, when (P, θ_t) is ergodic.

Define a *construction point* to be an arrival time T_n for which $W(T_n-) = 0$. It was shown in Chapter 2 that, under the stability condition, there are an infinite number of such construction points, both on the right and on the left of the origin of times. The existence of an infinity of construction points on the left allowed us to construct a number of point processes, mark sequences and stochastic processes, all compatible with the flow $\{\theta_t\}$. For instance (see Chapter 2, § 2) :
- The *system congestion process* $\{X(t)\}$, where $X(t)$ is the number of customers present in the system (waiting or being served) at time t.
- The *waiting room congestion process* $\{Q(t)\}$, where $Q(t)$ is the number of customers in the waiting room at time t.
- The *sojourn time sequence* $\{V_n\}$, where V_n is the sojourn time in the system of customer n.
- The *waiting time sequence* $\{\tilde{V}_n\}$, where $\tilde{V}_n$ is the amount of time spent in the waiting room by customer n.
- The *residual service time* process $\{R(t)\}$, where $R(t)$ is the amount of service remaining to be done at time t for the customer being served at time t; $R(t) = 0$ if the system is empty.
- D, the *departure point process* counting the departures from the system: if T_n' is the departure time of customer n, $D(C) = \sum_{n \in \mathbb{Z}} 1_C(T_n')$.

The construction of the above objects is possible for all 'reasonable' service disciplines (see Chapter 2, § 6.2). □

Example 1.1.2 *G/G input stream with priority classes.* Consider a G/G input stream $\{(T_n, \sigma_n, U_n\}, n \in \mathbb{Z}$, where σ_n is the amount of service required by customer n and U_n is its priority class : $U_n \in \{1, 2, ..., M\}$. Define

$$(1.1.5) \quad \begin{cases} \sigma(t) = \sigma_n & \text{if } t \in [T_n, T_{n+1}), \\ U(t) = U_n & \text{if } t \in [T_n, T_{n+1}) \end{cases}$$

and the point processes A and A_i $(1 \le i \le M)$ by

$$(1.1.6) \quad \begin{cases} A_i(C) = \sum_{n \in \mathbb{Z}} 1_C(T_n) 1_{\{i\}}(U_n), \\ A(C) = \sum_{n \in \mathbb{Z}} 1_C(T_n) = \sum_{i=1}^{M} A_i(C). \end{cases}$$

Let $\{T_{i,n}\}$ be the sequence associated with the arrival process A_i of customers of class i, with the usual convention $T_{i,0} \le 0 < T_{i,1}$. The quantity

$$(1.1.7) \quad \sigma_{i,n} = \sigma(T_{i,n})$$

is the amount of service required by customer n of type i arriving at time $T_{i,n}$.

Assume that $\lambda = E[A((0,1])] < \infty$ and therefore $\lambda_i = E[A_i((0,1])] < \infty$. This allows us to define the Palm probabilities P_A^0 and $P_{A_i}^0$. We have seen in Chapter 1, Example 5.2.1, that

$$(1.1.8) \quad \frac{\lambda_i}{\lambda} = P_A^0(U_0 = i).$$

Consider the traffic intensities $\rho_i = \lambda_i E_{A_i}^0[\sigma_0] = \lambda_i E_{A_i}^0[\sigma_{i,0}]$. Recall that $P_{A_i}^0(T_{i,0} = 0) = 1$ and therefore $\sigma_{i,0} = \sigma_0, P_{A_i}^0$-a.s. The traffic intensities and $\rho \overset{\text{def}}{=} \lambda E_A^0[\sigma_0]$ are linked by

$$(1.1.9) \quad \rho = \sum_{i=1}^{k} \rho_i$$

(see Chapter 1, Example 5.2.1). $\qquad\qquad\qquad\qquad\qquad\qquad\qquad\qquad\square$

Example 1.1.2 (cont'd) *G/G/s/∞ queueing system with priority classes.* In Chapter 2 (§ 3), we have seen that under the stability condition

$$(1.1.10) \quad \rho < s,$$

there exists at least one workload process $\{W(t)\}, t \in \mathbb{R}$, with values in $\mathbb{R}_+^s$ (and in particular *finite*), compatible with the flow $\{\theta_t\}$ and satisfying the evolution equation

$$(1.1.11) \quad W(t) = \mathcal{R}(W(T_n-) + \sigma(T_n)e - (t - T_n)i)^+,$$

for $t \in [T_n, T_{n+1})$, where $\mathcal{R}$, i and e were defined in Chapter 2, § 3.1.

It was shown that the cardinal of the set of indices $n \geq 1$ (resp. $n \leq 0$) such that $W_1(T_{n-}) = 0$ was P-a.s. infinite. As in Example 1.1.1, for 'reasonable' service disciplines and priority assignments, the existence of an infinity of construction points to the left allows us to construct the following point processes, stochastic processes and mark sequences, all compatible with the flow $\{\theta_t\}$:

- The workload process for class i, $\{W_i(t)\}$.
- The system congestion process for class i, $\{X_i(t)\}$.
- The waiting room congestion process for class i, $\{Q_i(t)\}$.
- The sojourn time sequence for class i, $\{V_{i,n}\}$.
- The waiting time sequence for class i, $\{\tilde{V}_{i,n}\}$.
- The departure (point) process for class i, D_i.
- The residual service time process for class i, $\{R_i(t)\}$.   □

We now proceed to the derivation of a basic result of queueing theory linking the time average congestion of a given system, the rate of arrival into this system, and the customer average sojourn time in the system.

1.2 $L = \lambda W$

The Campbell-Little-Mecke formula (3.3.3) of Chapter 1 is the source of a number of interesting queueing relations, including the Pollaczek-Khinchin formula, the formula of residual service times, Little's formula and Kleinrock's conservation law. For easy reference we reproduce it below

$$(1.2.1) \quad E\Big[\sum_{n \in \mathbb{Z}} f(T_n, Z_n)\Big] = \lambda \int \int_{\mathbb{R} \times K} f(t, z) P_N^0(Z_0 \in dz) dt.$$

In this formula, N is a stationary point process of finite intensity λ, $\{T_n\}$ is the sequence of its 'points', $\{Z_n\}$ is a sequence of marks with values in K, P_N^0 is the Palm probability associated with N, and $f(t, z)$ is an arbitrary non-negative measurable function from $\mathbb{R} \times K$ into $\mathbb{R}$.

The ingredients a Little type formula are the following: We need a stationary θ_t-framework with
- an arrival process A, represented by the sequence $\{T_n\}$, with finite intensity λ.
- a sojourn time sequence $\{V_n\}$,
where both A and $\{V_n\}$ are compatible with the flow $\{\theta_t\}$. The interpretation is that T_n is the arrival time, into some system, of a customer who remains in the system for the time V_n and then leaves the system. Therefore, the number of customers present in the system at time t is

$$(1.2.2) \quad X(t) = \sum_{n \in \mathbb{Z}} 1_{(-\infty, t]}(T_n) 1_{(t, +\infty)}(T_n + V_n).$$

Indeed a customer arriving at time T_n is in the system at time t if and only if he arrived before t $(T_n \leq t)$ and departed strictly after t $(T_n + V_n > t)$. Application of the Campbell-Little-Mecke formula (1.2.1) to the function $f(s, z) = 1_{(-\infty, t]}(s)1_{(t, +\infty)}(s + z)$ and to the mark sequence $\{Z_n\} = \{V_n\}$ implies, in view of Identity (1.2.2)

$$
\begin{aligned}
E[X(t)] &= \lambda \int \int_{\mathbb{R} \times \mathbb{R}_+} 1_{(-\infty, t]}(s)1_{(t, \infty)}(s + v)P_A^0(V_0 \in dv)ds \\
&= \lambda \int_{-\infty}^{t} \int_{(t-s, \infty)} P_A^0(V_0 \in dv)ds \\
&= \lambda \int_{-\infty}^{t} (1 - P_A^0(V_0 \leq t - s))ds \\
&= \lambda \int_{0}^{\infty} (1 - P_A^0(V_0 \leq u))du.
\end{aligned}
$$

Therefore $E[X(t)] = E[X(0)]$, which is expected since $\{X(t)\}$ is compatible with the flow $\{\theta_t\}$, and

(1.2.3) $E[X(0)] = \lambda E_A^0[V_0].$

When (P, θ_t) is ergodic (see Chapter 1, § 7), This formula can be read

(1.2.4) $E[X(0)] = \lambda \lim\limits_{n \to \infty} \dfrac{1}{n} \sum\limits_{k=1}^{n} V_k, \quad P\text{--a.s.}$

It has been customary among the queueing theory community to call $L = \lambda W$ a formula such as (1.2.3). It is however a rather imprecise terminology that we shall always make precise as in (1.2.3) or (1.2.4).

Example 1.2.1 *Little's waiting room formula.* If the 'system' is the waiting room of a queueing system, and if *the service of a customer is never inter-rupted,* then take $X(t) = Q(t)$, $V_n = \tilde{V}_n$ (the waiting time before service), and λ is the rate of arrivals into the waiting room and hence into the queueing system. Little's formula (1.2.3) reads

(1.2.5) $E[Q(0)] = \lambda E_A^0[\tilde{V}_0].$

If service interruptions are allowed, things become more complicated and it is better to use Formula (1.2.3), where the 'system' is the whole service station (waiting room plus servers), and use whatever relation there may exist between $Q(t)$ and $X(t)$, for instance, in a G/G/s/∞ queue, $(X(t) - s)^+ = Q(t)$. □

Example 1.2.2 *Little's server formula.* The system to which (1.2.3) now applies consists of the ticket booth. In a G/G/s/∞ queue, Little's formula (1.2.3) becomes

$$(1.2.6) \quad \sum_{i=1}^{s-1} iP(X(t) = i) + sP(X(t) \geq s) = \lambda \lim_{n \to \infty} \frac{1}{n} \sum_{k=0}^{\infty} \sigma_k = \lambda E_A^0[\sigma_0],$$

since all incoming customers eventually reach a ticket booth (and therefore the rate of arrivals into the 'system' is the rate of arrivals into the queue), and the sojourn time at a booth is the required service time.

In the $G/G/1/\infty$ case, recalling the definition of the traffic intensity $\rho = \lambda E_A^0[\sigma_0]$, we find that

$$(1.2.7) \quad P(X(t) = 0) = 1 - \rho.$$

□

Example 1.2.2 (cont'd). *G/G/s/c with loss.* Instead of a $G/G/s/\infty$ queue, we consider a queue with limited waiting room capacity $G/G/s/c$ where $c < \infty$. Equality (1.2.6) holds with λ being replaced by the rate of accepted arrivals, i.e. $\bar{\lambda} = \lambda P_A^0(X(0-) < s + c)$. For instance, in a $G/G/s/0$ queue, since $X(t)$ cannot exceed the number of servers, the left-hand side of (1.2.6) is $E[X(t)]$, and therefore taking into account the above remark concerning the rate of arrival $\bar{\lambda}$, we find

$$(1.2.8) \quad E[X(t)] = \rho(1 - P_A^0(X(0-) = s)).$$

□

Example 1.2.3 *Busy cycles via Little's formula.* Consider a G/G queue in equilibrium and let N be the point process counting the construction points, that is the arrival times at which a customer finds an empty queue

$$N(C) = \int_C 1_{\{0\}}(W(t-))A(dt).$$

Let $\{R_n\}$ be the sequence of points of N, and define C_n, the length of the n-th cycle, by

$$(1.2.9) \quad C_n = R_n - R_{n-1}.$$

It is the sum of an idle period I_n and of a busy period B_n (see Figure 1.2.1)

$$(1.2.10) \quad C_n = I_n + B_n.$$

Consider the following system: the arrival process is N, a customer arriving at time R_n requires the service time B_n, and is served at unit speed by a single server. Little's formula (1.2.3) can be applied to this system with the following identifications

$$\lambda \leftarrow \lambda P_A^0(X(0-) = 0),$$
$$V_n \leftarrow B_n,$$
$$X(t) \longleftarrow 1 - 1_{\{0\}}(X(t)).$$

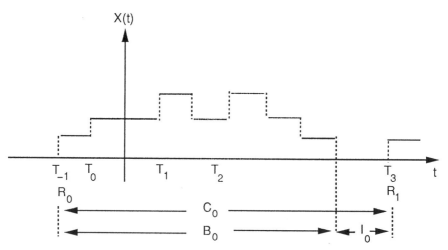

Fig. 1.2.1 Busy cycle

Therefore

$$(1.2.11) \quad 1 - P(X(0) = 0) = \lambda P_A^0(X(0-) = 0)E_N^0(B_0).$$

On the other hand, the intensity is the inverse of the mean inter-arrival time

$$(1.2.12) \quad \lambda P_A^0(X(0-) = 0)E_N^0[C_0] = 1$$

and therefore

$$(1.2.13) \quad P(X(0) = 0) = \frac{E_N^0[I_0]}{E_N^0[C_0]}.$$

$\square$

Example 1.2.4 *Attained service in* $GI/GI/1/\infty$ *Processor Sharing.* In this example, the arrival process is of a general nature, and the service time sequence is i.i.d., independent of the arrival process. The queueing discipline is of the processor sharing type (PS): all customers present in the system receive service, at a rate inversely proportional to their number. Thus a customer arriving at time $T_n < 0$ and requiring service σ_n will be present at time 0 and will have attained service not greater than a if and only if

$$\int_{T_n}^0 \frac{1}{X(s)} ds \leq \sigma_n \wedge a,$$

where $X(t)$ is the number of customers present at time t. Denoting by $X_a(t)$ the number of customers present at time t with attained service not greater than a

(1.2.14) $X_a(0) = \sum_{n \in \mathbb{Z}} 1_{T_n \leq 0} 1_{\int_{T_n}^0 \frac{1}{X(s)} ds \leq \sigma_n \wedge a}$.

Campbell-Little-Mecke formula gives

$$E[X_a(0)] = \lambda E_A^0 \left[\int_0^\infty 1_{\int_0^t \frac{1}{X(s)} ds \leq \sigma_0 \wedge a} dt \right] .$$

If we introduce the function $r(t)$ defined by

(1.2.15) $\int_0^{r(t)} \frac{1}{X^*(s)} ds = t,$

where $X^*(t) = X(t)$ if $t \leq W_0$ (the sojourn time of customer 0) and $X^*(t) = X(t) + 1$ if $t \geq W_0$, we have

(1.2.16) $r(\sigma_0) = W_0$

and $r(t)$ receives the interpretation of the sojourn time of customer 0 if its required service is t. We shall therefore call $\{r(t)\}_{t \geq 0}$ the response time process of customer 0. Also

$$\int_0^\infty 1_{\int_0^t \frac{1}{X(s)} ds \leq \sigma_0 \wedge a} dt = \int_0^\infty 1_{t \leq r(\sigma_0 \wedge a)} dt = r(\sigma_0 \wedge a) .$$

Now, the service sequence is i.i.d. and independent of the arrival process, and $r(t)$ depends on the input process except σ_0. Therefore

$$E_A^0[r(\sigma_0 \wedge a)] = E_A^0 \left[\int_0^a r(t) dG(t) \right] = \int_0^a \bar{r}(t) dG(t) + \bar{r}(a)(1 - G(a)),$$

where

(1.2.17) $\bar{r}(t) = E_A^0[r(t)]$

is the average response time to required service t. But

$$\int_0^a \bar{r}(t) dG(t) + \bar{r}(a)(1 - G(a)) = \int_0^a (1 - G(t)) d\bar{r}(t),$$

so that finally

(1.2.18) $E[X_a(0)] = \lambda \int_0^a (1 - G(t)) d\bar{r}(t) .$

$\square$

Example 1.2.5 Response time of $M/GI/1/\infty$ PS. Let the state at time t of a $M/GI/1/\infty$ PS system consist of (1) the number $X(t)$ of customers in the system, and (2) the elapsed and residual service times of these customers. The stationary distribution of the state under P (of course we assume $\rho < 1$)

can be computed by general methods of Palm theory (see the bibliographical comments). It is obtained as follows:

First select the number of customers present in the system to be n with probability $\rho^n(1 - \rho)$.

Then select n independent pairs of elapsed-residual service times distributed as a pair of backward-forward recurrence times of a renewal process with c.d.f. G, the c.d.f. of the service times. In particular the residual service times and the elapsed service times have the c.d.f. $G_e(x) = \mu \int_x^\infty (1 - G(x))dx$, where μ^{-1} is the mean service time.

We shall use this result to obtain the average response time. Indeed the probability for a given customer to have attained service no greater than a is $G_e(a)$, and therefore

$$(1.2.19) \quad E[X_a(0)] = E[X(0)]G_e(a) = \frac{1}{1 - \rho}G_e(a) \ .$$

Comparing with (1.2.18) gives

$$\frac{\lambda}{1 - \rho} \int_0^a (1 - G(t))dt = \lambda \int_0^a (1 - G(t))d\bar{r}(t)$$

and therefore, since $\bar{r}(0) = 0$

$$(1.2.20) \quad \bar{r}(t) = \frac{t}{1 - \rho} \ .$$

$\square$

1.3 The Swiss Army Formula

Depending on which blade is selected, a Swiss Army knife transforms itself into various useful tools. The general formula obtained in this subsection is called the Swiss Army formula of Palm calculus because it contains well-known formulas of this theory as well as some new ones. The main formulas of Palm theory are not just *derived* from the Swiss Army formula, they are in fact *avatars* of it in following sense : the Swiss Army formula features
- a 'queueing' process $\{X(t)\} = X$, with its arrival and departure point processes A and D respectively;
- a random measure B, and
- a non-negative stochastic process $\{Z(t)\} = Z$.

The objects X, B and Z can be considered as 'dummy variables' which, when assigned a 'value', give a classical formula. For instance, with $Z(t) \equiv 1$, $B(ds) \equiv ds$, we obtain Little's $L = \lambda W$ formula, and with $X(t) \equiv 1$, B a point process, we obtain Neveu's exchange formula between A and B. The Swiss Army formula has also the following avatars : Palm inversion formula $(X(t) \equiv 1, \ B(ds) = ds)$, as well as an ordinal version of Little's formula.

It extends the classical $L = \lambda W$ formula as well as the exchange formula. It finally collapses into Mecke's definition of Palm probability ($B = A$) and this is of course a tautology since the Swiss Army formula is derived from Mecke's definition of Palm probability.

Let $\{T_n\}$ and $\{\tau_n\}$ be two simple point processes on $\mathbb{R}$ and let A and D be the associated counting measures, assumed to put finite masses on bounded sets. The sequence $\{T_n\}$ is supposed to be ordered, with the convention $T_0 \leq 0 < T_1$, and such that $A(\mathbb{R}_+) = A(\mathbb{R} - \mathbb{R}_+) = \infty$, so that in particular $T_n \in \mathbb{R}$, for all $n \in \mathbb{Z}$. The sequence $\{\tau_n\}$ is also supposed to satisfy $D(\mathbb{R}_+ = D(\mathbb{R} - \mathbb{R}_+) = \infty$, but it need not be ordered. However, it is required that for each $n \in \mathbb{Z}$

$$(1.3.1) \quad \tau_n - T_n \stackrel{\text{def}}{=} W_n \geq 0 \ .$$

On could imagine that T_n is the arrival time of customer n in a system, and that τ_n is its departure time. With this interpretation, any process $\{X(t)\}$ satisfying $X(t) \geq 0$ and

$$(1.3.2) \quad X(b) - X(a) = A((a, b]) - D((a, b])$$

is a queueing process associated with the arrival and departure processes A and D respectively. However such an interpretation is not required. The processes A and D can have common points, and as a matter of fact we shall consider the situation where $\tau_n = T_{n+1}$, that is $W_n = T_{n+1} - T_n$ and therefore $X(t) \equiv$ constant.

Let now $\{B(t)\}$ be a right continuous with left limits (corlol), non-decreasing real-valued process. Denote $\int_{(a,b]} h(s)dB(s)$ the Stieltjes-Lebesgue integral of function h with respect to the measure canonically associated with $\{B(t)\}$. For the consistency of the notational system, we shall write $dA(t), dD(t)$ instead of $A(dt), D(dt)$.

Finally, let $\{Z(t)\}$ be a non-negative real-valued stochastic process.

Recall the Stieltjes-Lebesgue formula of integration by parts for two corlol real-valued functions f and g of locally finite variation

$$(f(t) - f(0))(g(t) - g(0)) = \int_{(0,t]} (f(s_-) - f(0))dg(s)$$
$$(1.3.3)$$
$$+ \int_{(0,t]} (g(s) - g(0))df(s).$$

We shall use Formula (1.3.3) in a way that generalizes the argument used in textbooks to explain Little's formula. This argument is based on the graph of the arrival and departure counting processes of the queue, and on the computation of the area in between in two different manners (see R.W. Wolff, *Stochastic Modeling and the Theory of Queues*, Prentice Hall, 1989, p. 235).

This picturesque proof is equivalent to the following argument, using Formula (1.3.3), which gives, if $X(0) = 0$

$$tX(t) = \int_{(0,t]} X(s)ds + \int_{(0,t]} s dX(s),$$

that is

$$\int_{(0,t]} X(s)ds = \int_{(0,t]} (t - s)dA(s) - \int_{(0,t]} (t - s)dD(s).$$

Therefore, if t is such that $X(t) = 0$ (this is a simplifying assumption; we shall go through the complete argument later),

$$\int_0^t X(s)ds = \sum_{n \in \mathbb{Z}} (\tau_n - T_n) 1_{(0,t]}(T_n),$$

or

$$\frac{1}{t} \int_0^t X(s)ds = \frac{A((0,t])}{t} \frac{1}{A((0,t])} \sum_{n=1}^{A((0,t])} W_n.$$

Such an argument can be significantly generalized. Indeed, when applying (1.3.3) with

$$f(t) - f(0) = X(t) - X(0), \quad g(t) = \int_{(0,t]} Z(s)dB(s),$$

we obtain

$$(X(t) - X(0)) \int_{(0,t]} Z(s)dB(s) = \int_{(0,t]} (X(s_-) - X(0)) Z(s)dB(s)$$
$$+ \int_{(0,t]} \{ \int_{(0,s]} Z(u)dB(u) \} dX(s).$$

Rewriting the left-hand side of the last equality as

$$\int_{(0,t]} \{ \int_{(0,t]} Z(s)dB(s) \} dX(s)$$

gives

$$\int_{(0,t]} \{ \int_{(s,t]} Z(u)dB(u) \} dX(s) + X(0) \int_{(0,t]} Z(s)dB(s)$$
$$(1.3.4)$$
$$= \int_{(0,t]} X(s_-)Z(s)dB(s).$$

Since $dX(t) = dA(t) - dD(t)$, we have,

$$\int_{(0,t]} \{\int_{(s,t]} Z(u)dB(u)\}dX(s) = \sum_{n\in\mathbb{Z}} \int_{(T_n,t]} Z(u)dB(u)1_{(0,t]}(T_n)$$

$$- \sum_{n\in\mathbb{Z}} \int_{(\tau_n,t]} Z(u)dB(u)1_{(0,t]}(\tau_n)$$

and therefore, after elementary computations, the left hand side of (1.3.4) is found to be

$$(1.3.5) \quad \sum_{n\in\mathbb{Z}}\{\int_{(T_n,\tau_n]} Z(u)dB(u)\}1_{(0,t]}(T_n) + R(0) - R(t),$$

where

$$(1.3.6) \quad R(t) = \sum_{i\in\mathcal{N}(t)} \int_{(t,\tau_i]} Z(u)dB(u),$$

and $\mathcal{N}(t)$ is the set of indices n corresponding to customers still in the system at time t (that is, such that $T_n \le t$ and $\tau_n > t$). Finally

$$(1.3.7) \quad \begin{aligned} &\sum_{n\in\mathbb{Z}}\{\int_{(T_n,\tau_n]} Z(u)dB(u)\}1_{T_n\in(0,t]} + R(0) \\ &= \int_{(0,t]} X(s_-)Z(s)dB(s) + R(t). \end{aligned}$$

All the above objects are now supposed to be given in the stationary θ_t- framework, and in particular, we assume that $\{Z(t)\}$ and A and D (and therefore $X(t)$) are θ_t compatible, and that the intensity λ_A of A is non-null and finite. We then have:

The Swiss Army Formula. With the above assumptions, for all $t \in \mathbb{R}$

$$(1.3.8) \quad \lambda_A E_A^0[\int_{(0,W_0]} Z(s)dB(s)] = \frac{1}{t}E[\int_{(0,t]} X(s_-)Z(s)dB(s)].$$

Proof: First suppose that

$$(1.3.9) \quad E[\int_{(0,t]} X(s_-)Z(s)dB(s)] < \infty, \quad E_A^0[\int_{(0,W_0]} Z(s)dB(s)] < \infty.$$

Then

$$R(0) - R(t) \in L^1(P)$$

and since $R(t) = R(0) \circ \theta_t$, it follows from Lemma 2.3.1, Chapter 2, that $E[R(0) - R(t)] = 0$, and this suffices to prove (1.3.8), taking expectations in (1.3.7).

For the general case, we need to introduce the following notation :

$$T_-(t) = \inf\{T_n;\ T_n \le t \text{ and } \tau_n > t\}$$

(thus $T_-(t)$ is the arrival date of the oldest customer in the system at time t). For any $c > 0$, we define

$$Z^c(t) = Z(t)1_{X(t_-)\le c}\ 1_{\int_{(T_-(t),t]} Z(s)dB(s)\le c}.$$

The process $\{Z^c(t)\}$ satisfies condition (1.3.9) and moreover

$$\lim_{c\uparrow\infty} \uparrow Z^c(t,\omega) = Z(t,\omega).$$

Thus (1.3.9) holds true for $\{Z^c(t)\}$, and the general case follows by monotone convergence. $\qquad\square$

Extended Little's Formula. Under the above assumptions, the following formula is true

$$(1.3.10)\quad \lambda_A E^0[\int_{(0,W_0]} Z(s)ds] = E[X(0)Z(0)].$$

Proof: Let $B(ds) = ds$ in the Swiss Army formula and observe that $\frac{1}{t}E[\int_0^t X(s_-)Z(s)ds] = \frac{1}{t}E[\int_0^t X(s)Z(s)ds] = E[X(0)Z(0)]$. $\qquad\square$

Remark 1.3.1 Formula (1.3.10) has a very simple interpretation. Suppose that when some item is stocked in a warehouse, its owner has to pay $Z(t)$ money units per time unit. In view of Formula (1.3.10), the average income of the warehouse owner per time unit is equal to the average fee paid by the owner of the items multiplied by λ_A, the number of customers entering the warehouse per unit time. $\qquad\square$

The Extended Exchange Formula. Under the above assumptions, and if moreover B is a point process with positive and finite intensity λ_B, the following formula is true

$$(1.3.11)\quad \lambda_A E_A^0[\int_{(0,W_0]} Z(s)dB(s)] = \lambda_B E_B^0[X(0_-)Z(0)].$$

Proof: Just observe that when B is a point process with intensity λ_B, the right hand sides of (1.3.9) and (1.3.11) are equal by definition of Palm probability. $\qquad\square$

By further specifications of the 'dummy variables' of the Swiss Army formula we obtain the classical formulas, which can be classified in two types, according to whether they descend from the Extended Little's formula or from the Extended Exchange formula.

We start with the descendents of the Extended Little's formula:

(α_1) **Little's $L = \lambda W$ formula.** Letting $Z(t) \equiv 1$ in (1.3.10), we have

$$\lambda_A E_A^0[W_0] = E[X(0)].$$

(β_1) **Palm Inversion Formula.** Defining D from A by

(1.3.12) $\tau_n = T_{n+1},$

we have $W_0 = \tau_0 - T_0 = T_1 - T_0 = T_1, P_A^0 - a.s.$, and $X(t) \equiv 1$, so that (1.3.10) becomes

$$\lambda_A E_A^0[\int_0^{T_1} Z(s)ds] = E[Z(0)].$$

We now list the descendents of the Extended Exchange formula.

(α_2) **An Ordinal $L = \lambda W$ Formula.** Taking $Z(t) \equiv 1$ and $B \equiv A$ in (1.3.11), we obtain

(1.3.13) $E_A^0[A((0, W_0])] = E_A^0[X(0-)].$

Similarly, with $Z(t) \equiv 1$ and $B = D$,

$$\lambda_A E_A^0[D((0, W_0])] = \lambda_D E_D^0[X(0-)]$$

that is, since $\lambda_A \equiv \lambda_D$,

(1.3.14) $E_A^0[D((0, W_0])] = E_D^0[X(0-)].$

Remark 1.3.2 A formula like (1.3.13) is called an ordinal $L = \lambda W$ formula for the following reason: time is counted in terms of units, one unit being the (random) time separating two arrivals. Therefore the left-hand side of (1.3.13) is the sojourn time counted in terms of these new units, that is the number of arrivals during the usual sojourn time. The intensity is 1 since there is one arrival per new unit time.

The Swiss Army formula also gives an ordinal formula for a stable $G/G/1/\infty$ queue, with the sequence of arrival times at which the system is empty (we denote $\{R_n\}$, N the associated counting process, see Example 1.2.3). Here $T_n = R_n$, $\tau_n = (T_{n+1} = R_{n+1}$. The corresponding queueing process is $X(t) \equiv 1$. Applying the Swiss Army formula with $B = A$, we have

$$\lambda P_A^0(X(0-) = 0) E_N^0 \left[\int_{(0, R_+]} dA(s)\right] = \lambda,$$

that is, the average number of customers served in a busy period is equal to $P_A^0(X(0-) = 0)$. Of course, this can be obtained as a direct application of Neveu's exchange formula between A and N.   □

(β_2) **Neveu's Exchange Formula.** By specializing D as in (1.3.12), we obtain from (1.3.11)

$$\lambda_A E_A^0[\int_{(0,T_1]} Z(s)dB(s)] = \lambda_B E_B^0[Z(0)].$$

(γ_2) **Mecke's Definition.** Taking $B \equiv A$, we obtain the definition of Palm probability

$$E_A^0[Z(0)] = \frac{1}{\lambda_A t} E[\int_{(0,t]} Z(s)dA(s)],$$

which takes us back where we started.

Remark 1.3.3 The Swiss Army formula can be given the simpler form

$$(1.3.15) \quad \lambda_A E_A^0[B((0, W_0])] = \frac{1}{t}E[\int_{(0,t]} X(s_-)dB(s)],$$

since an increment $Z(s)dB(s)$ is a particular case of an increment $dB(s)$. The latter formula is a natural extension of $L = \lambda W$ and it receives an interpretation similar to that given in Remark 1.3.1.   □

2 $H = \lambda G$

2.1 The Function Space Campbell-Little-Mecke Formula and the $H = \lambda G$ Formula

We shall take another look at the Campbell-Little-Mecke Formula (1.2.1) and observe that Z_n can take its values in an arbitrary measurable space $(K, \mathcal{K})$. This fact can be usefully exploited. Indeed, take $K = D(\mathbb{R}; \mathbb{R})$ the set of corlol functions from $\mathbb{R}$ into $\mathbb{R}$ with a suitable topology (Skorokhod's topology for instance) and let $\mathcal{K}$ be the Borel field associated with this topology. Define $f(t, z)$ of (1.2.1) by $f(t, z) = z(t)$. The Campbell-Little-Mecke formula then takes the form

$$(2.1.1) \quad E\left[\sum_{n\in\mathbb{Z}} Z_n(T_n)\right] = \lambda \int_{\mathbb{R}} E_N^0[Z_0(t)]dt$$

or

$$(2.1.1') \quad E\left[\sum_{n\in\mathbb{Z}} Z_n(T_n)\right] = \lambda E_N^0\left[\int_{\mathbb{R}} Z_0(t)dt\right].$$

We shall call Formula (2.1.1) or (2.1.1') the *function space Campbell-Little-Mecke formula.*

The formula $L = \lambda W$ has been extended by Brumelle and the extension is known as $H = \lambda G$. It rests upon the function space Campbell-Little-Mecke formula which is just another look at the usual Campbell-Little-Mecke formula, only with marks that are functions; taking $Z_n(t) = h_n(a - t)$, where $\{h_n\}$ is a sequence marks taking values in a function space, we obtain

$$(2.1.1'') \quad E\left[\sum_{n \in \mathbb{Z}} h_n(a - T_n)\right] = \lambda E_N^0\left[\int_{\mathbb{R}} h_0(t)dt\right].$$

Remark 2.1.1 We can associate a formula of the type $H = \lambda G$ with every functional Ψ which depends upon the past at time 0. More precisely:

Let $\tau_n = T_{n+1} - T_n$. Consider now a functional

$$(2.1.2) \quad \Psi = h(T_0, Z_0, \tau_{-1}, Z_{-1}, \tau_{-2}, Z_{-2}, ...),$$

called the H-functional. Using the notation

$$(2.1.3) \quad U_n = (\tau_n, Z_n, \tau_{n-1}, Z_{n-1}, ...),$$

define the G-functional:

$$(2.1.4) \quad g(T_0, Z_0, U_{-1}) = h(T_0, Z_0, U_{-1}) - h(T_0 - \tau_{-1}, Z_{-1}, U_{-2}).$$

Suppose that

$$(2.1.5) \quad \int_{-\infty}^0 E_N^0[|\, g(t, Z_0, U_{-1})\, |]dt < \infty.$$

Campbell's formula

$$E\left[\sum_{n=-\infty}^0 |\, g(T_n, Z_n, U_{n-1})\, |\right] = \lambda \int_{-\infty}^0 E_N^0[|\, g(t, Z_0, U_{-1})\, |]dt$$

and assumption (2.1.5) imply that $\sum_{n=-\infty}^0 |\, g(T_n, Z_n, U_{-n})\, | < \infty$ P–a.s., and therefore $h(T_n, Z_n, U_{n-1})$ has a finite limit as n goes to $-\infty$. We shall assume that

$$(2.1.6) \quad \lim_{n \to -\infty} h(T_n, Z_n, U_{n-1}) = 0$$

and therefore

$$\Psi = \sum_{n=-\infty}^0 g(T_n, Z_n, U_{n-1}).$$

Also, applying Campbell's formula once more gives

(2.1.7) $E[\Psi] = \lambda \int_{-\infty}^{0} E_N^0[g(t, Z_0, U_{-1})]dt.$

This is again a $H = \lambda G$ formula, which can be considered as an extension of Little's formula.   □

Example 2.1.1 *Light traffic derivative.* Formula (2.1.7) is the key to light traffic analysis and to a method of perturbation analysis. We shall consider a simple case which contains the basic ingredients of the method and the reader is referred to the bibliographical comments at the end of the chapter for further information.

Suppose that N is a Poisson process of intensity λ and that $\{Z_n\}$ is independent of N, and that conditions (2.1.5) and (2.1.6) are verified, so that

$$E_\lambda[\Psi] = \lambda \int_{-\infty}^{0} E_\lambda[g(t, Z_0, U_{-1})]dt,$$

where we have written down (2.1.7) using the fact that since N is Poisson P_N^0 and P agree on (Z_0, U_{-1}), and where we have appended an index λ to the expectation symbol E in order to emphasize dependency on the intensity of N. Define

(2.1.8) $U_{-1}^\lambda = (\frac{1}{\lambda}\tau_{-1}, Z_{-1}, \frac{1}{\lambda}\tau_{-2}, Z_{-2}, ...).$

Since the τ_n's are the inter-arrival times of a Poisson process of intensity λ

$$E_\lambda[g(t, Z_0, U_{-1})] = E_1[g(t, Z_0, U_{-1}^\lambda)].$$

Therefore

(2.1.9) $E_\lambda[\Psi] = \lambda \int_{-\infty}^{0} E_1[g(t, Z_0, U_{-1}^\lambda)]dt.$

We also suppose that

(2.1.10) $E_0[\Psi] = 0.$

The following result then holds: under assumption (2.1.5) and (2.1.10), and if there exists a function $g_0(t, Z)$ such that

(2.1.11) $\lim_{\lambda \downarrow 0} \int_{-\infty}^{0} E_1[|\, g(t, Z_0, U_{-1}^\lambda) - g_0(t, Z_0)\,|]dt = 0,$

the derivative at $\lambda = 0$ of $E_\lambda[\Psi]$ exists and is given by

(2.1.12) $\frac{dE_\lambda(\Psi)}{d\lambda}\big|_{\lambda=0} = \int_{-\infty}^{0} E[g(t, Z_0)]dt,$

(in the right-hand side, the index 1 has been suppressed since the distribution of Z_0 is independent of the intensity λ of the basic point process N). The proof of (2.1.12) is immediate since, in view of (2.1.10), (2.1.9) gives

$$\frac{E_\lambda[\Psi] - E_0[\Psi]}{\lambda - 0} = \int_{-\infty}^0 E_1[g(t, Z_0, U_{-1}^\lambda)]dt.$$

If we go back to the definition (2.1.4) of g, we see that

$$g(t, Z_0, U_{-1}^\lambda) = h(t, Z_0, \frac{1}{\lambda}\tau_{-1}, Z_{-1}, \frac{1}{\lambda}\tau_{-2}, Z_{-2}, ...) -$$
$$h(t - \frac{1}{\lambda}\tau_{-1}, Z_{-1}, \frac{1}{\lambda}\tau_{-2}, Z_{-2}, ...).$$

In reasonable situations

$$\lim_{\lambda \downarrow 0} h(t - \frac{1}{\lambda}\tau_{-1}, Z_{-1}, \frac{1}{\lambda}\tau_{-2}, Z_{-2}, ...) = 0$$

and therefore a reasonable guess is that

$$g_0(t, Z_0) = \lim_{\lambda \downarrow 0} h(t, Z_0, \frac{1}{\lambda}\tau_{-1}, Z_{-1}, ...),$$

with the interpretation that $g_0(t, Z_0)$ is equal to the functional Ψ when there is just one customer at time t with the random mark Z_0. However this interpretation is not needed in the theory, although in all applications it is the right one.

An Extension of $H = \lambda G$. We now give one further generalization of the Swiss Army formula (1.3.8). Instead of taking a classical queueing process $\{X(t)\}$, $t \in \mathbb{R}$, we shall consider a process of the form

$$(2.1.13) \quad X(t) = \int_\mathbb{R} \{h(t - s) \circ \theta_s\}dA(s),$$

where $h(t, \omega)$ is a non–negative function such that $E_A^0\left[\int_\mathbb{R} h(s)ds\right] < \infty$. In view of the generalized Campbell's formula and of the latter integrability condition, $\{X(t)\}$ is a finite process. Arguments, similar to those leading to formula (1.3.8) give the extended $H = \lambda G$ formula

$$(2.1.14) \quad \lambda_A^0 E_A^0\left[\int_\mathbb{R} h(s)Z(s)dB(s)\right] = \frac{1}{t}E\left[\int_{(0,t]} X(s_-)Z(s)dB(s)\right],$$

which reduces to (1.3.8) with the choice $h(t) = \mathbf{1}_{(T_0, T_0 + W_0]}$. This formula is therefore an extension of (1.3.8) and with the choice $B(ds) = ds$, $Z(t) = 1$, it gives $H = \lambda G$:

$$(2.1.15) \quad \lambda_A E_A^0\left[\int_\mathbb{R} h(s)ds\right] = E\left[\int_\mathbb{R} \{h(t - s) \circ \theta_s\}dA(s)\right].$$

2.2 Pollaczek–Khinchin's Mean Value Formulas

Consider a $G/G/s/c$ system, with a non-preemptive service discipline, that is, once started, the service of a customer cannot be interrupted. The contribution of customer $n, n \le 0$, to the workload $W(0)$ at time 0 is of the form $Z_n(-T_n)$, where Z_n is the function depicted in Figure 2.2.1. In this figure, $\tilde{V}_n$ is the waiting time of customer n.

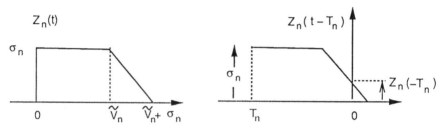

Fig. 2.2.1 The Z_n function

The workload at time 0 is the sum

$$(2.2.1) \quad W(0) = \sum_{n \in \mathbb{Z}} Z_n(-T_n) 1_{(-\infty, 0]}(T_n)$$

and therefore, by the function space Campbell-Little-Mecke formula (2.1.1)

$$E[W(0)] = \lambda E_A^0 \left[\int_{\mathbb{R}} Z_0(t) dt \right].$$

In view of the shape of $Z_0(t)$ and using the fact that $P_A^0(T_0 = 0) = 1$,

$$(2.2.2) \quad E_A^0 \left[\int_{\mathbb{R}} Z_0(t) dt \right] = E_A^0[\sigma_0 \tilde{V}_0 + \frac{1}{2}\sigma_0^2].$$

This results in Pollaczek–Khinchin's mean value formula:

$$(2.2.3) \quad E[W(0)] = \lambda E_A^0[\sigma_0 \tilde{V}_0] + \frac{1}{2}\lambda E_A^0[\sigma_0^2].$$

When σ_0 and $\tilde{V}_0$ are *independent*, for instance in a $GI/GI/1/\infty$ FIFO or LIFO *non-preemptive* queue (but not for SPT for instance)

$$(2.2.4) \quad E[W(0)] = \lambda E_A^0[\sigma_0] E_A^0[\tilde{V}_0] + \frac{1}{2}\lambda E_A^0[\sigma_0^2].$$

Example 2.2.1 *The $M/GI/1/\infty$ FIFO queue.* Because of the FIFO discipline and since there is only one server, the waiting time $\tilde{V}_n$ of customer n is equal to the system load that he sees in front of him upon arrival, i.e.

$W(T_n-)$. We will see in § 3 that, due to the Poisson nature of the arrival (point) process, the 'PASTA' property holds, that is

$$(2.2.5) \quad E^0_A[W(T_n-)] = E[W(0)]$$

and therefore, using (2.2.4) and the previous remarks

$$(2.2.6) \quad E^0_A[\tilde{V}_0] = \frac{\frac{1}{2}\lambda E^0_A[\sigma^2_0]}{1 - \rho}$$

or equivalently

$$(2.2.7) \quad E[W(0)] = \frac{\frac{1}{2}\lambda E[\sigma^2_0]}{1 - \rho}.$$

By Little's formula, $\lambda E^0_A[\tilde{V}_0] = E[Q(0)]$. Also, $E[Q(0)] = E[(X(0) - 1)^+] = E[X(0)] - 1 + P(X(0) = 0)$. Therefore in view of (1.2.7), $E[Q(0)] = E[X(0)] - \rho$. Combining all the above remarks, we find the expected number of customers in the system $M/GI/1/\infty$ FIFO:

$$(2.2.8) \quad E[X(0)] = \rho + \frac{\frac{1}{2}\lambda^2 E[\sigma^2_0]}{1 - \rho}.$$

Writing

$$\lambda^2 E[\sigma^2_0] = \lambda^2(Var(\sigma_0) + (E[\sigma_0])^2) = \lambda^2 Var(\sigma_0) + \rho^2$$

in the previous equality, we obtain

$$E[X(0)] = \rho + \frac{1}{2}\frac{\rho^2}{1 - \rho} + \frac{1}{2}\frac{\lambda^2}{1 - \rho}Var(\sigma_0).$$

This shows that for a fixed traffic intensity ρ, constant service times (such that $Var(\sigma_0) = 0$) give the smallest congestion in the $M/GI/1/\infty$ FIFO queue. We will come back to this in Chapter 4, § 1.   □

Residual Service Time. The function space Campbell-Little-Mecke formula can be applied to obtain the *residual service time formula*

$$(2.2.9) \quad E[R(0)] = \frac{1}{2}\lambda E^0_A[\sigma^2_0],$$

valid for a $G/G/s/\infty$ system with a non-preemptive discipline. Indeed defining $Z_n(t)$ as in Figure 2.2.2, we see that

$$(2.2.10) \quad R(0) = \sum_{n \in \mathbb{Z}} Z_n(-T_n)$$

and therefore, by (2.1.1), $E[R(0)] = \lambda E_A[\int_{\mathbb{R}} Z_0(t)dt]$, that is (2.2.9) since $\int_{\mathbb{R}} Z_n(t)dt = \frac{1}{2}\sigma^2_n$.

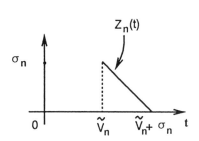
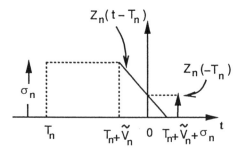

Fig. 2.2.2

2.3 Kleinrock's Conservation Law

This conservation formula is obtained exactly in the same way as Pollaczek
– Khinchin's mean value formula in the preceding subsection. It concerns the
$G/G/s/\infty$ queueing system with M priority classes of Example 1.1.2. If we
apply Pollaczek-Khinchin's formula to each of the priority classes, we obtain,
with the notations of Example 1.1.2

$$(2.3.1) \quad E[W_i(0)] = \lambda_i E^0_{A_i}[\sigma_{i,0}\tilde{V}_{i,0}] + \frac{1}{2}\lambda_i E^0_{A_i}[\sigma^2_{i,0}].$$

This formula applies when the service of a customer of any type cannot
be interrupted and the speed of service is one. The only requirement for
the discipline service among customers of the same class and for the priority
assignment between the M classes is that all the objects considered fit the θ_t-
framework. The simplest case would be a FIFO discipline among the members
of the same class, and a non-preemptive priority rule with given order of
priority, say $1 \gg 2 \gg ... \gg M$, where $i \gg j$ means that i has priority over j.
Summing up the M equations (2.3.1) and observing that $\sum_{i=1}^{M} W_i(t)$ is the
total workload, and that

$$(2.3.2) \quad \frac{1}{2}\sum \lambda_i E^0_{A_i}[\sigma^2_{i,0}] = \frac{1}{2}\lambda E^0_A[\sigma^2_0],$$

(since $\lambda_i E^0_{A_i}[\sigma^2_{i,0}] = \lambda\frac{\lambda_i}{\lambda}E^0_{A_i}[\sigma^2_0] = \lambda P^0_A(U_0 = i)E^0_A[\sigma^2_0 \mid U_0 = i]$, see Chapter 1, Example 5.2.1), we obtain

$$(2.3.3) \quad \sum_{i=1}^{M}\lambda_i E^0_{A_i}[\sigma_{i,0}\tilde{V}_{i,0}] = E[W(0)] - \frac{1}{2}\lambda E^0_A[\sigma^2_0].$$

The right-hand side does not depend upon service disciplines among members of the same class, and priority assignment, as long as the conditions
stated just after Formula (2.3.1) are in force. This constitutes Kleinrock's
conservation law

(2.3.4) $\displaystyle\sum_{i=1}^{M} \lambda_i E_{A_i}^0 [\sigma_{i,0} \tilde{V}_{i,0}] = \text{constant}.$

Of course, if for each class i, $\sigma_{i,0}$ and $\tilde{V}_{i,0}$ are independent (under P or $P_{A_i}^0$, this is equivalent), (2.3.3) takes the form

(2.3.5) $\displaystyle\sum_{i=1}^{M} \rho_i E_{A_i}^0 [\tilde{V}_{i,0}] = E[W(0)] - \frac{1}{2}\lambda E_A^0 [\sigma_0^2].$

This formula holds for instance in a $M/GI/1/\infty$ system with priority classes, no preemption, and FIFO discipline among the members of a given class (see also § 5.2).

Remark 2.3.1 Another derivation of Formula (2.3.1) from Pollaczek-Khinchin's formula (2.2.3) is as follows, using the results of § 5.1, Chapter 1:

$$E_A^0 [\sigma_0 \tilde{V}_0] = \sum_{i=1}^{M} E_A^0 [\sigma_0 \tilde{V}_0 \mid U_0 = i] P_A^0 [U_0 = i]$$

$$= \sum_{i=1}^{M} E_{A_i}^0 [\sigma_0 \tilde{V}_0] \frac{\lambda_i}{\lambda}$$

$$= \sum_{i=1}^{M} E_{A_i}^0 [\sigma_{i,0} \tilde{V}_{i,0}] \frac{\lambda_i}{\lambda}.$$

□

Example 2.3.2 *A continuous version of Kleinrock's conservation law.* This version is an immediate consequence of Pollaczek-Khinchin's (2.2.3). It is obtained by conditioning with respect to σ_0:

$$E_A^0 [\sigma_0 \tilde{V}_0] = \int_{\mathbb{R}_+} x E_A^0 [\tilde{V}_0 \mid \sigma_0 = x] P_A^0 (\sigma_0 \in dx).$$

Therefore

(2.3.6) $\displaystyle\lambda \int_{\mathbb{R}_+} x E_A^0 [\tilde{V}_0 \mid \sigma_0 = x] P_A^0 (\sigma_0 \in dx) = E[W(0)] - \frac{1}{2}\lambda E_A^0 [\sigma_0^2].$

Defining $\rho(dx) = \lambda x P_A^0 (\sigma_0 \in dx)$, the traffic intensity measure, this equation takes the form

(2.3.7) $\displaystyle\int_{\mathbb{R}_+} E_A^0 [\tilde{V}_0 \mid \sigma_0 = x] \rho(dx) = E[W(0)] - \frac{1}{2}\lambda E_A^0 [\sigma_0^2].$

We recall the conditions of validity of (2.3.7): a service is not interrupted when started, and the speed of service is one for a given customer. However, no condition of independence of σ_0 and $\tilde{V}_0$ is needed. For instance, Formula

(2.3.7) is valid for a *non-preemptive SPT discipline* (where the servers choose in the waiting room the customer with shortest processing time σ_n, and no preemption is allowed). □

Another Conservation Formula for Preemptive Resume Disciplines.
We consider a system in equilibrium, with a stationary G/G input. Other hypotheses will be introduced as need arises. The first one is:

(2.3.8) *Hypothesis: the discipline is non-preemptive, or preemptive resume.*

The contribution of customer n, arriving at $T_n \leq 0$, to the workload $W(0)$ is $Z_n(0 - T_n)$, where, according to the above hypotheses, $Z_n(t)$ has the form exhibited in Figure 2.3.1.

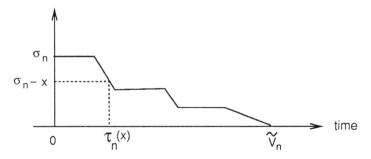

Fig. 2.3.1 The function $Z_n(t)$

The slopes of the decreasing parts of $Z_n(t)$ may be different. Also, in the non-preemptive case, there may be just one flat region (the first one), or no flat region at all. For $0 \leq x \leq \sigma_n$, $\tau_n(x)$ is defined as in Figure 2.3.1 and can be interpreted as the response time to a load x brought into the system at time T_n. We introduce the second hypothesis. It is a technical hypothesis, but it is not difficult to check (see the examples below).

(2.3.9) *Hypothesis: the random variables* $1_{0<x<\sigma_0}$ *and* $\tau_0(x)$ *are* P_A^0 *independent for all* x.

Under the assumptions (2.3.8) and (2.3.9)

$$E_A^0\left[\int_0^\infty Z_0(t)dt\right] = E_A^0\left[\int_0^{\sigma_0} \tau_0(x)dx\right]$$

$$= \int_0^\infty E_A^0[1_{0<x<\sigma_0}\tau_0(x)]dx$$

$$= \int_0^\infty E_A^0[\tau_0(x)]P_A^0(\sigma_0 > x)dx.$$

Since the workload at time 0 is

$$W(0) = \sum_{n \in \mathbb{Z}} 1_{T_n < 0} Z_n(-T_n),$$

the functional Campbell-Little-Mecke formula (2.1.1) implies $E[W(0)] = E_A^0[\int_0^\infty Z_0(t)dt]$, that is

$$(2.3.10) \quad \lambda \int_0^\infty E_A^0[\tau_0(x)] P_A^0(\sigma_0 > x) dx = E[W(0)].$$

In a number of interesting cases

$$(2.3.11) \quad E_A^0[\tau_0(x)] = E_A^0[\tilde{V}_0 \mid \sigma_0 = x]$$

and (2.3.10) then becomes

$$(2.3.12) \quad \lambda \int_0^\infty E_A^0[\tilde{V}_0 \mid \sigma_0 = x] P_A^0(\sigma_0 > x) dx = E[W(0)].$$

Example 2.3.3 *GI/GI/1/∞ Processor Sharing (PS).* For this system, at equilibrium, hypotheses (2.3.8), (2.3.9) and (2.3.11) hold. Only (2.3.9) requires a proof. This assumption is verified because $\{Z_0(t)\}, t \geq 0$, depends on σ_0 and on the congestion process $\{X(t)\}$ in the interval $[0, \tilde{V}_0)$. But in this interval, $\{X(t)\}$ depends only on the sequence of arrivals $\{T_n\}, n \in \mathbb{Z}$, and on the sequence of services $\{\sigma_n\}$ *except* σ_0 (for $t \geq \tilde{V}_0, X(t)$ actually depends on σ_0). □

Example 2.3.4 *GI/GI/s/c SRPT.* Here we assume that we are at equilibrium in the θ_t-framework. The same argument as in Example 2.3.2 gives the same conclusions. □

3 Event and Time Averages

3.1 PASTA

This classical result of queueing theory states, in rough terms, that if the arrival point process is Poissonian, operational characteristics of the system computed just before arrival times and at arbitrary times are the same (Poisson Arrivals See Time Averages). Some care must be exercised in the application of this principle, and we now give a precise statement, in the θ_t-framework. Let A be a point process, compatible with a flow $\{\theta_t\}$, and with finite intensity λ (we use the notation A because the PASTA theorem is mostly applied to arrival point processes).

Let $\{\mathcal{F}_t\}$ be a history of A that is compatible with the flow $\{\theta_t\}$ and with a predictable structure adapted to $\{\theta_t\}$ (see § 8.1 of Chapter 1). Let $\{Z(t)\}$ be a $\mathcal{F}_t$-predictable process compatible with the flow $\{\theta_t\}$, with values in a measurable space $(K, \mathcal{K})$, and let $f : K \to \mathbb{R}$ be a non-negative measurable function. Then if A admits the constant $\mathcal{F}_t$-intensity λ

(3.1.1) $E_A^0[f(Z(0))] = E[f(Z(0))].$

In the case when (P, θ_t) is ergodic, (3.1.1) becomes

$$(3.1.2)\quad \lim_{N \to \infty} \frac{1}{N} \sum_{n=1}^{N} f(Z(T_n)) = \lim_{T \to \infty} \frac{1}{T} \int_0^T f(Z(s)) ds,$$

(see § 7, Chapter 1).

Remark 3.1.1 By Watanabe's theorem, A admits a $\mathcal{F}_t$-intensity λ if and only if it is a Poisson process with rate λ *and* for all $(a, b] \subset \mathbb{R}$, $N(a, b]$ is independent of $\mathcal{F}_a$. In particular $N(a, b]$ is independent of $Z(a)$: this is the so-called *lack-of-bias* assumption.   □

Proof of (3.1.1):

$$E_A^0[f(Z(0))] = \frac{1}{\lambda} E\left[\int_{(0,1]} f(Z(s)) N(ds)\right] = \frac{1}{\lambda} E\left[\int_{(0,1]} f(Z(s)) \lambda ds\right]$$
$$= \int_{(0,1]} E[f(Z(s))] ds = E[f(Z(0))],$$

where the first equality is Mecke's definition of Palm probability, the second equality is the definition of stochastic intensity plus the stochastic intensity integration formula, and the last equality is the stationarity of $\{Z(t)\}$ under probability P.   □

Remark 3.1.2 Of course, as will be explicited in § 3.2, PASTA can be viewed as a consequence of Papangelou's Radon-Nikodým derivative theorem. However, we preferred to give the more elementary proof above, because PASTA is indeed a very elementary result.   □

In the usual applications to queueing theory, $Z(t)$ has the form

(3.1.3) $Z(t) = Y(t-),$

where $\{Y(t)\}$ is a corlol process adapted to $\{\mathcal{F}_t\}$ and moreover, $\{Y(t)\}$ is continuous at 0. In this case, (3.1.1) becomes

(3.1.4) $E_A^0[Y(0-)] = E[Y(0)].$

Example 3.1.1 The point process A is the input of a $M/GI/s/\infty$ queue in equilibrium $(\rho < s)$, and $Y(t) = 1_{X(t)=n}$, where $X(t)$ is the number of customers in the system at time t. The PASTA property then shows that

(3.1.5) $P(X(0) = n) = P_A^0(X(0-) = n).$

                                            □

Example 3.1.2 *Busy cycle in* $M/GI/1/\infty$. In a $GI/GI/1/\infty$ queue, we have $P(X(0) = 0) = 1 - \rho$, where ρ is the traffic intensity $\lambda E_A^0[\sigma_0] = \lambda E[\sigma_0]$, and if moreover the arrival point process is Poisson, $P_A^0[X(0-) = 0] = P[X(0) = 0]$. Using these remarks and Formula (1.2.11), we obtain

$$(3.1.6) \quad E_N^0[B_1] = \frac{E[\sigma_0]}{1 - \rho}$$

(recall that for this formula, N counts the arrival times into an empty system; see Example 1.2.3). $\qquad\qquad\qquad\qquad\qquad\qquad\qquad\qquad\qquad\qquad\qquad\square$

3.2 Applications of Papangelou's Formula

Necessary and Sufficient Condition for ESTA. ESTA means Events See Time Averages. It is the same property as PASTA, only without reference to an arrival process. The ESTA property is said to hold for the process $\{Z(t)\}$ and the point process N, both compatible with the flow $\{\theta_t\}$, if $E_N^0[f(Z(0))] = E[f(Z(0))]$, for all non-negative measurable functions f: $E \to \mathbb{R}$, where E is the state space of $\{Z(t)\}$.

Let $\{\mathcal{F}_t\}$ be a history of N and $\{Z(t)\}$, that is compatible with the flow $\{\theta_t\}$. Suppose that N admits a $\mathcal{F}_t$-intensity $\{\lambda(t)\}$ (which can be assumed compatible with the flow $\{\theta_t\}$; see Chapter 1, § 8). Recall that $E[\lambda(0)] = \lambda$. If $\{Z(0)\}$ is $\mathcal{F}_{0-}$-measurable, Papangelou's formula

$$(3.2.1) \quad E_N^0[f(Z(0))] = \frac{1}{\lambda}E[f(Z(0))\lambda(0)]$$

holds true for all bounded f. This shows that ESTA holds for N and $\{Z(t)\}$ if and only if the *lack of bias* condition

$$(3.2.2) \quad E[\lambda(0) \mid Z(0)] = E[\lambda(0)]$$

is satisfied.

When ESTA Does not Hold True. The basic formula to use is of course Papangelou's formula (3.2.1).

Example 3.2.1 This example is the same as Example 3.1.1 except that the waiting room has limited capacity: $c < \infty$, and therefore $X(t) \le s + c$. The arrival process into the system has the $\mathcal{F}_t$-intensity $\lambda(t) = \lambda 1_{X(t-) \le s+c-1}$ and (average) intensity $\lambda P(X(0) \le s + c - 1) = \lambda(1 - P(X(0) = s + c))$. Papangelou's formula immediately implies

$$(3.2.3) \quad P_A^0(X(0-) = n) = \frac{P(X(0) = n)}{(1 - P(X(0) = s + c))}, \quad 0 \le n \le s + c - 1$$

and of course $P_A^0(X(0-) = s + c) = 0$.   □

Example 3.2.2 *The 'job-observer' property of Gordon-Newell networks.*
Consider K interconnected queues forming a closed network (i.e. without
arrivals from, or departures to, the exterior) containing M customers who
circulate from one queue to another. When a customer has received the service he required in station (queue) i, he joins station j with probability r_{ij}
according to the result of a 'coin' toss. Of course

$$(3.2.4) \quad \sum_{j=1}^{K} r_{ij} = 1.$$

All the coin tosses and the service times are independent. The service times
in station i are exponential with the same mean μ_i^{-1}. In each station, there
is one server working at unit speed, and a waiting room of capacity larger
than M. Therefore, defining

$$X(t) = (X_1(t), ..., X_K(t)),$$

where $X_i(t)$ is the number of customers in station i (waiting or being
served) at time t, $\{X(t)\}$, $t \in \mathbb{R}_+$, is a Markov chain with state space
$E = \{n = (n_1, ..., n_K) \mid n_i \in \mathbb{N}, \sum_{i=1}^{K} n_i = M\}$ and with the infinitesimal characteristics:

$$q_{n,n-e_i+e_j} = \mu_i r_{ij} 1_{n_i > 0},$$

(here, e_k is the k-th canonical vector of $\mathbb{R}^K$). If the stochastic matrix R=
$\{r_{ij}\}$ is irreducible and all the μ_i's are strictly positive, the chain $\{X(t)\}$ is
irreducible, and since the state space is finite, it is ergodic. It is straightforward to check that the unique stationary distribution of $\{X(t)\}$ is given
by

$$(3.2.5) \quad \pi(n_1, ..., n_K) = \frac{1}{G(K, M)} \prod_{i=1}^{K} \alpha_i^{n_i},$$

where $\alpha = (\alpha_1, ..., \alpha_K)$ is the unique probability distribution solution of the
traffic equations

$$(3.2.6) \quad \alpha_i \mu_i = \sum_{j=1}^{K} \alpha_j \mu_j r_{ji}, \qquad (1 \le i \le K)$$

and $G(K, M) = \sum_{n_1 + ... + n_K = M} \alpha_i^{n_i}$ is a normalizing constant.

Let A_{ij} be the point process counting the transfers from station i to
station j. It admits the $\mathcal{F}_t^X$-intensity

$$\lambda_{ij}(t) = \mu_i r_{ij} 1_{X_i(t) > 0}$$

and by Papangelou's formula

$$\lambda_{ij} P^0_{A_{ij}}[X(0-) = n] = E[\mu_i r_{ij} 1_{X_i(0)>0} 1_{X(0)=n}],$$

where $\lambda_{ij} = \mu_i r_{ij} P(X_i(0) > 0)$ is the intensity of A_{ij}. Therefore

$$P^0_{A_{ij}}(X(0-) = n)P(X_i(0) > 0) = \begin{cases} P(X(t) = n) & \text{if } n_i > 0; \\ 0 & \text{otherwise.} \end{cases}$$

In view of the expression (3.2.5) for the stationary distribution of the network,

$$P^0_{A_{ij}}(X(0-) = n) = \begin{cases} \frac{1}{C}\left(\prod_{\substack{l=1 \\ l\neq i}}^{K} \alpha_l^{n_l}\right)\alpha_i^{n_i-1} & \text{if } n_i > 0; \\ 0 & \text{otherwise,} \end{cases}$$

where C is a constant obtained by normalization:

$$\sum_{n_1+\ldots+n_K=M, n_i>0} \left(\prod_{\substack{l=1 \\ l\neq i}}^{K} \alpha_l^{n_l}\right) \alpha_i^{n_i-1} = C.$$

After the change of summation variable $n_i \to n_i - 1$, the left-hand side of the above equality becomes

$$\sum_{n_1+\ldots+n_K=M-1} \left(\prod_{l=1}^{K} \alpha_l^{n_l}\right) = G(K, M - 1).$$

Therefore

$$(3.2.7) \quad P^0_{A_{ij}}(X(0-) = n) = \frac{1}{G(K, M - 1)}\left(\prod_{\substack{l=1 \\ l\neq i}}^{K} \alpha_l^{n_l}\right) \alpha_i^{n_i-1}(n_i > 0).$$

When a customer is transferred from i to j at time t, the situation he sees during his transfer (when he has left i but not yet reached j) for the rest of the network is not $X(t-)$ but $X(t-) - e_i$. Therefore, the state of the network observed by this customer (excluding him) is n with probability $\frac{1}{G(K,M-1)} \prod_{l=1}^{K} \alpha_l^{n_l}$. It is the same as the state of the same network with $M - 1$ customers observed at an arbitrary time by an external observer. $\square$

ANTIPASTA. ANTIPASTA is concerned with the converse of the ESTA property. The basic result is:

(3.2.8) *Let N be a point process and $\{X(t)\}$ be a stochastic process with a denumerable state space E, both compatible with the flow $\{\theta_t\}$. Suppose that N admits the $\mathcal{F}_t$-intensity $\lambda_t = \lambda(X(t))$, for some function λ and that $\{X(t)\}$ is $\mathcal{F}_t$-predictable. Then ESTA holds for $\{X(t)\}$ and N if and only if N is $\mathcal{F}_t$-Poisson.*

Proof: In view of what precedes, the only property to prove is the 'only if' part. Assume that ESTA holds, then for any bounded $f : E \to \mathbb{R}$, we have

$$E_N^0[f(X(0))] = E[f(X(0))],$$

that is, using Papangelou's theorem

$$\lambda_N E[f(X(0))] = E[f(X(0))\lambda(X(0))].$$

This being true for all f, we see that

$$\lambda(X(0)) = \lambda_N$$

and the conclusion follows from Watanabe's theorem.   □

Example 3.2.3 *ANTIPASTA for Markov chains.* The setting is the one described in Example 1.3.3 and § 5.3 of Chapter 1. We consider a Markov chain $\{X(t)\}$ with state space E, and we suppose that it is at equilibrium. Let N_H be the point process counting the transitions from state i to state j for all (i, j) belonging to a given set $H \subset E \times E - diag(E \times E)$.

As was shown in Example 8.2.2 of Chapter 1, the $\mathcal{F}_t^X$-intensity of N_H is

$$\lambda_H(t) = \sum_{(k,j) \in H} 1_{X(t)=k} q_{kj},$$

where $\{q_{ij}\}$ is the infinitesimal generator of $\{X_t\}$. According to the ANTIPASTA theorem, ESTA holds for $\{X(t)\}$ and N_H if and only if N_H is $\mathcal{F}_t^X$-Poisson.   □

Conditional PASTA. We consider a point process N with the $(P, \mathcal{F}_t)$-predictable intensity $\{\lambda(t)\}$ of the form

(3.2.9) $\lambda(t) = g(Y(t))$,

where $\{Y(t)\}$ is some $\mathcal{F}_t$-predictable process taking its values in a denumerable set E, of the form $Y(t, \omega) = Y(0, \theta_t \omega)$. For fixed $i \in E$, we consider the point process N_i defined by

(3.2.10) $N_i(C) = \int_C 1_{Y(s)=i} N(ds), \quad C \in \mathcal{B}(\mathbb{R})$.

The intensity of $N_i(C)$ is

$$\lambda_i = E[N_i(0, 1]] = E\left[\int_0^1 1_{Y(s)=i} \, g(Y(s))ds\right],$$

that is

$$\lambda_i = g(i)P(Y(0) = i).$$

In view of the general results concerning conditional Palm probabilities (Chapter 1, § 5.2), for any $\mathcal{F}_t$-predictable process $\{X(t)\}$ of the form $X(t, \omega) = X(0, \theta_t \omega)$, where $X(0)$ is $\mathcal{F}_{0-}$-measurable and for all bounded functions f

$$E^0_{N_i}[f(X(0))] = E^0_N[f(X(0)) \mid Y(0) = i],$$

that is

$$E^0_{N_i}[f(X(0))] = \frac{E^0_N[f(X(0))1_{\{Y(0)=i\}}]}{P^0_N[Y(0) = i]}.$$

From Papangelou's formula

$$\lambda_N P^0_N[Y(0) = i] = g(i)P(Y(0) = i)$$

and

$$\lambda_N E^0_N[f(X(0))1_{\{Y(0)=i\}}] = g(i)E[f(X(0))1_{\{Y(0)=i\}}],$$

and therefore

$$E^0_{N_i}[f(X(0))] = \frac{E[f(X(0))1_{\{Y(0)=i\}}]}{P[Y(0) = i]}.$$

If (P, θ_t) is ergodic, the above equality reads

$$(3.2.11) \quad \lim_{t \to \infty} \frac{1}{N_i(0, t]} \int_{(0,t]} f(X(s))N_i(ds) = \lim_{t \to \infty} \frac{\int_0^t f(X(s))1_{\{Y(s)=i\}}ds}{\int_0^t 1_{\{Y(s)=i\}}ds}.$$

Example 3.2.4 *Insensitivity of $M/GI/1/\infty$ LIFO preemptive.* The service time sequence $\{\sigma_n\}$ is i.i.d. with c.d.f. $G(x)$ and mean μ^{-1} and the input process N is Poisson with intensity λ. Assume that $\rho = \lambda\mu^{-1} < 1$ and that the system is in equilibrium. Call $X(t)$ the number of customers in the system at time t. For fixed $k \geq 1$, denote N_k the point process counting the arrivals that make the congestion process $\{X(t)\}$ reach level k, i.e.

$$N_k(C) = \sum_{n \in \mathbb{Z}} 1_C(T_n)1_{\{X(T_n-)=k-1\}}.$$

Let $\{T_n^{(k)}\}$ be the sequence of points N_k, with the usual convention $T_0^{(k)} \leq 0 < T_1^{(k)}$. A customer arriving at time $T_n^{(k)}$ requires the service $\sigma_n^{(k)}$. The following fact is true: $\{\sigma_n^{(k)}\}$ is i.i.d. with the same distribution as $\{\sigma_n\}$ (we shall admit this, although it requires a proof).

Because of the LIFO preemptive rule, customer $T_n^{(k)}$ receives all his service when the queue is at level k (Figure 3.2.1).

Since k is recurrent (under the stability hypothesis), the law of large numbers give

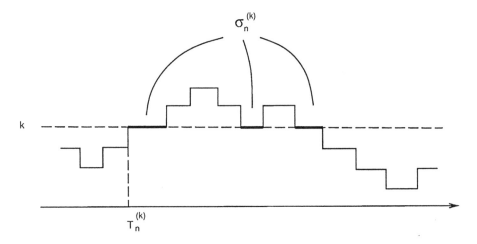

Fig. 3.2.1 The LIFO Queue

$$\lim_{t\to\infty} \frac{\int_0^t 1_{\{X(s)=k\}}ds}{\int_{(0,t]} 1_{\{X(s-)=k-1\}}N(ds)} = \mu^{-1} \quad \text{a.s.}$$

Since the input stream M/GI is ergodic,

$$\lim_{t\to\infty} \frac{1}{t}\int_0^t 1_{\{X(s)=k\}}ds = \pi(k),$$

where π is the stationary distribution of $\{X(t)\}$. Moreover,

$$\lim_{t\to\infty} \frac{1}{t}\int_{(0,t]} 1_{\{X(s-)=k-1\}}N(ds) = \lim_{t\to\infty} \frac{N(t)}{t}\frac{1}{N(t)}\int_{(0,t]} 1_{\{X(s-)=k-1\}}N(ds).$$

But $\lim_{t\to\infty} \frac{N(t)}{t} = \lambda$, and in view of the PASTA property

$$\lim_{t\to\infty} \frac{1}{N(t)}\int_{(0,t]} 1_{\{X(s-)=k-1\}}N(ds) = \lim_{t\to\infty} \frac{1}{t}\int_0^t 1_{\{X(s)=k-1\}}ds = \pi(k-1),$$

so that

(3.2.12) $\dfrac{\pi(k)}{\pi(k-1)} = \rho, \qquad k \geq 1.$

This leads to

$$(3.2.13) \quad \pi(k) = (1 - \rho)\rho^k, \qquad k \geq 0,$$

showing in particular the insensitivity of the $M/GI/1/\infty$ LIFO preemptive queue, i.e. π depends on G only through its mean. The proof of insensitivity can be extended to the situation where the input process N admits the $(P, \mathcal{F}_t)$ intensity

$$\lambda(t) = \lambda_{X(t)},$$

where $\{\mathcal{F}_t\}$ is the history recording the past of N at time t and the whole sequence $\{\sigma_n\}$. Now, we have to use Papangelou's version of PASTA

$$\lim_{t \to \infty} \frac{1}{N(t)} \int_0^t 1_{\{X(s-)=k-1\}} N(ds)$$

$$= \lim_{t \to \infty} \frac{t}{N(t)} \frac{1}{t} \int_0^t 1_{\{X(s)=k-1\}} \lambda_{k-1} ds$$

$$= \pi(k-1) \frac{\lambda_{k-1}}{\lambda},$$

showing insensitivity. $\square$

PASTA and the Martingale SLLN. The following result can be considered as a non-stationary version of the classical PASTA result (3.1.2). The framework is that of § 9.3 of Chapter 1 and in particular no stationarity is assumed for $\{Z(t)\}$. Assume that

$$(3.2.14) \quad \exists \lim_{t \to \infty} \frac{N_t}{t} = \lambda, \quad \text{where } 0 < \lambda < \infty.$$

Therefore $\exists \lim_{t \to \infty} \frac{\int_0^t \lambda(s) ds}{t} = \lambda$ (from the results in the examples of § 9.3 of Chapter 1). Assume moreover that f is bounded, so that condition (9.3.7) of Chapter 1 is verified. Then, if either limit involved exists, the other exists, and

$$(3.2.15) \quad \lim_{t \to \infty} \frac{1}{N_t} \int_{(0,t]} f(Z(s)) N(ds) = \lim_{t \to \infty} \frac{1}{t} \int^t f(Z(s)) \lambda(s) ds.$$

This result immediately follows from the general theory of § 9.3, Chapter 1.

4 Formulas Derived from Conservation Equations

4.1 First Order Equivalence

Congestion at Arrivals and at Departures. There are a number of formulas which follow directly from the definition of Palm probability, which we recall here under its expectation form

$$(4.1.1) \quad E_N^0[Z(0)] = \frac{1}{\lambda t} E\Big[\sum_{n \in \mathbb{Z}} Z(T_n) 1_{(0,t]}(T_n)\Big],$$

where N and $\{Z(t)\}$ are compatible with the flow $\{\theta_t\}$, λ is the intensity (finite and non-null) of N, and $\{T_n\}$ is the sequence of times associated with N.

For instance, take the situation described in Example 1.1.1 or Example 1.1.2. More generally consider a θ_t-framework with two simple point processes A and D and a stochastic process $\{X(t)\}$, all compatible with the flow $\{\theta_t\}$, and linked by the relations

$$(4.1.2) \quad X(t) = X(0) + A((0,t]) - D((0,t]),$$

$$(4.1.3) \quad A((0,t]) \geq D((0,t]).$$

Moreover, $X(0) \geq 0$, so that $X(t) \geq 0$. Also assume that A and D have no common points.

Let us write down the evolution equation of a stochastic process of the form $\{f(X(t))\}$. Since a change occurs only at a point of A or D

$$f(X(t)) = f(X(0)) + \int_{(0,t]} (f(X(s)) - f(X(s-)))A(ds)$$
$$+ \int_{(0,t]} (f(X(s)) - f(X(s-)))D(ds).$$

At a point of A, $f(X(t)) = f(X(t-) + 1)$ and at a point of D, $f(X(t)) = f(X(t-) - 1)$. Therefore

$$f(X(t)) = f(X(0)) + \int_{(0,t]} \{f(X(s-) + 1) - f(X(s-))\}A(ds)$$
$$+ \int_{(0,t]} \{f(X(s-) - 1) - f(X(s-))\}D(ds).$$

Dividing by λt, taking expectations with respect to P, observing that $E[f(X(t))] = E[f(X(0))]$, and using (4.1.1), we find that

$$E_A^0[f(X(0-) + 1) - f(X(0-))] = E_D[f(X(0-) - 1) - f(X(0-))].$$

Taking for instance $f(x) = 1_{\{n\}}(x)$, where $n \geq 1$, and denoting

$$\pi_A^0(n) = P_A^0(X(0-) = n) \,, \quad \pi_D^0(n) = P_D^0(X(0-) = n),$$

we obtain

(4.1.4) $\pi_A^0(n-1) - \pi_A^0(n) = \pi_D^0(n) - \pi_D^0(n+1).$

As for $n = 0$, taking into account the fact that $X(0-) \geq 0$, and that $X(0-) > 0$ if 0 is a departure time (which it is under P_D^0) :

(4.1.4') $\pi_A^0(0) = \pi_D^0(1).$

Summing up the last two equalities, we obtain for all $i \geq 0$

(4.1.5) $\pi_A^0(i) = \pi_D^0(i+1).$

First Order Equivalent of a Queue and Norton's Theorem. Suppose that A and D admit the $\mathcal{F}_t$-intensities $\{\lambda(t)\}$ and $\{\mu(t)\}$ respectively, where $\{\mathcal{F}_t\}$ is a history of $\{X(t)\}$ that is compatible with the flow $\{\theta_t\}$. In particular, the stochastic processes $\{\lambda(t)\}$ and $\{\mu(t)\}$ can be chosen compatible with $\{\theta_t\}$. By Papangelou's formula

$$\lambda P_A^0(X(0-) = i) = E[1_{\{i\}}(X(0-))\lambda(0)] = E[1_{\{i\}}(X(0))\lambda(0)] \,,$$
$$\lambda P_D^0(X(0-) = i) = E[1_{\{i\}}(X(0-))\mu(0)] = E[1_{\{i\}}(X(0))\mu(0)] \,.$$

where we have used the fact that at point 0 there are no arrivals or departures under P. Defining

(4.1.6) $\begin{cases} \hat{\lambda}_i = E[\lambda(0) \mid X(0) = i], \\ \hat{\mu}_i = E[\mu(0) \mid X(0) = i], \\ \pi(i) = P(X(0) = i), \end{cases}$

we obtain

(4.1.7) $\lambda \pi_A^0(i) = \hat{\lambda}_i \pi(i) \,, \quad \lambda \pi_D^0(i) = \hat{\mu}_i \pi(i)$

and therefore, in view of (4.1.4) and (4.1.4')

(4.1.8) $\begin{cases} \hat{\lambda}_0 \pi(0) - \hat{\mu}_1 \pi(1) = 0, \\ \hat{\lambda}_{i-1} \pi(i-1) - (\hat{\lambda}_i + \hat{\mu}_i)\pi(i) + \hat{\mu}_{i+1}\pi(i+1) = 0. \end{cases}$

Therefore π is the stationary distribution of a birth and death process with parameters $\{\hat{\lambda}_n\}$ and $\{\hat{\mu}_n\}$, called the *first order equivalent* birth and death process of $\{X(t)\}$.

If (P, θ_t) is ergodic, Equalities (4.1.7) become

$$(4.1.7') \quad \begin{cases} \hat{\lambda}_i = \lim_{t\to\infty} \dfrac{\int_{(0,t]} 1_{X(s-)=i}\, A(ds)}{\int_0^t 1_{X(s)=i}\, ds}, \\[2ex] \hat{\mu}_i = \lim_{t\to\infty} \dfrac{\int_{(0,t]} 1_{X(s-)=i}\, D(ds)}{\int_0^t 1_{X(s)=i}\, ds}. \end{cases}$$

Example 4.1.1 *Norton's theorem for Gordon-Newell networks.* Consider the Gordon-Newell network of Example 3.2.2. If we let $\mathcal{F}_t = \mathcal{F}_t^X$, the $\mathcal{F}_t$-intensities of the input and output flows of station K are $\sum_{i=1}^{K-1} \mu_i r_{iK} 1_{X_i(t)>0}$ and $\mu_K(1 - r_{KK})1_{X_K(t)>0}$. Here we have implicitly assumed that the station 'includes' the feedback loop, so that the input and output flows do not have common jumps, as required in the theory of the present subsection. Our goal is to compute the parameters $\hat{\lambda}_{n_K}$ and $\hat{\mu}_{n_K}$ of the birth and death process equivalent to station K at the first order. Clearly $\hat{\lambda}_{n_K} = \mu_K(1-r_{KK})1_{n_K>0}$ and, by the results obtained above,

$$(4.1.9) \quad \hat{\mu}_{n_K} = E\Big[\sum_{i=1}^{K-1} \mu_i r_{iK} 1_{X_i(t)>0} \mid X_K(t) = n_K \Big].$$

In the computation of the right-hand side of the above equality, we shall need to compute

$$\pi(n \mid n_K) \stackrel{\text{def}}{=} P(X(t) = n \mid X_K(t) = n_K).$$

We will show that

$$(4.1.10) \quad \pi(n \mid n_K) = \frac{1}{G(K-1, M - n_K)} \prod_{i=1}^{K-1} (\hat{\alpha}_i)^{n_i},$$

where $\hat{\alpha} = (\hat{\alpha}_1, ..., \hat{\alpha}_{K-1})$ is the probability vector satisfying the traffic equations

$$(4.1.11) \quad \hat{\alpha}_i \mu_i = \sum_{j=1}^{K-1} \hat{\alpha}_j \mu_j \hat{r}_{ji} \quad (1 \le i \le K-1),$$

relative to the same network as the original one, except for queue K which has been short-circuited (see Figure 4.1.1).

Therefore $\pi(n \mid n_K)$ is equal to $\pi(n_1, \ldots, n_{K-1}; n_K)$, where for fixed n_K, $\pi(n_1, ..., n_{K-1}; n_K)$ is the stationary distribution of the short-circuited network of Figure 4.1.1.b, with $M - n_K$ circulating customers; note that $\hat{\mu}_{n_K}$ is the intensity in the short-circuit (i.e. branch AB of Figure 4.1.1.b). This is the content of the so called Norton's theorem of Gordon-Newell queueing networks.

We now proceed to the proof of statement (4.1.10). First, we compute the routing parameters of the short circuited network. We have

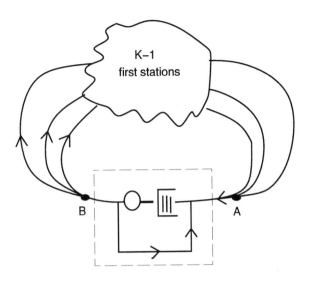

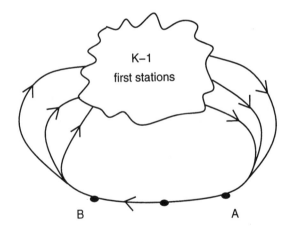

Fig. 4.1.1 A short circuited queue

$$(4.1.12) \quad \hat{r}_{ij} = r_{ij} + \frac{r_{iK} r_{Kj}}{1 - r_{KK}}.$$

This expresses the fact that the routes $ij, iKj, iKKj, iKKKj, \ldots$ of the original network collapse into a single route from i to j in the short-circuited network. The corresponding probability is therefore $r_{ji} + r_{iK} r_{Kj}(1 + r_{KK} + r_{KK}^2 + \ldots)$ that is, the right-hand side of (4.1.12).

We can check that

$$\hat{\alpha}_i = \frac{\alpha_i}{\sum_{j=1}^{K-1} \alpha_j}, \quad (1 \le j \le K-1),$$

is the unique probability distribution solution of the traffic equations (4.1.11). Therefore, for any n with the last coordinate fixed equal to n_K, we obtain

$$\pi(n \mid n_K) \stackrel{\text{def}}{=} \frac{\pi(n)}{\sum_{m/m_K=n_K} \pi(m)} = \frac{1}{C} \prod_{i=1}^{K-1} (\hat{\alpha}_i)^{n_i},$$

for some C depending only upon M, K, n_K and the routing probabilities. The constant C must be equal to $G(K-1, M-n_K)$ since $\sum \pi(n \mid n_K) = 1$ and $\sum_{i=1}^{K-1} n_i = M - n_K$.   □

Example 4.1.2 *Equivalent birth and death process for GI/M/1/∞ FIFO.* Let $H(x) = P_A^0(T_1 \le x)$ be the inter-arrival cumulative distribution function. From the classical theory of queues (see N.V. Prabhu, *Queues and Inventories*, Wiley, 1965, p. 43–44), we know that

$$(4.1.13) \quad \pi^0(i) = P^0(X(0-) = i) = \xi^i(1-\xi),$$

where ξ is the unique solution in $]0,1[$ of

$$(4.1.14) \quad \xi = \int_0^\infty e^{\mu t(\xi-1)} dH(t),$$

(recall that we are considering a system in equilibrium, and in particular $\rho = \lambda E_A^0[\sigma] < 1$). We shall now compute $\pi(i) = P(X(0) = i)$ using the extension of PASTA theorem and the relation $\pi_A^0(i) = \pi_D^0(i+1)$ (Formula (4.1.6)). Indeed, the $\mathcal{F}_t^X$-intensity of D is $\mu 1_{\{X(t)>0\}}$, and therefore

$$\pi_A^0(i) = \pi_D^0(i+1) = P_D^0[X(0-) = i+1] = E[\frac{\mu}{\lambda} 1_{X(0)>0} 1_{X(0)=i+1}].$$

That is to say

$$\pi_A^0(i) = \frac{1}{\rho}\pi(i+1), \quad (i \ge 1)$$

and therefore

$$(4.1.15) \quad \pi(i) = \rho\xi^{i-1}(1-\xi), \quad (i \ge 1)$$

and, as we already know from (1.2.7)

$$(4.1.16) \quad \pi(0) = 1 - \sum_{i=1}^\infty \pi(i) = 1 - \rho.$$

Finally, from the extended PASTA theorem, $\lambda \pi_A^0(i) = \hat{\lambda}_i \pi(i)$, so that

$$(4.1.17) \quad \begin{cases} \hat{\lambda}_0 = \lambda \dfrac{1-\xi}{1-\rho}, \\[2mm] \hat{\lambda}_i = \lambda \dfrac{\xi}{\rho} \quad (i \geq 1). \end{cases}$$

□

Remark 4.1.1 Observe that since $P_A^0(X(0-) > 0) = \xi$, the parameter ξ can be estimated by

$$(4.1.18) \quad \xi = \lim_{t \to \infty} \frac{1}{A(t)} \int_{(0,t]} 1_{X(s-)>0} A(ds).$$

□

Remark 4.1.2 From (4.1.15) we see that if $\xi = \rho$, then $\pi_A^0 \equiv \pi$. In this case, we have the ESTA property without the arrival process being Poisson.   □

4.2 Brill and Posner's Formula

Let $\{Z(t)\}$ be a corlol, real-valued stochastic process compatible with the flow $\{\theta_t\}$, and let N contain all the discontinuity points of $\{Z(t)\}$, in the sense that

$$N(C) \geq \sum_{s \in C} 1_{Z(s) \neq Z(s-)},$$

for all Borel sets C. Assume that N has a finite non-null intensity λ. Call $\{T_n\}$ the sequence of points of N and suppose that there exists a stochastic process $\{Z'(t)\}$ compatible with $\{\theta_t\}$ and such that for all $n \in \mathbb{Z}$,

$$(4.2.1) \quad Z(t) = Z(T_n) + \int_{T_n}^t Z'(s)ds, \quad t \in [T_n, T_{n+1}).$$

Let now $f : \mathbb{R} \to \mathbb{R}$ be a function such that for all $n \in \mathbb{Z}$

$$(4.2.2) \quad f(Z(t)) = f(Z(T_n)) + \int_{T_n}^t f'(Z(s))Z'(s)ds, \ t \in [T_n, T_{n+1}),$$

for some function $f' : \mathbb{R} \to \mathbb{R}$ which is to be interpreted as the derivative of f. Therefore, for all $t \geq 0$

$$(4.2.3) \quad \begin{aligned} f(Z(t)) = f(Z(0)) + \int_0^t f'(Z(s))Z'(s)ds \\ + \sum_{n \geq 1} \{f(Z(T_n)) - f(Z(T_n-))\} 1_{T_n \leq t} \ . \end{aligned}$$

We assume that

(4.2.4) $Z'(t) = g(Z(t))$,

for some function $g : \mathbb{R} \to \mathbb{R}$ satisfying, for all $a, b, \in \mathbb{R}_+$

(4.2.5) $\displaystyle\int_a^b \frac{1}{|g(y)|} dy < \infty.$

We also suppose that for some a and b

(4.2.6) $g(a) \neq 0, \; g(b) \neq 0$,

so that $\{Z(t)\}$ does not stick to the boundaries a and b. The function

(4.2.7) $\displaystyle f(x) = \int_a^b 1_{y<x} \frac{1}{g(y)} dy$

is well defined and in (4.2.3) we can take

$$f'(x) = 1_{[a,b]}(x) \frac{1}{g(x)} \; .$$

The evolution equation (4.2.3) then takes the special form

(4.2.8)
$$f(Z(t)) = f(Z(0)) + \int_0^t 1_{[a,b]}(Z(s))ds$$
$$+ \sum_{n\geq 1} \left\{ \int_a^b 1_{Z(T_n)>y} \frac{1}{g(y)} dy - \int_a^b 1_{Z(T_n-)>y} \frac{1}{g(y)} dy \right\} 1_{T_n \leq t} \; .$$

Taking expectations in (4.2.8) leads to

(4.2.9)
$$P(Z(0) \in [a,b]) =$$
$$- \frac{1}{t} E \left[\sum_{n\geq 1} \left\{ \int_a^b 1_{Z(T_n)>y} \frac{1}{g(y)} dy - \int_a^b 1_{Z(T_n-)>y} \frac{1}{g(y)} dy \right\} 1_{T_n \leq t} \right]$$

For each $y \in \mathbb{R}$, define the point processes D_y^+ and D_y^- by

(4.2.10)
$$\begin{cases} D_y^+(C) = \displaystyle\sum_{n\geq 1} 1_{Z(T_n-)\leq y, \; Z(T_n)>y} 1_{T_n \leq t}, \\ D_y^-(C) = \displaystyle\sum_{n\geq 1} 1_{Z(T_n-)>y, \; Z(T_n)\leq y} 1_{T_n \leq t} \; . \end{cases}$$

The point process D_y^+ counts the upcrossings of level y (from $\leq y$ to $> y$) by $\{Z(t)\}$ which are located at a discontinuity of $\{Z(t)\}$. A similar interpretation holds for D_y^-. Using (4.2.9), the observation that

$$\sum_{n\geq 1}\left\{\int_a^b 1_{Z(T_n)>y}\frac{1}{g(y)}dy - \int_a^b 1_{Z(T_n-)>y}\frac{1}{g(y)}dy\right\}1_{T_n\leq t}$$

$$= \int_a^b\left[\sum_{n\geq 1}\{1_{Z(T_n)>y} - 1_{Z(T_n-)>y}\}1_{T_n\leq t}\right]\frac{1}{g(y)}dy$$

$$= \int_a^b\{D_y^+((0,t]) - D_y^-((0,t])\}\frac{1}{g(y)}dy$$

implies

$$P(Z(0)\in[a,b]) = -\int_a^b(\lambda_y^+ - \lambda_y^-)\frac{1}{g(y)}dy,$$

where $\lambda_y^\pm$ is the intensity of $D_y^\pm$. In particular the P–distribution of $Z(0)$ admits the density

$$(4.2.11)\quad f_Z(y) = -(\lambda_y^+ - \lambda_y^-)\frac{1}{g(y)}\ .$$

From a simulation point of view, it is preferable to give the following ergodic form to the above identity, which of course requires the ergodicity of (P,θ_t) :

$$(4.2.12)\quad g(y)f_Z(y) = -\lim_{t\to\infty}\frac{1}{t}\sum_{n\geq 1}\{1_{Z(T_n)>y} - 1_{Z(T_n-)>y}\}1_{T_n\leq t}\ .$$

Example 4.2.1 *The workload level crossing formula.* If $Z(t) = W(t)$, where $W(t)$ is the load at time t of a single server queue, $g(y)\equiv -1$ and

$$\sum_{n\geq 1}\{1_{W(T_n)>y} - 1_{W(T_n-)>y}\}1_{T_n\leq t}$$

counts the number of upcrossings (from $\leq y$ to $> y$) at arrival instants or equivalently, the number of downcrossings of level y (from $> y$ to $\leq y$). Thus

$$(4.2.13)\quad f_W(y) = \lim_{t\uparrow\infty}\frac{1}{t}\sum_{s>0}1_{W(s-)=y}\,1_{(0,t]}(s)\ .$$

More generally, if g is strictly negative and if the jumps of $\{Z(t)\}$ are all upwards

$$(4.2.14)\quad g(y)f(y) = -\lim_{t\uparrow\infty}\frac{1}{t}\sum_{s>0}1_{Z(s-)=y}\,1_{(0,t]}(s)\ .$$

$\square$

Remark 4.2.1 Defining the Palm c.d.f.'s of $Z(T_n-)$ and $Z(T_n)$ respectively by $F_{0,Z}^-$ and $F_{0,Z}^+$, and the stationary c.d.f. of $Z(t)$ by F_Z , Equation (4.2.9) can be written

$$(4.2.15) \quad F_Z(b) - F_Z(a) = \lambda \int_a^b (F_{0,Z}^+(y) - F_{0,Z}^-(y)) \frac{1}{g(y)} dy .$$

$\square$

Example 4.2.2 If we apply (4.2.15) to the case when $Z(t) = W(t)$, the workload of a $GI/GI/1/\infty$ FIFO queue, we obtain

$$(4.2.16) \quad F_W(b) - F_W(a) = \lambda \int_a^b (F_{V_0}(y) - F_{\tilde{V}_0}(y)) dy ,$$

where F_W is the stationary c.d.f. of $W(t)$, F_{V_0} is the Palm c.d.f. of the sojourn time V_n and $F_{\tilde{V}_0}$ is the Palm c.d.f. of the waiting time $\tilde{V}_n$. $\square$

4.3 Takács' Formula and Queues with Vacations

System without Vacations. Let $\{W(t)\}$ be the workload process of a stationary $G/G/1/\infty$ stationary queue. The evolution equation of $X(t) = e^{iuW(t)}$ is

$$(4.3.1) \quad \begin{aligned} e^{iuW(t)} &= e^{iuW(0)} - iu \int_0^t e^{iuW(s)} 1_{W(s)>0} ds \\ &\quad + \sum_{n\in\mathbb{Z}} \{e^{iuW(T_n)} - e^{iuW(T_n-)}\} 1_{T_n \leq t}. \end{aligned}$$

Taking expectations, observing that in the stationary regime

$$E[e^{iuW(t)}] = E[e^{iuW(0)}]$$

and that

$$e^{iuW(s)} 1_{W(s)>0} = e^{iuW(s)} - 1_{X(s)=0},$$

we obtain

$$-iuE[e^{iuW(0)}] + iuP(X(0) = 0) + \lambda E_A^0[e^{iuW(0)} - e^{iuW(0-)}] = 0$$

Suppose that σ_n is independent of $W(T_n-)$ (this is the case in a $GI/GI/1/\infty$ queue). Then

$$(4.3.2) \quad \begin{aligned} E_A^0[e^{iuW(0)} - e^{iuW(0-)}] &= E_A^0[e^{iuW(0-)}(e^{iu\sigma_0} - 1)] \\ &= E_A^0[e^{iuW(0-)}](E_A^0[e^{iu\sigma_0}] - 1). \end{aligned}$$

In a $GI/GI/1/\infty$ queue, $E_A^0[e^{iu\sigma_0}] = E[e^{iu\sigma_0}]$, and therefore, taking into account $P(X(0) = 0) = 1 - \rho$

$$(4.3.3) \quad iuE[e^{iuW(0)}] = \lambda E_A^0[e^{iuW(0-)}](E[e^{iu\sigma_0}] - 1) + iu(1 - \rho).$$

This formula is due to Takačs. In the special case when the arrival process is Poissonian ($M/GI/1/\infty$), the PASTA property gives $E_A^0[e^{iuW(0-)}] = E[e^{iuW(0)}]$ and therefore

$$(4.3.4) \quad E[e^{iuW(0)}] = \frac{iu(1-\rho)}{iu - \lambda(\Psi_\sigma(u) - 1)} \,,$$

where $\Psi_\sigma(u)$ is the characteristic function of σ_0. This formula is referred to as Pollaczek–Khinchin's characteristic function formula

System with Multiple Vacations : Cooper's Formula. Let now $\{W(t)\}$ be the workload process of a $M/GI/1/\infty$ stationary queue with multiple server vacations : as soon as the queue becomes empty, the server takes a vacation. The sequence of vacation times $\{V_k\}$ is assumed i.i.d. and independent of the arrival process. It is supposed that if at the end of a vacation, the server finds the queue still empty, he takes another vacation ; and so on, as long as the queue remains empty.

Call N_V the point process counting the starting times t_k of vacations. The workload process verifies the evolution equation

$$(4.3.5) \quad W(t) = W(0) + \sum_{n\geq 1} \sigma_n 1_{T_n \leq t} + \sum_{k\geq 1} V_k 1_{t_k \leq t} - t \,.$$

If equilibrium is assumed, $E[W(t)] = E[W(0)]$, and therefore, denoting by λ_V the intensity of the vacation process N_V, we have

$$\rho t + \lambda_V t E[V_0] - t = 0,$$

which gives

$$(4.3.6) \quad \lambda_V = \frac{1-\rho}{E[V_0]} \,.$$

The evolution equation of $\{\exp(iu\,W(t))\}$ is

$$\exp(iu\,W(t)) = \exp(iu\,W(0)) + \sum_{n\geq 1} \exp(iu\,W(T_n-))(e^{iu\,\sigma_n} - 1)1_{T_n \leq t}$$

$$(4.3.7)$$
$$+ \sum_{k\geq 1} \exp(iu\,W(t_k-))(e^{iu\,V_k} - 1)1_{t_k \leq t} - iu \int_0^t e^{iu\,W(s)}1_{W(s)>0} ds \,.$$

Observing that $W(t_k-) = 0$ and that the Lebesgue measure of $\{t \mid W(t) = 0\}$ is a.s. null, we obtain the following formula after computations similar to those performed in the derivation of Takačs' formula, and when assuming the existence of a stationary state :

$$E[\exp(iu\,W(0))] = \frac{\lambda_V(\Psi_V(u) - 1)}{iu - \lambda(\Psi_\sigma(u) - 1)} \,,$$

where $\Psi_V(u)$ and $\Psi_\sigma(u)$ are the characteristic functions of V_0 and σ_0 respectively. Therefore, using the expression (4.3.6) for the intensity of vacation process

$$(4.3.8) \quad E[\exp(iu\,W(0))] = \frac{1-\rho}{iu - \lambda(\Psi_\sigma(u)-1)} \times \frac{\Psi_V(u)-1}{E[V_0]} \ .$$

Remark 4.3.1 Observing that

$$(4.3.9) \quad \frac{\Psi_V(u)-1}{E[V_0]} = \int_0^\infty e^{iux} \frac{1}{E[V_0]}(1 - F_V(x))dx,$$

where $F_V(x)$ is the c.d.f. of V_0, we see, from formulas (4.2.4a) and (4.2.4b) of Chapter 1, that the above expression is that of the characteristic function of the forward (or equivalently : of the backward) recurrence time of a stationary (delayed) renewal process corresponding to the c.d.f. F_V.   □

Remark 4.3.2 From expressions (4.3.8), (4.3.9) and the previous remark, and also observing that in the vacation system as well as in the original system, $W(T_n-) = \tilde{V}_n$ is the waiting time before service when a FIFO discipline is assumed, we find that, with obvious notations

$$(4.3.10) \quad \Psi_{\tilde{V}_0}(u)|_{FIFO,\ VAC} = \Psi_{\tilde{V}_0}(u)|_{FIFO,\ noVAC} \times \Psi_Y(u) \ ,$$

where Y is a random variable having the same distribution as the forward recurrence time of a stationary renewal process corresponding to the c.d.f. F_V. In words :
(4.3.11) *The waiting time of a $M/GI/1/\infty$ FIFO system with multiple independent vacations of c.d.f. F_V is distributed as the sum of two independent random variables X and Y, where*

- X *is distributed as the waiting time in the same $M/GI/1/\infty$ FIFO system without vacations;*
- Y *is distributed as the forward recurrence time of a stationary renewal process corresponding to the c.d.f. F_V.*

□

A General Case. Let us go back to the general situation described in Chapter 2, § 6.3, with the same notation. In the FIFO discipline, the waiting time of the customer arriving at time T_n is

$$(4.3.12) \quad W(T_n-) = W_1(T_n-) + F_n,$$

where F_n is defined by this relation; see also Figure 4.3.1.
　　Therefore

$$(4.3.13) \quad E\left[e^{iu\,W(T_n-)}\right] = E\left[e^{iu\,W_1(T_n-)} E[e^{iu\,F_n}|\mathcal{F}_{W_1}]\right],$$

where $\mathcal{F}_{W_1}$ is the σ–field generated by $\{W_1(t)\}$, $t \geq 0$. Observe that

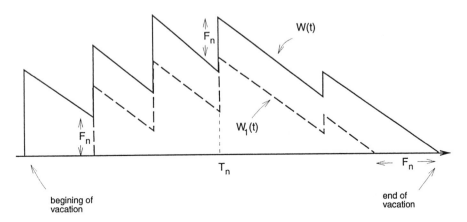

Fig. 4.3.1. A vacation queue

$$(4.3.14) \quad F_n = F\left(\int_0^{T_n} 1_{W(s)=0}ds\right) = F(U_n),$$

where $F(t)$ is the forward recurrence time at time t of the point process with time sequence $\{V_1 + \ldots + V_n\}$, $n \geq 1$. Call $\varphi_{F*}(u)$ the characteristic function of the stationary forward recurrence time, assumed to exist. In other words, we assume that

$$(4.3.15) \quad \lim_{t\uparrow\infty} E\left[e^{iu\, F(t)}\right] = \psi_{F*}(u),$$

for a characteristic function φ_{F*}. In view of the $\mathcal{F}_{W_1}$-measurability of U_n and of the independence of the $\mathcal{F}_{W_1}$ and $\{V_k\}$, $k \geq 1$, we have:

$$E\left[e^{iu\, W(T_n-)}\right] = E\left[e^{iu\, W_1(T_n-)}\psi_{F*}(u)\right]$$
$$+ E\left[e^{iu\, W_1(T_n-)}(\psi_F(u, U_n) - \psi_{F*}(u))\right],$$

where $\psi_F(u, t)$ is the characteristic function of $F(t)$. Therefore, by bounded convergence,

$$(4.3.16) \quad \lim_{t\uparrow\infty} E\left[e^{iu\, W(T_n-)}\right] = \lim_{t\uparrow\infty} E\left[e^{iu\, W_1(T_n-)}\right]\psi_{F*}(u),$$

provided $\lim_{t\uparrow\infty} E\left[e^{iu\, W_1(T_n-)}\right]$ exists. In other words, under the conditions

$$(4.3.17) \quad W_1(T_n-) \xrightarrow{D}_{n\uparrow\infty} X_1, \quad F(t) \xrightarrow{D}_{n\uparrow\infty} Y_1,$$

we have

(4.3.18) $\tilde{V}_n = W(T_{n^-}) \xrightarrow{D} X + Y,$

where X and Y are independent and are distributed as X_1 and Y_1 respectively. This clearly generalizes (4.3.11).

Remark 4.3.3 If we do not wish to make an assumption such as (4.3.17), we can instead consider the stationary system constructed in § 6.3 of Chapter 2, and obtain the relation

(4.3.19)
$$
\begin{aligned}
E\left[e^{iu\, W_1(0)} \mid W_1(0) > 0\right] (EV)^{-1} \frac{\phi_V(u) - 1}{iu} \\
= \quad E_A^0\left[e^{iu\, W(0-)}\right] (E\sigma)^{-1} \frac{\phi_\sigma(u) - 1}{iu}.
\end{aligned}
$$

This relation is obtained by first observing that

$$
E\left[e^{iu\, W(0)}\right] = E\left[e^{iu\, W_1(0)}\right] (EV)^{-1} \frac{\phi_V(u) - 1}{iu}
$$

(since $W(0) = W_1(0) + F(0)$), and then by taking expectation in (4.3.7), and using (4.3.6).   ☐

4.4 Backward and Forward Recurrence Times

Let N be a stationary simple point process with finite intensity $\lambda > 0$. Another way of obtaining the joint distribution of the stationary distribution of the backward and forward recurrence time at time 0, $B(0)$ and $F(0)$ respectively is the following:
Write the evolution equation

$$
e^{i(u\, B(t)+v\, F(t))} = e^{i(u\, B(0)+v\, F(0))} + (iu - iv) \int_0^t e^{i(u\, B(s)+v\, F(s))} ds
$$

$$
+ \sum_{n\in\mathbb{Z}} \left\{ e^{i(u\, B(T_n)+v\, F(T_n))} - e^{i(u\, B(T_{n^-})+v\, F(T_{n^-}))} \right\} 1_{[0,t]}(T_n) .
$$

Observing that $B(T_{n^-}) = T_n - T_{n-1}$, $B(T_n) = 0$, $F(T_{n^-}) = 0$, $F(T_n) = T_{n+1} - T_n$ and taking expectations, we obtain

$$
i(v - u)E\left[e^{i(u\, B(0)+v\, F(0))}\right] = \lambda \left\{ E_N^0\left[e^{iv\, T_1}\right] - E_N^0\left[e^{-iu\, T_{-1}}\right] \right\}.
$$

But T_1 and $-T_{-1}$ have the same distribution under P_N^0. Therefore

(4.4.1)
$$
\begin{aligned}
i(v - u)E\left[e^{i(u\, B(0)+v\, F(0))}\right] &= \lambda \left\{ E_N^0\left[e^{iv\, T_1}\right] - E_N^0\left[e^{iu\, T_1}\right] \right\} \\
&= \lambda \left\{ \Psi_{T_1}^0(v) - \Psi_{T_1}^0(u) \right\},
\end{aligned}
$$

with obvious notations. In particular, with $v = 0$

$$(4.4.2) \quad E\left[e^{iu\,B(0)}\right] = \frac{E_N^0\left[e^{iu\,T_1}\right]}{iu\,E_N^0[T_1]}\,.$$

5 Queueing Applications
of the Stochastic Intensity Integration Formula

5.1 Reminder

In this section, we shall demonstrate how the stochastic intensity integration formula can be useful in obtaining queueing relations. For instance, we shall provide a proof of Cobham's formulas in § 5.2.

First recall the notion of a $\mathcal{F}_t$-intensity kernel for a marked point process $(N, \{Z_n\})$. Defining $\{Z(t)\}$, $t \in \mathbb{R}$, by $Z(t) = \sum_{n\in\mathbb{Z}} Z_n 1_{[T_n, T_{n+1})}(t)$, it is assumed that $\{\mathcal{F}_t\}$ is a history of $(N, \{Z_n\})$ that is to say

$$\mathcal{F}_t \supset \mathcal{F}_t^N \vee \mathcal{F}_t^Z\,.$$

A stochastic $\mathcal{F}_t$-intensity kernel of $(N, \{Z_n\})$ is a function $\lambda : \mathbb{R} \times \Omega \times \mathcal{E} \longrightarrow \mathbb{R}_+$ (where $(E, \mathcal{E})$ is the measurable state space of $\{Z(t)\}$) such that

(a) $(t, \omega) \rightarrow \lambda(t, \omega, C)$ is $\mathcal{F}_t$- progressively measurable for all $C \in \mathcal{E}$,
(b) $C \rightarrow \lambda(t, \omega, C)$ is a measure on $(E, \mathcal{E})$ for all $(t, \omega) \in \mathbb{R} \times \Omega$,
(c) $\int_a^b \lambda(t, E)dt < \infty$, P-a.s for all $[a, b] \subset \mathbb{R}$,

and for all $C \in \mathcal{E}, \{\lambda(t, C)\}$ is a $\mathcal{F}_t$-intensity of N_C, where $N_C(A) = \sum_{n\in\mathbb{Z}} 1_A(T_n) 1_C(Z_n)$ (see Chapter 1, § 8, for the definition of stochastic intensity). Denoting

$$N(A \times C) = N_C(A),$$

the stochastic intensity integration formula states that

$$(5.1.1) \quad E\left[\int_{\mathbb{R}} \int_E H(t, z) N(dt \times dz)\right] = E\left[\int_{\mathbb{R}} \int_E H(t, z)\lambda(t, dz)dt\right],$$

for all non-negative functions $(t, \omega, z) \rightarrow H(t, \omega, z)$ from $\mathbb{R} \times \Omega \times E$ into $\mathbb{R}$ that are $\mathcal{P}(\mathcal{F}_t) \bigotimes \mathcal{E}$-measurable, where $\mathcal{P}(\mathcal{F}_t)$ is the $\mathcal{F}_t$-predictable σ-field on $\mathbb{R} \times \Omega$ (see Chapter 1, § 8). Recall that the left-hand side of (5.1.1) is by definition equal to $E[\sum_{n\in\mathbb{Z}} H(T_n, Z_n)]$.

Example 5.1.1 *Mean busy period in* $M/GI/1/\infty$. Let $\{(T_n, \sigma_n)\}, n \in \mathbb{N}$, be an M/GI input flow with $T_0 = 0$, and let $\{W(t)\}, t \in \mathbb{R}_+$, be the non-stationary workload process, with $W(0-) = 0$ and $W(0) = \sigma_0$. Let R_1 be the first strictly positive time at which the system is empty (∞ if the system never empties). Assuming that there is a unique server working at unit speed, we have, for any $K > 0$,

$$R_1 \wedge K \leq \sigma_0 + \sum_{k \geq 1} \sigma_k 1_{(0, R_1 \wedge K]}(T_k)$$

(5.1.2)

$$= \sigma_0 + \int_0^\infty \int_E \sigma 1_{(0, R_1 \wedge K]}(t) N(dt \times d\sigma).$$

Clearly R_1 is a $\mathcal{F}_t^A \vee \mathcal{F}_t^\sigma$-stopping time, where A is the arrival process (with associated arrival sequence $\{T_n\}$): indeed $\{R_1 \leq t\}$ only depends on the variables T_k, σ_k, where k is such that $T_k \leq t$. Therefore

$$H(t, \sigma) = 1_{(0, R_1 \wedge K]}(t)\sigma,$$

verifies the assumptions for (5.1.1) with respect to $\mathcal{F}_t = \mathcal{F}_t^A \vee \mathcal{F}_t^\sigma$. Since the $\mathcal{F}_t$-intensity kernel of $(A, \{\sigma_n\})$ is $\lambda G(dz)$ where λ is the intensity of A and G is the common c.d.f. of the service times, we obtain from (5.1.1) and (5.1.2)

(5.1.3)
$$E[R_1 \wedge K] \leq E[\sigma_0] + E\left[\int_0^\infty \int_E \sigma 1_{(0, R_1 \wedge K]}(t) \lambda G(d\sigma) dt\right]$$
$$= E[\sigma_0] + \lambda E[\sigma_0] E[R_1 \wedge K].$$

If $\lambda E[\sigma_0] < 1$

$$E[R_1 \wedge K] \leq \frac{E[\sigma_0]}{1 - \lambda E[\sigma_0]},$$

and therefore ER_1 is finite and given by

(5.1.4) $E[R_1] = \dfrac{E[\sigma_0]}{1 - \lambda E[\sigma_0]}$

(set $K = \infty$ in (5.1.2) and (5.1.3), with an equality instead of an inequality). Thus $\rho < 1$ is a sufficient condition for $E[R_1]$ to be finite in a $M/GI/1/\infty$ queue. It is also a necessary condition, in view of $E[R_1] = E[\sigma_0] + \rho E[R_1]$ and $E[\sigma_0] > 0$.   □

Although, the above proof does not teach us anything new, it shows how martingale calculus can be used. The next application contains a more elaborate usage of the stochastic intensity integration theorem.

5.2 Priorities in $M/GI/1/\infty$

The Non-Preemptive Case: Cobham's Formula. Cobham's formulas give the average waiting time of a customer of a given type in a $M/GI/1/\infty$ system with M priority classes. More precisely, we consider the situation of Example 1.1.2, with the additional feature that the M input flows corresponding to the M classes of priority are independent and of the M/GI

type. There is one server operating at unit speed, the service discipline is non-preemptive, FIFO for the customers of the same class, and priority is given to customers of class i over customers of class j if $i < j$. Equilibrium is assumed, and in particular

$$\rho = \sum_{i=1}^{M} \rho_i < 1 \ .$$

Recall the definition

$$\sigma_i(t) = \sigma_{i,n}, \quad \text{if } t \in [T_{i,n}, T_{i,n+1}) \ .$$

Define the history $\{\mathcal{F}_{i,t}\}$ by

$$(5.2.1) \quad \mathcal{F}_{i,t} = \mathcal{F}_t^{\sigma_i, A_i} \vee \Big(\bigvee_{\substack{k=1 \\ k \neq i}}^{M} \mathcal{F}_\infty^{\sigma_k, A_k} \Big).$$

Defining $N_i(A \times C) = \sum_{n \in \mathbb{Z}} 1_A(T_{i,n}) 1_C(\sigma_{i,n})$, then (see Example 8.2.3 of Chapter 1) the marked point process, $(A_i, \{\sigma_{i,n}\})$ admits the $\mathcal{F}_{i,t}$-intensity kernel $\lambda_i G_i(d\sigma)$, that is to say

$$E\Big[\int_{\mathbb{R}} \int_{\mathbb{R}_+} H(t, \sigma) N_i(dt \times d\sigma)\Big] = E\Big[\int_{\mathbb{R}} \int_{\mathbb{R}_+} H(t, \sigma) \lambda_i G_i(d\sigma) dt\Big],$$

for all non-negative functions $H : \mathbb{R} \times \Omega \times \mathbb{R}_+ \to \mathbb{R}$ that is $\mathcal{P}(\mathcal{F}_{i,t}) \otimes \mathcal{B}(\mathbb{R}_+)$-measurable.

Define the virtual i-customer at time t as follows: it is a customer arriving at time t with the required service

$$\hat{\sigma}_i(t) = \sigma_{i,n+1} \quad \text{if } t \in (T_{i,n}, T_{i,n+1}].$$

Thus, if $t = T_{i,n}, \hat{\sigma}_i(T_{i,n}) = \sigma_{i,n}$.

Call $\tilde{V}_i(t)$ the waiting time of the virtual i-customer at time t (all priority rules being respected), $C_i(t)$ the time required to clear all customers of class $1, 2, ..., i$ present in the waiting room (therefore excluding the customer presently served) at time t and $D_i(t)$ the additional delay incurred by the virtual i-customer due to those customers of class $1, ..., i-1$, arriving during the time interval $(t, t + \tilde{V}_i(t)]$ (such customers with higher priority than i arrive in the system whereas the virtual i-customer at time t is still waiting, and pass in front of him in the line). Accounting gives

$$(5.2.2) \quad \tilde{V}_i(t) = R(t) + C_i(t) + D_i(t),$$

where $R(t)$ is the residual service at time t. The residual service time formula (2.2.9) gives

$$(5.2.3) \quad E[R(0)] = \frac{1}{2} \lambda E[\sigma_0^2].$$

The clearing time $C_i(t)$ has the following expression

$$C_i(t) = \sum_{l=1}^{i} \sum_{n \in \mathbb{Z}} \sigma_{l,n} 1_{(t,\infty)}(T_{l,n} + \tilde{V}_{l,n}) 1_{(-\infty,t]}(T_{l,n}),$$

where $\tilde{V}_{i,n}$ is the waiting time of the customer of type i arriving at time $T_{i,n}$. Taking expectation and observing that $\sigma_{l,n}$ is independent of $T_{l,n}$ and $\tilde{V}_{l,n}$, and also that

$$\sum_{n \in \mathbb{Z}} 1_{(t,\infty)}(T_{l,n} + \tilde{V}_{l,n}) 1_{(-\infty,t]}(T_{l,n}) = Q_l(t),$$

the number of type l customers in the waiting room, we obtain

(5.2.4) $E[C_i(t)] = \displaystyle\sum_{l=1}^{i} E[\sigma_l] E[Q_l(t)].$

The additional delay $D_i(t)$ has the following expression

$$D_i(t) = \sum_{l=1}^{i-1} \int_{\mathbb{R}} \int_{\mathbb{R}_+} \sigma 1_{(t,t+\tilde{V}_i(t)]}(u) N_l(du \times d\sigma).$$

Now, the process $\{1_{(t,t+\tilde{V}_i(t)]}(u), u \in \mathbb{R}\}$ is adapted to $\{\mathcal{F}_{i,u}\}$ (in order to check whether $u \in (t, t + \tilde{V}_i(t)]$ or not, it suffices to observe $\mathcal{F}_{i,u}$) and left-continuous. Therefore, from the above expression of $D_i(t)$ and the stochastic intensity integration formula,

(5.2.5)
$$E[D_i(t)] = \sum_{l=1}^{i-1} E\left[\int_{\mathbb{R}} \int_{\mathbb{R}_+} \sigma 1_{(t,t+\tilde{V}_i(t)]}(u) \lambda_l G_l(d\sigma) du \right]$$
$$= \left(\sum_{l=1}^{i-1} \rho_l \right) E[\tilde{V}_i(t)].$$

Little's formula and the PASTA property (see the remark after the proof) give

(5.2.6) $E[Q_l(t)] = \lambda_l E[\tilde{V}_l(t)].$

Combining equations (5.2.2) to (5.2.6), we obtain Cobham's formula (non-preemptive case):

(5.2.7) $E[\tilde{V}_i(t)] = \dfrac{\frac{1}{2} \lambda E[\sigma_0^2]}{\left(1 - \sum_{l=1}^{i-1} \rho_l\right)\left(1 - \sum_{l=1}^{i} \rho_l\right)}.$

From the PASTA property, we obtain as above

(5.2.8) $E[\tilde{V}_i(t)] = E_{A_i}^0[\tilde{V}_{i,0}].$

Recall that (see Chapter 1, § 5.2)

(5.2.9) $E^0_{A_i}[\tilde{V}_{i,0}] = E^0_A[\tilde{V}_0 \mid$ customer arriving at $T_0 = 0$ is of type $i]$,

where $\tilde{V}_n$ is the waiting time of a customer arriving at time T_n.   □

Remark 5.2.1 In order to show that $E[\tilde{V}_l(0)] = E^0_{A_l}[\tilde{V}_{l,0}]$, using the PASTA property, some care must be exercised. Indeed A_l is a $\mathcal{F}_{l,t}$-Poisson process with intensity λ_l and $\tilde{V}_{l,0} = \tilde{V}_l(T_{l,0}) = \tilde{V}_l(0)\ P^0_{A_l}$-a.s. . However $\{\tilde{V}_l(t)\}$ is not a $\mathcal{F}_{l,t}$-predictable process, when $\mathcal{F}_{l,t}$ is defined by (5.2.1). This problem is easily circumvented by introducing the σ-field

$$\mathcal{G}_{l,t} = \mathcal{F}_{l,t} \vee \mathcal{F}^{\sigma_l}_\infty$$

(we add to $\mathcal{F}_{l,t}$ the future of the service process). The point process is a $\mathcal{G}_{l,t}$-Poisson process of intensity λ_l, and this time $\{\tilde{V}_l(t)\}$ is a left-continuous process adapted to $\mathcal{G}_{l,t}$, and therefore $\mathcal{G}_{l,t}$-predictable.   □

Example 5.2.1 $M/GI/1/\infty$ *SPT non-preemptive.* In this discipline the customer with smallest required service (Smallest Processing Time) has non-preemptive priority over the others. Calling $G(x)$ the c.d.f. of the required service time, we have

(5.2.10)
$$E^0_A\left[\tilde{V}_0 \mid \sigma_0 \in (x-h, x]\right] = \frac{\frac{1}{2}\lambda E[\sigma^2_0]}{\left(1 - \lambda \int_{(0,x-h]} y dG(y)\right)\left(1 - \lambda \int_{(x-h,x]} y dG(y)\right)}.$$

Proof: Consider 3 priority classes: in class 1, put all customers with required service less than or equal to $x - h$, in class 2 those with required service in $(x - h, x]$, and in class 3 the rest of the customers. Thus (ignoring class 3)

$$\rho_1 = \lambda \int_{(0,x-h]} y dG(y), \quad \rho_2 = \lambda \int_{(x-h,x]} y dG(y).$$

Applying (5.2.7)–(5.2.9), we obtain (5.2.10). In the case when x is not a discontinuity point of $G(x)$, letting h go to 0 in (5.2.10), we obtain

(5.2.11) $E^0_A[\tilde{V}_0 \mid \sigma_0 = x] = \dfrac{\frac{1}{2}\lambda E[\sigma^2_0]}{(1 - \lambda \int_{(0,x]} y dG(y))^2}.$

□

The Preemptive Case: Phipps' Formula. In the preemptive case, the virtual sojourn time of a customer of class i arriving at time t is

(5.2.12) $V_i(t) = F_i(t) + G_i(t),$

where $F_i(t)$ is the time between t and the first time the customer receives attention from the server, and $G_i(t)$ is the sum of the service $\tilde{\sigma}_i(t)$ and of the service of all customers of class $1, .., i - 1$ arriving in the system in the interval $(t + F_i(t), t + F_i(t) + G_i(t)]$. Clearly in the computation of $E[F_i(t)]$, the customers of class $i + 1, ..., K$ do not play a role, and therefore $E[F_i(t)]$ is the average waiting time of a class i virtual customer arriving at time t in a system with only customers of type $1, ..., i$, in the non-preemptive case

(5.2.13) $E[F_i(t)] = \dfrac{\frac{1}{2} \sum_{k=1}^{i} \lambda_k E[\sigma_k^2]}{\left(1 - \sum_{k=1}^{i-1} \rho_k\right)\left(1 - \sum_{k=1}^{i} \rho_k\right)}.$

The term $G_i(t)$ can be expressed as

$$G_i(t) = \tilde{\sigma}_i(t) + \sum_{k=1}^{i-1} \int_{\mathbb{R} \times \mathbb{R}_+} \int \sigma 1_{(t+F_i(t), t+F_i(t)+G_i(t)]}(u) N_k(du \times d\sigma)$$

and arguing as in the non-preemptive case, we obtain

$$E[G_i(t)] = E[\tilde{\sigma}_i(t)] + \sum_{k=1}^{i-1} \lambda_k E[\sigma_k] E[G_i(t)].$$

Therefore, observing that $E[\tilde{\sigma}_i(t)] = E[\sigma_i]$ (PASTA), we obtain

(5.2.14) $E[G_i(t)] = \dfrac{E[\sigma_i]}{1 - \sum_{k=1}^{i-1} \rho_k}.$

Combining (5.2.12)-(5.2.14), we obtain

(5.2.15) $E[V_i(t)] = \dfrac{\frac{1}{2} \sum_{k=1}^{i} \lambda_k E[\sigma_k^2]}{\left(1 - \sum_{k=1}^{i-1} \rho_k\right)\left(1 - \sum_{k=1}^{i} \rho_k\right)} + \dfrac{E[\sigma_i]}{1 - \sum_{k=1}^{i-1} \rho_k}.$

Here also, in view of PASTA

(5.2.16)
$E[V_i(t)] = E^0_{A_i}[V_{i,0}]$
$\qquad = E^0_A[V_0 \mid \text{the customer arriving at } T_0 = 0 \text{ is of type } i],$

where $V_{i,n}$ is the sojourn time of the customer of type i arriving at time $T_{i,n}$ and V_n is the sojourn time of the customer (of any type) arriving at time T_n.   □

Application: the c/ρ Rule. Consider the $M/GI/1/\infty$ system with M priority classes with non-preemptive priority as described at the beginning of the present subsection. For simplicity, denote $E[\tilde{V}_i(0)]$ by $\tilde{V}_i$. Our objective is to minimize the functional

$$(5.2.17) \quad C = \sum_{i=1}^{M} c_i \tilde{V}_i,$$

where $c_i > 0$, among all possible rankings (in terms of priority) of the M classes. We will show that the classes should be ranked according to the value of c/ρ, that is non-preemptive priority is given to class i over class j if and only if $\frac{c_i}{\rho_i} > \frac{c_j}{\rho_j}$ (in the case of equality $\frac{c_i}{\rho_i} = \frac{c_j}{\rho_j}$, give highest priority to i or j indifferently).

To prove this result, compare two rankings A and B differing only in two adjacent classes. More precisely, suppose (for convenience) that ranking A corresponds to

$$1 \gg 2 \gg ... \gg M,$$

where $i \gg j$ means that class i has (non-preemptive) priority over class j, and suppose that ranking B exchanges classes i and $i + 1$

$$1 \gg 2 \gg ... \gg i - 1 \gg i + 1 \gg i \gg i + 2 \gg ... \gg M.$$

Call $\tilde{V}_j^A$ and $\tilde{V}_j^B$ the average waiting time for a customer of class j under the rankings A and B respectively. Also denote

$$C^A = \sum_{j=1}^{M} c_j \tilde{V}_j^A, \quad C^B = \sum_{j=1}^{M} c_j \tilde{V}_j^B.$$

From the expression (5.2.7), we see that $\tilde{V}_k^A = \tilde{V}_k^B$, for all k, $1 \le k \le M$, $k \ne i$, $k \ne i + 1$, so that

$$(5.2.18) \quad C^A - C^B = c_i(\tilde{V}_i^A - \tilde{V}_i^B) + c_{i+1}(\tilde{V}_{i+1}^A - \tilde{V}_{i+1}^B).$$

Kleinrock's conservation law (§ 2.3) gives

$$\sum_{j=1}^{M} \rho_j \tilde{V}_j^A = \sum_{j=1}^{M} \rho_j \tilde{V}_j^B,$$

that is, in view of the previous remark

$$(5.2.19) \quad \rho_i(\tilde{V}_i^A - \tilde{V}_i^B) = -\rho_{i+1}(\tilde{V}_{i+1}^A - \tilde{V}_{i+1}^B).$$

From (5.2.18) and (5.2.19), we obtain

$$(5.2.20) \quad C^A - C^B = \rho_i(\tilde{V}_i^A - \tilde{V}_i^B)\left(\frac{c_i}{\rho_i} - \frac{c_{i+1}}{\rho_{i+1}}\right).$$

Now $\tilde{V}_i^A - \tilde{V}_i^B < 0$ (think, or use Formula (5.2.7)) and therefore $C^A - C^B < 0$ if and only in $\frac{c_i}{\rho_i} > \frac{c_{i+1}}{\rho_{i+1}}$.

This proves the result since, for any ranking not satisfying the $\frac{c}{\rho}$ condition, we can find two adjacent classes i and $i+1$ violating the condition, and exchanging these two classes would give a better ranking.

Example 5.2.2 *The μc rule.* Suppose we wish to minimize

$$(5.2.21) \quad C = \sum_{i=1}^{M} c_i Q_i,$$

where $Q_i = E[Q_i(t)]$, the average number of customers of class i in the waiting room at time t. From Little's formula

$$C = \sum_{i=1}^{M} c_i \lambda_i \tilde{V}_i$$

and therefore, from the previous results, we see that priority should be given to class i over class j if $\mu_i c_i > \mu_j c_j$. $\qquad \square$

Example 5.2.3 *Optimality of SPT non-preemptive.* Consider a $M/GI/1/\infty$ queueing system. Then among all the non-preemptive service disciplines based on the required service time, SPT non-preemptive minimizes the average number of customers in the system. This result follows from the μc rule of Example 5.2.2 which $c_i \equiv 1$ (minimizing the average number of customers $E[Q(t)]$ in the waiting room is same as minimizing the average number $E[X(t)]$ of customers in the system, when there is one server). Thus in Example 5.2.2, in order to minimize $E[Q(t)]$, we must give highest priority to the class with smallest average service time. A limiting argument (with class i formed of those customers with required service between ih and $(i+1)h$) gives the optimality of SPT non-preemptive. $\qquad \square$

Bibliographical Comments

Little's formula (1.2.3), or (1.2.4), seems to have been well known by practitioners before a proof appeared in Little [86]. A number of proofs with varying degrees of generality and rigor followed this article, the history of which is recorded in the review article [133]. The proof given in § 1.2 follows the general ideas expressed in [47], were the reader will find abundant historical comments. The derivation of the response time for $M/GI/1/\infty$ PS in Example 1.2.5 is borrowed from Wolff [136] which contains many other examples of this type. Formula (1.2.18) of Example 1.2.4 is sometimes proved by a statement like: "it follows from $L = \lambda W$ that ..." and this is why we presented it in the section devoted to Little's formula. The Swiss Army Formula

(1.3.15) was given in [28]; considering the obvious interpretation of Remark 1.3.1, and the numerous formulas that it generates, it is only surprising that it was not discovered earlier. The ordinal $L = \lambda W$ Formula (1.3.13) is due to Halfin and Whitt [51]. The insensitivity problem has a long history recorded in the monograph [47] (see also [115], [116], [117]). The theory of insensitivity by Palm calculus can be found in the paper of Jensen, König and Nawrotzki [59]; (see also the monograph [4]). The $H = \lambda G$ formula was discovered by Brumelle [32]. It is equivalent to the generalized Campbell's formula (Equation (3.3.1) of Chapter 1, due to Mecke [93], Satz 2-3 thereof). The light traffic analysis of Example 2.1.1 comes from [5]; more complete results using analytical methods are given in [108] (see also [18]). The treatment of the conservation formulas of § 2.2 and § 2.3 is inspired by Kalähne [62] and Chapter 11 of the book by Heyman and Sobel [55] (see also [33]). A fundamental article in the area of work conservation is that of Wolff [134]. For applications and references concerning the conservation formula (2.3.5), see Kleinrock [75]. As mentioned in [27], the ESTA results when there exists a stochastic intensity are implicit in the work of Papangelou [105]. An ESTA result not contained in Papangelou's work and containing PASTA as special case can be found in the article by König and Schmidt [76], which contains the first rigorous proof of PASTA in the general case. The proof of PASTA in the non-stationary case is an extension, in the martingale parlance, of the proof of Wolff [135]. As is now well known, the result of [135] is a consequence of the martingale strong law of large numbers, and in this respect, Theorem 8.3.22, p. 250, of Dacunha-Castelle and Duflo [36] gives all the details without mention of PASTA. For the job observer property of § 3 we refer for bibliographical comments and additional information to the book of Mitrani, [95]. More details and references concerning PASTA can be found in the review article [29]. The first order equivalence result of § 4 first appeared in the monograph [26] and was used in the proof of Norton's theorem by Lazar and Hsiao, [81]. For Norton's theorem of § 4, we refer to the monograph of Walrand [129], which contains additional details, bibliographical comments, and also a nice heuristic proof. The result of § 4.2 are those of Brill and Posner, [31]. The proof presented in the present monograph only slightly differs from that of Lazar and Ferrandiz [81]. The proof of Takács formula (4.3.4) using evolution equations comes from Brémaud and Jacod [25]. This proof was extended by Kella and Whitt [68] to cover the case with vacations. The basic decomposition (4.3.11) for the $M/GI/1/\infty$ queue with multiple vacations is due to Fuhrmann and Cooper [48]. A review of systems with vacations is given by Doshi [39], the general spirit of which inspires our treatment. In the non-preemptive case, the priority formulas of § 5 can be found in Cobham [35]. For the preemptive case, see the paper by Phipps, [106]. The proof presented in the present monograph is new. For applications, see [75] and [95].

4 Stochastic Ordering and Comparison of Queues

Introduction

Since many queueing systems are analytically untractable, one often has to resort to more qualitative properties such as the monotonicity of the waiting or sojourn times with respect to the service or inter-arrival times. This often leads to the derivation of bounds which may give useful information on the behavior of a system which cannot be exactly computed. Another application of stochastic comparison is optimal design, where one does not necessarily want to compute the performance of a particular system, but one only wishes to show that the system is the best, for some criteria, among a given class of systems. Such optimality results are collected in § 1.

A systematic approach to the comparison of queues goes through the study of stochastic ordering of random variables or of their cumulative distribution functions (c.d.f.). A stochastic order can first be seen as a partial order on a set of c.d.f., like for instance the integral orderings defined in § 2.1. The simplest example on $\mathbb{R}$ is the *increasing stochastic order* $\leq_i$ defined as follows: two c.d.f. F and G on $\mathbb{R}$ are such that $F \leq_i G$ if $1 - F(x) \leq 1 - G(x)$, for all x. Such stochastic orders often admit a simple pointwise representation; for instance, it is easy to see that that $F \leq_i G$ if and only if one can find two random variables A and B defined on a common probability space, with c.d.f. F and G respectively, and such that $A \leq B$ a.s. In that, we shall say that $\leq_i$ is the *pathwise* stochastic order associated with the partial order $\leq$ on $\mathbb{R}$,

As we shall see in § 2, there are several other types of stochastic orders which are useful in queueing theory, like for instance, the *convex stochastic order* $\leq_{icx}$, which admits the following pointwise representation: two integrable c.d.f. F and G on $\mathbb{R}^n$ are such that $F \leq_{icx} G$ if we can find random variables A and B defined on a common probability space $(\Omega, \mathcal{F}, P)$, with respective c.d.f. F and G, and such that $A \leq E[B|\mathcal{G}]$ a.s., for some sub σ-field $\mathcal{G}$ of $\mathcal{F}$. We will say that $\leq_{icx}$ is the *projection* stochastic order associated with the partial order $\leq$ on $\mathbb{R}^n$.

The following example illustrates how this projection stochastic order can be used to establish a general extremal property of $G/G/1/\infty$ queues, which finds its origin in a 'folk theorem' of queueing theory stating that determinism minimizes waiting or sojourn times in many queueing systems. For $M/GI/1/\infty$ systems for instance, whenever the traffic intensity is fixed, it follows from the Pollaczek-Khinchin mean value formula that deterministic service times minimize the mean stationary workload (see § 2.2, Chapter 3).

Consider two independent sequences of non-negative integrable random variables $\{\sigma_n\}$ and $\{\tau_n\}$, all defined on the same probability space $(\Omega, \mathcal{F}, P)$, and define

$$\xi_n = E[\sigma_n] - \tau_n$$

and

$$\widetilde{\xi}_n = \sigma_n - \tau_n.$$

Let $\mathcal{G}$ be the σ-field generated by the variables $\{\xi_n\}$ or, equivalently, by the random variables $\{\tau_n\}$. From the independence assumption, $E[\widetilde{\xi}_i|\mathcal{G}] = \xi_i$ a.s. for all $i = 0, 1, \ldots, n$, so that the c.d.f. of the vector $\xi = (\xi_1, \ldots, \xi_n)$ is less than that of the vector $\widetilde{\xi}$ in the projection stochastic order sense.

Let $\{W_n\}$ and $\{\widetilde{W}_n\}$, $n \geq 0$ be the associated workload sequences, that is, the non-negative random variables defined by

$$W_{n+1} = [W_n + \xi_n]^+$$

and

$$\widetilde{W}_{n+1} = [\widetilde{W}_n + \widetilde{\xi}_n]^+,$$

with $W_0 = \widetilde{W}_0 = 0$.

The stochastic order relation between ξ and $\widetilde{\xi}$ is inherited by the workload sequence in that

$$W_n \leq E[\widetilde{W}_n \mid \mathcal{G}] \quad \text{a.s.},$$

for all n. The proof proceeds by induction. The property trivially holds for $n = 0$, since $W_0 = \widetilde{W}_0 = 0$. Assuming that it holds true for some $n \geq 0$, Jensen's inequality implies

$$E[\widetilde{W}_{n+1} \mid \mathcal{G}] \geq \left[E[\widetilde{W}_n \mid \mathcal{G}] + E[\widetilde{\xi}_n \mid \mathcal{G}] \right]^+,$$

since the function $x \to x^+$ is convex. The observation $E[\widetilde{\xi}_n|\mathcal{G}] = \xi_n$ and the induction assumption lead to

$$E[\widetilde{W}_{n+1} \mid \mathcal{G}] \geq \left[W_n + \xi_n \right]^+ = W_{n+1}, \quad \text{a.s.},$$

which completes the proof.

Therefore, the relation $E[f(W_n)] \leq E[f(\widetilde{W}_n)]$ holds, for all convex functions f, and this can be seens as a generalization of the extremal property which was mentioned above. It is now seen to be true for general arrival and service processes, provided they are independent.

1 Comparison of Service Disciplines

1.1 Partial Orderings on $\mathbb{R}^n$

Let $\mathcal{R}$ be binary relation on a set S, such that
(a) $x\mathcal{R}x$, for all $x \in S$ (reflexivity);
(b) $x\mathcal{R}y$ and $y\mathcal{R}z$ imply $x\mathcal{R}z$ (transitivity);
Then S is called a *partial semi-ordering* on S. If moreover
(c) $x\mathcal{R}y$ and $y\mathcal{R}x$ imply $x = y$ (antisymmetry),
then $\mathcal{R}$ is called a *partial ordering* on S.

In general, for arbitrary x and y, $x\mathcal{R}y$ and/or $y\mathcal{R}x$ need not be verified, and this is the meaning of the qualification 'partial'. When either $x\mathcal{R}y$ or $y\mathcal{R}x$ hold for any pair (x, y) of elements of S, one then talks about semi-ordering or ordering depending on whether just (a) and (b), or (a)-(c) are true.

For $S = \mathbb{R}^n$, the *coordinatewise* partial ordering, denoted $\leq$, is defined by

(1.1.1) $x \leq y$ if and only if $x_1 \leq y_1, \ldots, x_n \leq y_n$.

On $S = \mathbb{R}^n$, the *majorization* partial semi-ordering, denoted $\prec$, is defined by $x \prec y$ if

$$
\begin{aligned}
\sum_{k=l}^{n} x_{\gamma(k)} &\leq \sum_{k=l}^{n} y_{\beta(k)}, \quad l = 2, \ldots, n, \\
\sum_{k=1}^{n} x_{\gamma(k)} &= \sum_{k=1}^{n} y_{\beta(k)},
\end{aligned}
$$

(1.1.2)

where γ and β are permutations of the indices $1, \ldots, n$ that reorder x and y respectively, that is

$$x_{\gamma(1)} \leq x_{\gamma(2)} \leq \cdots \leq x_{\gamma(n)}, \quad y_{\beta(1)} \leq y_{\beta(2)} \leq \cdots \leq y_{\beta(n)}.$$

Remark 1.1.1 Equation (1.1.2) holds true for all permutations γ, provided β is a permutation which reorders y.   □

Remark 1.1.2 The majorization partial ordering has a simple interpretation in economics: assume that a given amount of money has to be distributed among n individuals and let $x_1, \ldots, x_n$ and $y_1, \ldots, y_n$ be two such repartitions with $\sum_{i=1}^{n} x_i = \sum_{i=1}^{n} y_i$. The property $x \prec y$ means that the richest individual is richer in y than in x, that the two richest are richer in y than in x and so on, although the total wealth is the same. In other words, the repartition x is more 'socialistic' than y.   □

A function $f : \mathbb{R}^n \to \mathbb{R}^m$ is said to be $\leq$ (resp. $\prec$)-non-decreasing if $x \leq y$ coordinatewise (resp. $x \prec y$) in $\mathbb{R}^n$ implies $f(x) \leq f(y)$ coordinatewise in $\mathbb{R}^m$. A similar definition is adopted for non-increasing functions.

A $\prec$-non-decreasing (resp. non-increasing) function is also called *Schur-convex* (resp. *Schur-concave*).

Example 1.1.1 The functions $f(x) = \sum x_i$ or $f(x) = \max x_i$ are Schur-convex functions. More generally, for all $1 \leq k \leq n$, the function

$$\max_{1 \leq i_1, \ldots, i_k \leq n} \sum_{l=1}^{k} x_{i_l}$$

is Schur-convex (use Remark 1.1.1). □

Equivalent definitions of the majorization partial order are given below. Let Γ be the collection of permutations of $\{1, \ldots, n\}$, and for $\gamma \in \Gamma$, $z \in \mathbb{R}^n$, denote $z_\gamma = (z_{\gamma(1)}, \ldots, z_{\gamma(n)})$. Also call $\phi : \mathbb{R}^n \to \mathbb{R}$ symmetric if $\phi(x) = \phi(x_\gamma)$ for all $\gamma \in \Gamma$ and all $x \in \mathbb{R}^n$.

(1.1.3) *The following properties are equivalent*
    (a) $x \prec y$;
    (b) x *lies in the convex hull of the set* $\{y_\gamma, \ \gamma \in \Gamma\}$;
    (c) $\phi(x) \leq \phi(y)$ *for all convex symmetric functions* ϕ.

Proof: $(a) \Rightarrow (b)$. The point x lies in the convex hull $\mathcal{C}$ of the points $\{y_\gamma, \ \gamma \in \Gamma\}$ if and only if

$$\sum_{i=1}^{n} c_i x_i \leq \sup_{z \in \mathcal{C}} \sum_{i=1}^{n} c_i z_i, \quad \forall c \in \mathbb{R}^n,$$

or equivalently if

$$(1.1.4) \quad \sum_{i=1}^{n} c_i x_i \leq \max_{\gamma \in \Gamma} \sum_{i=1}^{n} c_i y_{\gamma(i)}, \quad \forall c \in \mathbb{R}^n.$$

Without loss of generality, take y such that $y_1 \leq \cdots \leq y_n$. Let β be a permutation of Γ such that $c_{\beta(1)} \leq \cdots \leq c_{\beta(n)}$. The maximum in the right-hand side of (1.1.4) is reached for $\gamma = \beta^{-1}$ (see the proof of (3.3.7), Chapter 2). From Remark (1.1.1), we obtain that for all $\alpha \in \Gamma$,

$$(1.1.5) \quad \sum_{i=1}^{n} x_{\alpha(i)} = \sum_{i=1}^{n} y_i$$

and that for all $l = 2, \ldots, n$ and $\alpha \in \Gamma$,

$$(1.1.6) \quad \sum_{i=l}^{n} x_{\alpha(i)} \leq \sum_{i=l}^{n} y_i.$$

Multiplying (1.1.5) (resp. the l-th inequality of (1.1.6)) by $c_{\beta(1)}$ (resp. $c_{\beta(l)} - c_{\beta(l-1)} \geq 0$) and summing up the n resulting inequalities, we obtain that for all $\alpha \in \Gamma$,

$$\sum_{i=1}^{n} c_{\beta(i)} x_{\alpha(i)} \leq \sum_{i=1}^{n} c_{\beta(i)} y_i = \max_{\gamma \in \Gamma} \sum_{i=1}^{n} c_i y_{\gamma(i)}.$$

Taking $\alpha = \beta$ in the last relation allows us to conclude the proof.
$(b) \Rightarrow (c)$. If x lies in the convex hull of $\{y_\gamma, \ \gamma \in \Gamma\}$, then

$$x = \sum_{\gamma \in \Gamma} p_\gamma y_\gamma,$$

where the real numbers p_γ are non-negative and sum up to one. If ϕ is symmetric and convex, we then have

$$\phi(y) = \sum_{\gamma \in \Gamma} p_\gamma \phi(y_\gamma) \geq \phi\left(\sum_{\gamma \in \Gamma} p_\gamma y_\gamma\right) = \phi(x).$$

$(c) \Rightarrow (a)$. It suffices to observe that the functions

$$\max_{1 \leq i \leq n} x_i, \quad \max_{1 \leq i, j \leq n} x_i + x_j, \quad \cdots, \quad \max_{1 \leq i_1, \ldots, i_{n-1} \leq n} \sum_{k=1}^{n-1} x_{i_k}, \quad \sum_{i=1,\ldots,n} x_i$$

are all symmetric and convex. □

1.2 Optimality of the SRPT Discipline in $G/G/1/\infty$

In § 4.2 of Chapter 2, we constructed a state representation which features the most common service disciplines including FIFO, LIFO and SRPT. We now show how elementary sample path arguments can be used in order to compare these disciplines using the partial orderings introduced above. The notations and definitions of this section are those of § 6.2, Chapter 2.

$(1.2.1)$ *If ψ denotes the SRPT discipline, then for any other admissible discipline ϕ, $S_\phi \prec S_\psi$, P^0 a.s.*

Remark 1.2.1 We only defined majorization for finite dimensional vectors. The property $S_\phi \prec S_\psi$ should be understood as the comparison of two vectors of dimension J, where J is the smallest integer such that $S_\psi^i = S_\phi^i = 0$, for all $i > J$. □

Proof of (1.2.1) We want to prove that the event $\{S_\phi \prec S_\psi\}$ is of probability one. For this, it is enough to prove that this event is $\theta-$contracting, since on $\{W = 0\}$, $0 = S_\phi \prec S_\psi = 0$ and $P^0(W = 0) > 0$.

Let $\widetilde{S}$ be a reordering of $S \in \mathbb{R}^{\mathbb{N}}$ in decreasing order, i.e. $\widetilde{S}^1 \geq \widetilde{S}^2 \geq \cdots$. Observe that $\widetilde{S}_\psi = S_\psi$ by definition of ψ=SRPT. On the event $\{\widetilde{S}_\phi \prec \widetilde{S}_\psi\}$, by definition of $\prec$,

$$(1.2.2) \quad \sum_{i=k}^{\infty} \widetilde{S}_\phi^i \geq \sum_{i=k}^{\infty} \widetilde{S}_\psi^i = \sum_{i=k}^{\infty} S_\psi^i,$$

for all $k > 1$, and

$$(1.2.3) \quad \sum_{i=1}^{\infty} \widetilde{S}_{\phi}^{i} = \sum_{i=1}^{\infty} \widetilde{S}_{\psi}^{i}.$$

From Equation (6.2.8), Chapter 2, for all $k \geq 1$, and all disciplines ϕ,

$$\sum_{i=k}^{\infty} S_{\phi}^{i} \circ \theta = \Big(\sum_{i=k}^{\infty} (S_{\phi}^{+})^{i} - \tau \Big)^{+},$$

where

$$S_{\phi}^{+} = \phi(S_{\phi} + \sigma e_{I+1}).$$

From the definition of the SRPT discipline ψ, we obtain from the last two relations that for all $k > 1$

$$\sum_{i=k}^{\infty} \widetilde{S}_{\psi}^{i} \circ \theta = \Big(\sum_{i=k}^{\infty} \widetilde{S}_{\psi}^{i} + \sigma - \tau \Big)^{+} \wedge \Big(\sum_{i=k-1}^{\infty} \widetilde{S}_{\psi}^{i} - \tau \Big)^{+},$$

whereas for ϕ,

$$\sum_{i=k}^{\infty} \widetilde{S}_{\phi}^{i} \circ \theta \geq \Big(\sum_{i=k}^{\infty} \widetilde{S}_{\phi}^{i} + \sigma - \tau \Big)^{+} \wedge \Big(\sum_{i=k-1}^{\infty} \widetilde{S}_{\phi}^{i} - \tau \Big)^{+}.$$

When using this together with (1.2.2), we obtain that $\sum_{i=k}^{\infty} \widetilde{S}_{\phi}^{i} \circ \theta \geq \sum_{i=k}^{\infty} \widetilde{S}_{\phi}^{i} \circ \theta$. For $k = 1$, we have

$$\sum_{i=1}^{\infty} S_{\phi}^{i} \circ \theta = \sum_{i=1}^{\infty} S_{\psi}^{i} \circ \theta = W \circ \theta.$$

Therefore $\{S_{\phi} \prec S_{\psi}\} \subset \{S_{\phi} \circ \theta \prec S_{\psi} \circ \theta\}$.   □

Since $\{S_{\phi,n} \prec S_{\psi,n}, \ n \in \mathbb{Z}\} \equiv \{S_{\phi}(t) \prec S_{\psi}(t), \ t \in \mathbb{R}\}$, another application of the invariance results of § 7.2, Chapter 1, implies the following result, in view of (1.2.1):

(1.2.4) *If ψ is the SRPT discipline and ϕ is any other admissible discipline*

$$S_{\phi}(t) \prec S_{\psi}(t), \quad t \in \mathbb{R}, \quad P\text{--a.s.}$$

In particular let $\{X_{\phi}(t), t \in \mathbb{R}\}$ be the process counting the number of customers present in the system at time t under discipline ϕ. Since for all $k \geq 1$

$$\sum_{i=k}^{\infty} S_{\psi}(t) \leq \sum_{i=k}^{\infty} S_{\phi}(t),$$

we see that $I_{\psi} \leq I_{\phi}$. Since $I_{\phi} = X_{\phi}$

(1.2.5) $X_\psi(t) \leq X_\phi(t), \quad t \in \mathbb{R}, \quad P-\text{a.s.}.$

A direct application of Little's formula shows that

(1.2.6) $E^0[V_\psi] \leq E^0[V_\phi],$

for all admissible disciplines ϕ, where V_ϕ denotes the stationary sojourn time under discipline ϕ.

These optimality results should be stated together with their counterpart that for all Schur-convex functions f,

(1.2.7) $E^0[f(S_\psi)] \geq E^0[f(S_\phi)].$

For instance

(1.2.8) $E^0[\max_{i \geq 1} S_\psi^i] \geq E^0[\max_{i \geq 1} S_\phi^i].$

1.3 Optimality of the FIFO Discipline

Reordering of Vectors and Majorization. We start with two technical lemmas on majorization

(1.3.1) *Let $x_1 \leq x_2 \leq \cdots \leq x_n$ and $y_1 \leq y_2 \leq \cdots \leq y_n$ be real numbers. For any permutation γ on $(1, 2, \ldots, n)$, such that there exist some i, j, $1 \leq i < j \leq n$, with $\gamma(i) > \gamma(j)$, let γ' be the permutation of $(1, 2, \ldots, n)$ which is obtained from γ by interchanging the values of γ on i and j:*

$$\gamma'(i) = \gamma(j), \quad \gamma'(j) = \gamma(i), \quad \text{and} \quad \gamma'(k) = \gamma(k), \quad k \neq i, \quad k \neq j.$$

Then

(1.3.2) $(y_{\gamma'} - x) \prec (y_\gamma - x).$

Proof: Since $y_{\gamma(i)} - y_{\gamma(j)} \geq 0$ and $x_i - x_j \leq 0$, there exists a real number $0 \leq \epsilon \leq 1$ such that

$$\epsilon(y_{\gamma(i)} - y_{\gamma(j)}) + (1 - \epsilon)(x_i - x_j) = 0.$$

This relation can be rewritten under the two equivalent forms

$$y_{\gamma'(i)} - x_i = y_{\gamma(j)} - x_i = (1 - \epsilon)(y_{\gamma(j)} - x_j) + \epsilon(y_{\gamma(i)} - x_i)$$

and

$$y_{\gamma'(j)} - x_j = y_{\gamma(i)} - x_j = (1 - \epsilon)(y_{\gamma(i)} - x_i) + \epsilon(y_{\gamma(j)} - x_j),$$

which imply that $(y_{\gamma'} - x)$ lies in the convex hull of the points $\{(y_\gamma - x)_\nu, \nu \in \Gamma\}$. This in turn implies that $(y_{\gamma'} - x) \prec (y_\gamma - x)$ in view of (1.1.3). $\square$

As an immediate application of the preceding lemma, we obtain

(1.3.3) *Let* $x_1 \leq x_2 \leq \cdots \leq x_n$ *and* $y_1 \leq y_2 \leq \cdots \leq y_n$ *be real numbers. Then, for all* $\gamma \in \Gamma$

(1.3.4) $(y - x) \prec (y_\gamma - x) \prec (y_- - x),$

where y_- *is defined by* $y_- = (y_n, \ldots, y_1)$.

The Interchange Argument. Consider a $GI/GI/1/\infty$ queue with an admissible discipline ϕ, for which we use the same type of notations as in § 6.2, Chapter 2. In particular, $\{I_t\}$ denotes the corlol congestion process whereas

$$(S_{\phi,t}^{1-}, \ldots, S_{\phi,t}^{I_{t-}-}) \quad \text{and} \quad (S_{\phi,t}^{1+}, \ldots, S_{\phi,t}^{I_t+})$$

denote the non-zero part of the residual service time vector at time $t-$ and t respectively, when starting with an empty queue at $T_0- = 0$ (the first subscript ϕ will be omitted when possible).

We assume that ϕ is *non-preemptive* and uses *no information on the service times* (like for instance FIFO, LIFO or RANDOM), and we denote ψ the FIFO discipline. Let A denote the GI/GI input of the queue; we show below that there exists a point process A', equivalent in law to A, and such that $S_{\phi,t}(A) = S_{\psi,t}(A')$ for all t. The proof of this property (from this point to Lemma (1.3.10) below) may be skipped on the first reading.

Let V_σ be the characteristic function of σ_0 and let $\mathcal{G}_t$ be the σ-field

$$\mathcal{G}_t = \sigma\left(A(u),\ u \geq 0\right) \bigvee \sigma\left(S_{\phi,u}^{I_u+},\ 0 \leq u \leq t\right).$$

In words, this is the σ-field generated by the arrival process and by the history of the residual service times of the customers who started their service before time t. The key property of non-preemptive policies using no information on service times, which we will need below, is that conditionally on $\mathcal{G}_{T_n}$, the required service times of the 'fresh' customers (those who have not yet started their service) are i.i.d. and with the same c.d.f. as σ_0:

(1.3.5) *For all sequences of real numbers* $\{u_l\}$, *on the event* $I_{T_n} = j > 1$, *which belongs to* $\mathcal{G}_{T_n}$,

$$E\left[\exp\left(iu_1 S_{T_n}^{1+} + \ldots + iu_{j-1} S_{T_n}^{j-1+}\right) \mid \mathcal{G}_{T_n}\right] = \prod_{l=1}^{j-1} V_\sigma(u_l).$$

Note that here, I_{T_n} is the number of customers at time T_n+.

Example 1.3.1 *FIFO.* In the FIFO case, (1.3.5) is a direct consequence of the fact that for all $j > 1$, on $I_{T_n} = j > 1$,

$$\mathcal{G}_{T_n} = \sigma\left(A(u),\ u \geq 0\right) \bigvee \sigma\left(\sigma_l,\ 0 \leq l \leq n - j + 1\right)$$

and

$$(S_{T_n}^{1+}, \ldots, S_{T_n}^{j-1+}) = (\sigma_n, \sigma_{n-1}, \ldots, \sigma_{n-j+2}).$$

$\square$

Example 1.3.2 *LIFO non-preemptive.* The random variables $\{U_n\}$, denoting the successive jump times of $\{I_t\}$, are $\mathcal{G}_t$-stopping times. We prove by induction on n that

$$(1.3.6) \quad E\left[\exp\left(iu_1 S_{U_n}^{1+} + \ldots + iu_{I_{U_n}-1} S_{U_n}^{I_{U_n}-1+}\right) \mid \mathcal{G}_{U_n}\right] = \prod_{l=1}^{I_{U_n}-1} V_\sigma(u_l),$$

with the convention that both sides are zero on $I_{U_n} \leq 1$.

Assume that the property holds for n. On $I_{U_{n+1}} = I_{U_n} + 1 > 1$ (that is, U_{n+1} is an arrival time, say $U_{n+1} = T_m$), we have $\mathcal{G}_{U_{n+1}} = \mathcal{G}_{U_n}$ and since ϕ is LIFO non-preemptive

$$(S_{U_{n+1}}^{1+}, \ldots, S_{U_{n+1}}^{I_{U_{n+1}}-1+}) = (S_{U_n}^{1+}, \ldots, S_{U_n}^{I_{U_n}-1+}, \sigma_m),$$

and so by the induction assumption

$$E\left[\exp\left(iu_1 S_{U_{n+1}}^{1+} + \ldots + iu_{I_{U_{n+1}}-1} S_{U_{n+1}}^{I_{U_{n+1}}-1+}\right) \mid \mathcal{G}_{U_{n+1}}\right]$$

$$= E\left[\exp\left(iu_1 S_{U_n}^{1+} + \ldots + iu_{I_{U_n}-1} S_{U_n}^{I_{U_n}-1+} + iu_{I_{U_n}} \sigma_m\right) \mid \mathcal{G}_{U_n}\right]$$

$$= \prod_{l=1}^{I_{U_n}} V_\sigma(u_l) = \prod_{l=1}^{I_{U_{n+1}}-1} V_\sigma(u_l),$$

where we also used the fact that σ_m is then independent of $\mathcal{G}_{U_n} \bigvee \sigma(S_{U_n}^+)$. Similarly, if U_{n+1} is a departure time such that $I_{U_{n+1}} > 1$, then $\mathcal{G}_{U_{n+1}} = \mathcal{G}_{U_n} \bigvee \sigma(S_{U_n}^{I_{U_n}-1+})$ and using the induction assumption,

$$E\left[\exp\left(iu_1 S_{U_{n+1}}^{1+} + \ldots + iu_{I_{U_{n+1}}-1} S_{U_{n+1}}^{I_{U_{n+1}}-1+}\right) \mid \mathcal{G}_{U_{n+1}}\right]$$

$$= E\left[\exp\left(iu_1 S_{U_n}^{1+} + \ldots + iu_{I_{U_n}-2} S_{U_n}^{I_{U_n}-2+}\right) \mid \mathcal{G}_{U_{n+1}}\right]$$

$$= \prod_{l=1}^{I_{U_{n+1}}-1} V_\sigma(u_l).$$

We obtain (1.3.5) by restricting (1.3.6) to arrival times. $\square$

Let A be the following counting measure on $\mathbb{R} \times \mathbb{R}$ associated with the GI/GI input:

$$A = \sum_{n \geq 0} \delta_{T_n, \sigma_n}.$$

Let $S_{\phi,n}^{+} \overset{\text{def}}{=} S_{\phi,T_n}^{+}$.

(1.3.7) *There exists a sequence of random permutations* $\gamma_n : \mathbb{N} \to \mathbb{N}$, $n \geq 1$, *where* γ_n *differs from identity on* $\{0, 1, \ldots, n-1\}$ *only, and such that for all n, the counting measure*

$$A^n(\omega) = \sum_{k \geq 0} \delta_{T_k, \sigma_{\gamma_n(k)}}$$

is such that

(a) $S_{\phi,k}^{-}(A) = S_{\psi,k}^{-}(A^n)$ *for all* $k = 0, \ldots, n$;

(b) A *and* A^n *are equivalent in law.*

Proof: The proof is by induction. For $n = 1$, $S_{\phi,0}^{-}(A) = S_{\psi,0}^{-}(A) = 0$, so that we can take γ_1 equal to the identity and (a) and (b) trivially hold. Assume the property holds true for n. Then in particular $S_{\phi,n}^{-}(A) = S_{\psi,n}^{-}(A^n)$. Define

$$(\beta_{n-1}^{-}, \ldots, \beta_{n-j+1}^{-}, 0, 0, \ldots) = S_{\phi,n}^{-}(A) = S_{\psi,n}^{-}(A^n),$$

where $j = I_{\phi,n}(A) = I_{\psi,n}(A^n) \overset{\text{def}}{=} I_n$ and

$$(\beta_n^{+}, \ldots, \beta_{n-j+1}^{n+}) = S_{\phi,n}^{+}(A) = \phi(\beta_{n-1}^{-}, \ldots, \beta_{n-j+1}^{-}, \sigma_n).$$

Since ϕ is non-preemptive, $\beta_{n-j+1}^{+} = \beta_{n-j+1}^{-}$, if $j > 0$. Let γ_{n+1} be a permutation which differs from the identity on $\{0, 1, \ldots, n\}$ only, and which is such that:

- If $I_n = 1$, then $\gamma_{n+1} = \gamma_n$;
- If $I_n > 1$, then $\gamma_{n+1}(l) = \gamma_n(l)$, for $0 \leq l \leq n - j + 1$ and

$$(\sigma_{\gamma_{n+1}(n-j+2)}, \ldots, \sigma_{\gamma_{n+1}(n)}) = (\beta_{n-j+2}^{+}, \ldots, \beta_n^{+}),$$

with $\gamma_{n+1}(l) = l$ elsewhere.

Then by construction, $S_{\phi,k}^{-}(A) = S_{\psi,k}^{-}(A^{n+1})$, for all $0 \leq k \leq n+1$, which completes the proof of (a). In order to complete the proof of (b), we now show that for all bounded $f : \mathbb{R}^{\infty} \times \mathbb{R}^{\infty} \to \mathbb{R}$,

$$E\left[f(\tau_0, \tau_1, \ldots, \sigma_0, \sigma_1, \ldots)\right] = E\left[f(\tau_0, \tau_1, \ldots, \sigma_{\gamma_{n+1}(0)}, \sigma_{\gamma_{n+1}(1)}, \ldots)\right].$$

Taking f of the form

$$f(\tau_0, \tau_1, \ldots, \sigma_0, \sigma_1, \ldots) = \prod_{l \geq 0} 1_{C_l}(\tau_l) \prod_{l \geq 0} 1_{D_l}(\sigma_l),$$

we obtain

$$E\left[f(\tau_0, \tau_1, \ldots, \sigma_{\gamma_{n+1}(0)}, \sigma_{\gamma_{n+1}(1)}, \ldots)\right]$$

(1.3.8)
$$= \sum_{j=0}^{\infty} E\left[f_1(\tau_0, \tau_1, \ldots, \sigma_{\gamma_{n+1}(0)}, \sigma_{\gamma_{n+1}(1)}, \ldots, \sigma_{\gamma_{n+1}(n-j+1)}) 1_{I_n = j}\right.$$

$$\left. \times f_2(\sigma_{\gamma_{n+1}(n-j+2)}, \sigma_{\gamma_{n+1}(n-j+3)}, \ldots)\right],$$

where f_1 and f_2 are appropriate product functions. In view of the definition of γ_{n+1}, for $j > 1$, the right hand side of the last expression is also

$$E\left[f_1(\tau_0, \tau_1, \ldots, \sigma_{\gamma_n(0)}, \sigma_{\gamma_n(1)}, \ldots, \sigma_{\gamma_n(n-j+1)})1_{I_n=j}\right.$$
$$\left.\times f_2(\beta^+_{n-j+2}, \ldots, \beta^+_n, \sigma_{n+1}, \sigma_{n+2}, \ldots)\right]$$
$$= E\left[f_1(\tau_0, \tau_1, \ldots, \sigma_{\gamma_n(0)}, \sigma_{\gamma_n(1)}, \ldots, \sigma_{\gamma_n(n-j+1)})1_{I_n=j}\right]$$
$$\times E\left[f_2(\sigma_{n-j+2}, \ldots, \sigma_n, \sigma_{n+1}, \sigma_{n+2}, \ldots)\right],$$

where the last factorization comes from (1.3.5). From (b) of the induction assumption, for all values of j

$$E\left[f_1(\tau_0, \tau_1, \ldots, \sigma_{\gamma_n(0)}, \sigma_{\gamma_n(1)}, \ldots, \sigma_{\gamma_n(n-j+1)})1_{I_n=j}\right]$$
$$= E\left[f_1(\tau_0, \tau_1, \ldots, \sigma_0, \sigma_1, \ldots, \sigma_{n-j+1})1_{I_n=j}\right].$$

Therefore, the right hand side of (1.3.8) is simply $E\left[f(\tau_0, \tau_1, \ldots, \sigma_0, \sigma_1, \ldots)\right]$ and the proof is concluded from the monotone class theorem. $\qquad\square$

Let $A' \stackrel{\text{def}}{=} \sum_{k \geq 0} \delta_{T_k, \sigma'_k}$ be the point process defined by

(1.3.9) $\quad A'(C \times K) = \lim_{n \to \infty} A^n(C \times K)$

for C and K Borel sets of $\mathbb{R}$. If $\rho < 1$, this a.s. limit is well defined since the permutations γ_n are then such that $\gamma_n(k)$ does not depend on n after a finite rank (indeed, γ_n only permute indices within a busy period). Using this and (1.3.7) (b), we obtain:

(1.3.10) *The point process A' is equivalent in law to A, and such that for all t, $S_{\phi,t}(A) = S_{\psi,t}(A')$.*

Let T_μ be the first positive construction point of the queue. Then, the process $\{S_{\phi,t}\}$, $0 \leq t \leq T_\mu$, fully determines the time $B_{\phi,n}$ at which customer n, $0 \leq n \leq \mu - 1$, begins its service (see (6.2.9), Chapter 2.). Let B_ϕ denote the vector $(B_{\phi,n}, n = 0, \ldots, \mu-1)$ and let V_ϕ be the waiting time vector $V_\phi = (B_{\phi,n} - T_n, n = 0, \ldots, \mu - 1)$. In the particular case of policy ψ, the waiting time of the n-th customer is also the workload at the arrival of customer n, that is $V_{\psi,n} = W_n$.

We shall add a 'prime' to denote a variable associated with A'. For instance, $\{W'_n\}$ will be the stationary workload sequence, $B'_{\psi,n}$ the time at which the service of customer n begins under policy ψ, all for the arrival point process A' etc. Let $T_{\mu'}$ be the the first positive construction point of $\{W'_n\}$. We have $\mu(\omega) = \mu'(\omega)$ and more generally, all construction points of $\{W_n\}$ are construction points of $\{W'_n\}$ and conversely. By construction

$$B_{\phi,\gamma(n)} = B'_{\psi,n}, \quad (0 \leq n < \mu(\omega))$$

(see Figure 1.3.1, for the particular case when ϕ if LIFO non-preemptive).

Thus, it follows from (1.3.3) that (with obvious notations)

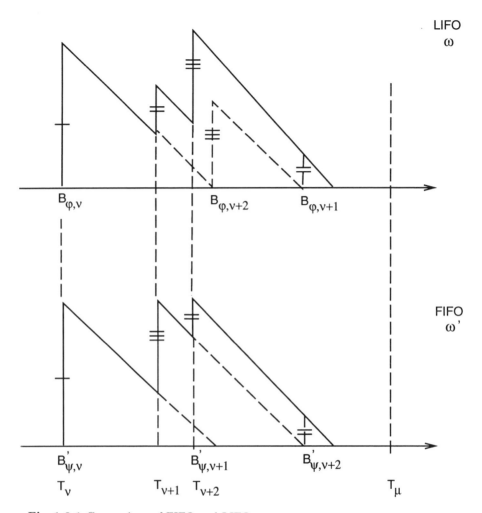

Fig. 1.3.1 Comparison of FIFO and LIFO

(1.3.11) $V'_\psi = (B'_\psi - T) \prec (B_\phi - T) = V_\phi.$

From (1.1.3), this in particular implies that

$$\sum_0^{\mu-1} f(V'_{\psi,n}) \le \sum_0^{\mu-1} f(V_{\phi,n}),$$

for all convex functions $f : \mathbb{R} \to \mathbb{R}$, so that

$$E\left[\sum_0^{\mu-1} f(V'_{\psi,n}) \mid S_0^{-'} = 0\right] \le E\left[\sum_0^{\mu-1} f(V_{\phi,n}) \mid S_0^- = 0\right].$$

Owing to the fact that A and A' are equivalent in law, we also have

$$E\left[\sum_0^{\mu-1} f(V'_{\psi,n}) \mid S_0^{-'} = 0\right] = E\left[\sum_0^{\mu-1} f(V_{\psi,n}) \mid S_0^- = 0\right].$$

The last two relations and the cycle formula allow us to conclude that the stationary sojourn time $V_{\psi,0}$ satisfy the following optimality property:

(1.3.12) $E^0[f(V_{\psi,0})] \leq E^0[f(V_{\phi,0})]$, for all convex functions f such that the expectations exist.

Let $R_{\psi,0}$ and $R_{\phi,0}$ be the stationary sojourn times of customer 0 under disciplines ψ and ϕ respectively.

(1.3.13) $E^0[f(R_{\psi,0})] \leq E^0[f(R_{\phi,0})]$, for all convex functions f such that the expectations exist.

Proof: We have $R_{\phi,0} = V_{\phi,0} + \sigma$, where $V_{\phi,0}$ and σ are independent (see Example 2.2.1 below). □

Remark 1.3.1 We can define the same service disciplines in $GI/GI/s/\infty$ queues, and prove that within the class of disciplines which use no information on service times, FIFO is optimal in the same sense as in (1.3.12)-(1.3.13). □

2 Comparison of Queues

2.1 Integral Stochastic Orderings

Let $\mathcal{D}(\mathbb{R}^n)$ denote the set of c.d.f. on $\mathbb{R}^n$ and $\mathcal{L}$ be a set of Borel mappings from $\mathbb{R}^n$ onto $\mathbb{R}$. Consider the binary relation $\leq_{\mathcal{L}}$ on $\mathcal{D}(\mathbb{R}^n)$ defined by the integral relation

$$F \leq_{\mathcal{L}} G \quad \text{if and only if} \quad \int_{\mathbb{R}^n} f(x)F(dx) \leq \int_{\mathbb{R}^n} f(x)G(dx),$$

for all $f \in \mathcal{L}$ such that the integrals are well defined.

The binary relation $\leq_{\mathcal{L}}$ is clearly reflexive and transitive, so that it always defines a partial semi-ordering on $\mathcal{D}(\mathbb{R}^n)$ (if the set $\mathcal{L}$ is rich enough to imply the anti-symmetry property, $\leq_{\mathcal{L}}$ defines a partial ordering). Such an order will be referred to as an *integral order* on $\mathcal{D}(\mathbb{R}^n)$. It will also be understood as a partial order on the set of $\mathbb{R}^n$-valued random variables via the usual definition: $X \leq_{\mathcal{L}} Y$ if $P[X \leq .] \leq_{\mathcal{L}} P[Y \leq .]$.

Three basic instances of sets $\mathcal{L}$ are first considered.

- The set $\{i\} = \{f : \mathbb{R}^n \to \mathbb{R} \mid f \text{ non} - \text{decreasing}\}$ generates the *increasing (partial) integral order* on $\mathcal{D}(\mathbb{R}^n)$.

- The set $\{cx\} = \{f : \mathbb{R}^n \to \mathbb{R} \,|\, f \text{ convex }\}$ generates the *convex integral order* on $\mathcal{D}(\mathbb{R}_+^n)$, and is closely related to the projection stochastic order associated with $\le$, alluded to in the introduction.
- The set $\{scx\} = \{f : \mathbb{R}^n \to \mathbb{R} \,|\, f \text{ Schur} - \text{convex }\}$ defines the *Schur-convex integral order*, which will be seen to be closely related to the pathwise stochastic order associated with $\prec$).

Remark 2.1.1 Traditionally, the initials 'st' (for stochastic) are used in place of 'i' (increasing). We will see that the $\le_i$ order is in some sense equivalent to the pathwise stochastic order associated with $\le$; we will thus often refer to it as the *strong ordering*. $\qquad\square$

The following subsets of the above sets will also be used:

- The set $\{icx\} = \{i\} \bigcap \{cx\}$, which generates the *increasing convex* ordering on $\mathcal{D}(\mathbb{R}^n)$, and which coincides with the projection stochastic order associated with the partial ordering $\le$.

- The set $\{cxs\} = \{f : \mathbb{R}^n \to \mathbb{R} \,|\, f \text{ convex symmetric}\}$, generates the *convex symmetric* ordering and coincides with the projection stochastic order associated with the partial ordering $\prec$ on $\mathbb{R}^n$.

- The set $\{ip\} = \{f : \mathbb{R}^n \to \mathbb{R}_+ \,|\, f = \prod_{i=1}^n f_i(x_i),\ f_i : \mathbb{R} \to \mathbb{R}_+ \in \{i\}\}$ generates the *increasing product form* partial ordering.

Example 2.1.1 *Exponential and Erlang Distributions.* Let $\Gamma_{\lambda,n}(x)$ be the Gamma c.d.f. of parameters λ and n, and $E_\lambda(x)$ be the exponential c.d.f. with parameter λ. If $n \in \mathbb{N}$, we have

$$\Gamma_{\lambda n, n} \le_{cx} E_\lambda.$$

Indeed let $Y_1, \ldots, Y_n$ be i.i.d. random variables, with c.d.f. E_λ, and let $X = Y_1 + \ldots + Y_n$. Then if f is convex,

$$f\left(\frac{1}{n} \sum_{i=1}^n Y_i\right) \le \frac{1}{n} \sum_{i=1}^n f(Y_i),$$

so that that $E[f(X/n)] \le E[f(Y)]$. Therefore $X/n \le_{cx} Y$. $\qquad\square$

Example 2.1.2 *Optimality of the FIFO discipline.* The setting is that of § 1.3. From (1.3.10), for all Schur-convex functions f (like for instance the maximum of the coordinates), $f(V'_\psi) \le f(V_\phi)$, and therefore, in view of the equivalence in law between A and A', for all increasing functions $g : \mathbb{R} \to \mathbb{R}$, $E[g \circ f(V_\psi)] \le E[g \circ f(V_\phi)]$. Thus, for all Schur convex functions, $f(V_\psi) \le_i f(V_\phi)$. $\qquad\square$

Some obvious relations between these (semi)orderings are quoted below for future reference:

(2.1.1) $\le_i \Rightarrow \le_{icx}$ and $\le_i \Rightarrow \le_{ip}$

and

(2.1.2) $\leq_{cx} \Rightarrow \leq_{icx}$.

In addition, the fact that convex symmetric functions are Schur-convex (see (1.1.3)) implies

(2.1.3) $\leq_{scx} \Rightarrow \leq_{cxs}$.

In general, these implications have no converse.

Remark 2.1.2 For *non-negative* random variables, each of the inequalities $F \leq_i G$, $F \leq_{cx} G$, $F \leq_{icx} G$ and $F \leq_{ip} G$ implies the corresponding inequality between the moments (of any order) of the coordinates of F and G. For the $\leq_{cx}$ ordering, we have the stronger property that, for all $i = 1, \ldots, n$

$$(2.1.4) \quad F \leq_{cx} G \implies \int_{\mathbb{R}^n} x_i F(dx) = \int_{\mathbb{R}^n} x_i G(dx),$$

provided these moments exist (indeed, both functions $x \to x_i$ and $x \to -x_i$ are convex). Thus, we will say that the *variability* of F is smaller than the variability of G since their mean values coincide and any even moment of F is smaller that the corresponding moment of G.   □

The preceding definitions will naturally extend to random vectors: the random vector $X = (X_1, \ldots, X_n)$ is $\leq_{\mathcal{L}}$-dominated by $Y = (Y_1, \ldots, Y_n)$ if $F(x) = P[X_0 \leq x_0, \ldots, X_n \leq x_n]$ and $G(x) = P[Y_0 \leq x_0, \ldots, Y_n \leq x_n]$, satisfy the ordering relation $F \leq_{\mathcal{L}} G$, or equivalently if

$$E[f(X_1, \ldots, X_n)] \leq E[f(Y_1, \ldots, Y_n)],$$

for all $f : \mathbb{R}^n \to \mathbb{R} \in \mathcal{L}$. This definition does not require that the random vectors X and Y be defined on the same probability space.

If we replace increasing functions by decreasing functions and/or convex functions by concave functions in the above definitions, we obtain the *decreasing concave, concave symmetric, increasing concave, decreasing convex*, etc. partial orderings, which are respectively denoted $\leq_d$, $\leq_{cv}$, $\leq_{cvs}$, $\leq_{icv}$, $\leq_{dcx}$, etc. Using the last definition, we see that the relation $X \leq_{cx} Y$ is equivalent to $-X \leq_{cx} -Y$, since if the function $f(x)$ si convex, so is $f(-x)$. Using the fact that $-f(x)$ is concave if f is convex, we obtain the more general equivalences

$$X \leq_{icx} Y \quad \Leftrightarrow \quad -X \leq_{dcx} -Y$$

(2.1.5) $\quad\quad \Updownarrow \quad\quad\quad\quad\quad\quad \Updownarrow$

$$Y \leq_{dcv} X \quad \Leftrightarrow \quad -Y \leq_{icv} -X$$

For all the integral orders considered above, if $f : \mathbb{R}^n \to \mathbb{R}$ is in $\mathcal{L}$, so is $f \circ \gamma$, where γ is any permutations of $\{1, \ldots, n\}$. Therefore $X \leq_{\mathcal{L}} Y$ implies that $X_\gamma \leq_{\mathcal{L}} Y_\gamma$, where $X_\gamma \stackrel{\text{def}}{=} (X_{\gamma(1)}, \ldots, X_{\gamma(n)})$.

Thus, the above definitions can then be extended as follows:

- Let $X^1, \ldots, X^n$ be $\mathbb{R}^k$ valued random vectors, all defined on the same probability space. Let $Y^1, \ldots, Y^n$ in $\mathbb{R}^k$ be another sequence, possibly defined on a different probability space. Let X be the matrix $(X^1, \ldots, X^n)$, with a similar notation for Y. We will say that $X \leq_{\mathcal{L}} Y$ if

$$(X_1^1, \ldots, X_k^1, X_1^2, \ldots, X_k^2, \ldots, X_1^n, \ldots, X_k^n)$$
$$\leq_{\mathcal{L}} (Y_1^1, \ldots, Y_k^n, Y_1^2, \ldots Y_k^2, \ldots, Y_1^n, \ldots, Y_k^n).$$

In this definition, the elements of the matrices were ordered in columns. Any other order would lead to an equivalent definition.

- Let $\{X^n\}$, $n \geq 1$ and $\{Y^n\}$, $n \geq 1$ be $\mathbb{R}^k$-valued stochastic sequences, possibly defined on different probability spaces. The sequence $\{Y^n\}$ is said to dominate $\{X^n\}$ for the $\leq_{\mathcal{L}}$ ordering (which will be denoted $(X^1, X^2, \ldots) \leq_{\mathcal{L}} (Y^1, Y^2, \ldots)$) if for all $n \geq 1$, the following matrix comparison property holds:

$$(X^1, \ldots, X^n) \leq_{\mathcal{L}} (Y^1, \ldots, Y^n).$$

2.2 Analytical Characterizations

An integral ordering property can be checked directly through the definition of § 2.1, but this is rarely the most efficient way. On $\mathcal{D}(\mathbb{R})$, there are simple analytical characterizations for the three integral orderings $\leq_i$, $\leq_{cx}$ and $\leq_{icx}$ of interest in dimension 1, which boil down to simple tests on the distribution functions.

The following result shows that we can restrict the set of test functions for the strong order:

(2.2.1) *If the relation*

$$(2.2.2) \qquad \int_{\mathbb{R}} f(x) F(dx) \leq \int_{\mathbb{R}} f(x) G(dx)$$

holds for all functions $f : \mathbb{R} \to \mathbb{R}_+$ which are non-decreasing and continuous, then $F \leq_i G$.

Proof: It suffices to prove (2.2.2) for f non-decreasing, continuous and non-negative (if (2.2.2) is satisfied by $f_n(x) = (-n) \vee f(x) + n$, which is positive, then it is satisfied by $f(x)$ as can be seen when letting n tend to ∞). Any non-negative non-decreasing function $f : \mathbb{R} \to \mathbb{R}_+$ can be represented as the sum

$$f(x) = g(x) + \sum_{n \geq 0} u_n(x),$$

where $g(x) : \mathbb{R} \to \mathbb{R}_+$ is non-decreasing and continuous and the functions $u_n(x)$ are step functions of the form

$$v_{a,b,\alpha}(x) = \begin{cases} 0, & \text{for } x < a; \\ \alpha b, & \text{for } x = a; \\ b, & \text{for } x > a. \end{cases}$$

with $0 \le \alpha b \le b$. Thus in view of the monotone convergence theorem, it is enough to check (2.2.2) for all continuous functions and all step functions in this class.

A step function in this class is left-continuous if $\alpha = 0$, right-continuous if $\alpha = 1$. If $\alpha \in (0,1)$, this function admits a representation as the sum of a right-continuous function and a left-continuous one within this class via the relation $v_{a,b,\alpha} = v_{a,\alpha b,1} + v_{a,(1-\alpha)b,0}$. The proof is now completed if we observe that each step function with either $\alpha = 0$ or $\alpha = 1$ is the monotone limit of a sequence of non-decreasing continuous functions. $\qquad\square$

Let F and G be in $\mathcal{D}(\mathbb{R})$ and $\bar{F}$ denote the function $\bar{F}(x) = 1 - F(x)$, $x \in \mathbb{R}$.

(2.2.3) $F \le_i G$ if and only if $\bar{F}(x) \le \bar{G}(x)$ for all $x \in \mathbb{R}$.

Proof: The necessary part is obvious since the indicator function $t \to 1(t > x)$ is non-decreasing. Conversely, each right-continuous (and a fortiori continuous) non-decreasing function $f : \mathbb{R} \to \mathbb{R}$ such that $f(-\infty) > -\infty$ admits the Stieltjes-Lebesgue integral representation

$$f(u) = f(-\infty) + \int_{(-\infty,u]} f(dt) = f(-\infty) + \int_{\mathbb{R}} 1(t \le u) f(dt)$$

and so

$$\int_{\mathbb{R}} f(u) F(du) = f(-\infty) + \int_{\mathbb{R}} \bar{F}(t-) f(dt).$$

The fact that $\bar{F}(t) \le \bar{G}(t)$ for all $t \ge 0$ implies $\bar{F}(t-) \le \bar{G}(t-)$ for all $t \ge 0$. Therefore, the last relation implies that (2.2.2) holds for all f as above, which concludes the proof in view of (2.2.1). $\qquad\square$

(2.2.4) *Assume that F and G have a finite first moment. Then $F \le_{icx} G$ if and only if*

$$\int_x^\infty \bar{F}(u)du \le \int_x^\infty \bar{G}(u)du, \quad \forall x \in \mathbb{R}.$$

Proof: The identity $\int_x^\infty \bar{F}(u)du = \int_{\mathbb{R}} (u-x)^+ F(du)$, (obtained from (1.3.3), Chapter 3 and the integrability assumption) establishes the necessary part since $u \to (u-x)^+$ is non-decreasing and convex. To prove the converse, it is enough to consider f bounded from below (otherwise take $f \vee (-n)$ and let n go to ∞). We have

$$f(u) = f(-\infty) + \int_{-\infty}^{u} g(x)dx = \int_{\mathbb{R}} (u - x)^+ g(dx),$$

where g, the right-derivative of f, is a non-decreasing function which can be assumed right-continuous without loss of generality. Thus, by Fubini's Theorem

$$\int_{\mathbb{R}} f(u)F(du) = f(-\infty) + \int_{\mathbb{R}} \int_{\mathbb{R}} (u - x)^+ F(du)g(dx)$$

$$= f(-\infty) + \int_{\mathbb{R}} \left(\int_{x}^{\infty} \bar{F}(u)du \right) g(dx).$$

Therefore $\int_{x}^{\infty} \bar{F}(u)du \le \int_{x}^{\infty} \bar{G}(u)du$, for all x implies

$$\int_{\mathbb{R}} f(u)F(du) \le \int_{\mathbb{R}} f(u)G(du).$$

□

In view of (2.2.4):

(2.2.5) *If X and Y are integrable, $X \le_{\text{icx}} Y$ is equivalent to $E[(X - x)^+] \le E[(Y - x)^+]$, for all $x \in \mathbb{R}$.*

In higher dimension, only the independent case follows from what is known in dimension 1:

(2.2.6) *Let $X = (X_1, \ldots, X_n)$ and $\tilde{X} = (\tilde{X}_1, \ldots, \tilde{X}_n)$ be two random vectors with mutually independent coordinates. Then for each of the stochastic orders $\mathcal{L} = \{i\}, \{cx\}, \{icx\}, X \le_{\mathcal{L}} \tilde{X}$ if and only if $X_i \le_{\mathcal{L}} \tilde{X}_i$ for all $i = 1, \ldots, n$.*

This property extends to random sequences in the obvious manner.

Example 2.2.1 *Stability of integral orders by convolution* If the real-valued random variables $X_1, \ldots, X_n$ (resp. $\tilde{X}_1, \ldots, \tilde{X}_n$) are mutually independent, then for any of the above orders, $X_i \le_{\mathcal{L}} \tilde{X}_i$ for all i implies

$$(X_1, \ldots, X_n) \le_{\mathcal{L}} (\tilde{X}_1, \ldots, \tilde{X}_n),$$

so that in particular

$$X_1 + \ldots + X_n \le_{\mathcal{L}} \tilde{X}_1 + \ldots + \tilde{X}_n.$$

So these integral orders are stable by convolution.   □

2.3 Strassen's Pointwise Representation Theorems

The pointwise representations which are discussed in this subsection provide a natural way for handling integral ordering in higher dimension, at least whenever the independence assumptions of (2.2.6) are not satisfied. These representations are particularly useful to establish comparison properties of imbedded sequences in various queueing systems by simple induction arguments, which replace the usual analytical proofs, based on stability properties of the integral order with respect to convolutions or products of c.d.f.

The first result, already mentioned in the introduction, is that the $\leq_i$-ordering corresponds to the pathwise stochastic order associated with $\leq$:

(2.3.1) *For F and G two c.d.f. in $\mathcal{D}(\mathbb{R}^n)$, $F \leq_i G$ if and only if there exist two $\mathbb{R}^n$-valued random variables X and Y defined on the same probability space with c.d.f. F and G respectively and such that $X \leq Y$ a.s.*

Proof: See § 5.   □

Remark 2.3.1 In dimension 1, the proof boils down to the following classical construction: take U to be a random variable uniformly distributed on the interval $[0, 1]$, defined on some probability space $(\Omega, \mathcal{F}, P)$. Let $X = F^{-1}(U)$, $Y = G^{-1}(U)$, where the inverse of the non-decreasing function F is defined by

$$F^{-1}(u) = \inf\{x \mid F(x) > u\}.$$

It follows from the assumption $F \leq_i G$ that $F^{-1}(U) \leq G^{-1}(U)$. Conversely, if $X \leq Y$ a.s., then $P(X \leq x) = F(x) \geq G(x) = P(Y \leq x)$ for all $x \geq 0$, which is equivalent to $F \leq_i G$.   □

Similarly, the Schur-convex ordering corresponds to the pathwise ordering associated with $\prec$: $F \leq_{scx} G$ if and only if there exist two $\mathbb{R}^n$-valued random variables X and Y defined on the same probability space, with c.d.f. F and G respectively, and such that $X \prec Y$ a.s. The proof is similar to that of (2.3.1).

The following characterizations of $\leq_{cx}$ and $\leq_{icx}$ in terms of the *projection stochastic order* associated with $\leq$ are also proved in § 5:

(2.3.2) *Let F and G be two integrable c.d.f. in $\mathcal{D}(\mathbb{R}^n)$; $F \leq_{cx} G$ (resp. $F \leq_{icx} G$) if and only if there exist two $\mathbb{R}^n$-valued random variables X and Y defined on the same probability space with c.d.f. F and G respectively, and such that $E[Y \mid X] = X$ (resp. $E[Y \mid X] \geq X$) a.s.*

Example 2.3.1 *Exponential and Erlang Distributions.* We give a second proof of the comparison of Example 2.1.1, based on the construction of the variables of the last theorem: by symmetry, we have $E[Y_i \mid X] = \Psi(X)$ a.s., for some function Ψ independent of i. Therefore $n\Psi(X) = \sum_i E[Y_i \mid X] = X$, so that

$$E[nY_i \mid X] = X.$$

Since X is $\Gamma_{\lambda,n}$, the proof is concluded from (2.3.2).   □

These results have the following immediate corollaries:

(2.3.3) *If $F \leq_i G$ and F and G have the same finite first moment, then $F = G$.*

Proof: Use (2.3.1) which allows us to chose X and Y distributed according to F and G respectively and such that $X \leq Y$ a.s. This and $E[X] = E[Y]$ imply $X = Y$ a.s.   □

(2.3.4) *If* $F \leq_{icx} G$ *and* F *and* G *have the same finite first moment, then* $F \leq_{cx} G$.

Proof: From (2.3.2), we can chose X and Y distributed according to F and G respectively and such that $E[Y|X] \geq X$ a.s. If in addition $E[X] = E[Y]$, then the random variables $E[Y|X]$ and Y have the same mean, so that necessarily, $E[Y|X] = X$ a.s., which concludes the proof in view of (2.3.2).   □

2.4 Comparison of Stochastic Recurrences

The ideas developed in §§ 2.1-2.3 provide the underpinings of various bounding techniques. Before specializing them to queues, we describe these techniques within the framework of stochastic recurrences introduced in § 4.2 of Chapter 2. The quantities of interest are described by $\mathbb{R}^K$-valued sequences $\{y_n\}$, $n \geq 0$, generated by the recurrence equation

(2.4.1) $y_{n+1} = h(y_n, \xi_n), \quad n \geq 0.$

The $\mathbb{R}^M$-valued driving sequence $\{\xi_n\}$, $n \geq 0$, and the initial condition $y_0 = \eta$ are defined on the probability space (Ω, F, P).

   Consider another stochastic recurrence, say

(2.4.2) $\widetilde{y}_{n+1} = h(\widetilde{y}_n, \widetilde{\xi}_{n+1}), \quad n \geq 0,$

with the same dynamics h, and which only differs from the first one by its initial condition $\widetilde{\eta}$ and its driving sequence $\{\widetilde{\xi}_n\}$, $n \geq 0$, (all the tilde variables are possibly defined on another probability space). Under what conditions on h does the ordering relation

   $(\eta, \xi_0, \ \xi_1, \ldots) \leq_{\mathcal{L}} (\widetilde{\eta}, \widetilde{\xi}_0, \ \widetilde{\xi}_1, \ldots),$

imply that

   $(y_0, \ y_1, \ldots) \leq_{\mathcal{L}} (\widetilde{y}_0, \widetilde{y}_1, \ldots).$

Assuming in addition that the sequences y_n and $\widetilde{y}_n$ converge in some sense to the stationary limits y_∞ and $\widetilde{y}_\infty$ respectively, when does the relation

   $y_\infty \leq_{\mathcal{L}} \widetilde{y}_\infty,$

hold? These questions can be addressed directly from Strassen's Theorems by constructing the two sequences on the same probability space.

2.5 Bounds Based on Integral Orderings

Strong Bounds.

(2.5.1) *Assume that $(y, \xi) \to h(y, \xi)$ is non-decreasing. If $(\eta, \xi_0, \xi_1, \cdots) \leq_i (\widetilde{\eta}, \widetilde{\xi}_0, \widetilde{\xi}_1, \ldots)$, then $(y_0, y_1, \ldots) \leq_i (\widetilde{y}_0, \widetilde{y}_1, \ldots)$.*

Proof: From Strassen's Theorem (2.3.1), for all n, we can find random variables $(\eta', \xi'_0, \xi'_1, \ldots, \xi'_n)$ and $(\widetilde{\eta}', \widetilde{\xi}'_0, \widetilde{\xi}'_1, \ldots, \widetilde{\xi}'_n)$ defined on the same probability space and such that

α) The distribution of $(\eta, \xi_0, \xi_1, \ldots, \xi_n)$ (resp. $(\widetilde{\eta}, \widetilde{\xi}_0, \widetilde{\xi}_1, \ldots, \widetilde{\xi}_n)$) coincides with the distribution of $(\eta', \xi'_0, \xi'_1, \ldots, \xi'_n)$ (resp. $(\widetilde{\eta}', \widetilde{\xi}'_0, \widetilde{\xi}'_1, \ldots, \widetilde{\xi}'_n)$);

β) $\eta' \leq \widetilde{\eta}'$ a.s. and $\xi'_i \leq \widetilde{\xi}'_i$ a.s. for all $i = 0, 1, \ldots, n$.

The property $y'_n \leq \widetilde{y}'_n$ a.s. is now established by induction as follows: $y'_0 \leq \widetilde{y}'_0$ a.s. since $\eta' \leq \widetilde{\eta}'$ a.s. Assume that the property holds up to rank $i < n$. Since h is non-decreasing, we obtain

$$y'_{i+1} = h(y'_i, \xi'_i) \leq h(\widetilde{y}'_i, \xi'_i) \leq h(\widetilde{y}'_i, \widetilde{\xi}'_i) = \widetilde{y}'_{i+1},$$

where we successively used the induction assumption and the pathwise ordering between ξ' and $\widetilde{\xi}'$. □

Bounds by Projection. The following result generalizes the example considered in the introduction:

(2.5.2) *Assume that the random variables $(\eta, \xi_0, \xi_1, \ldots)$ are integrable, and that*
(a) The function $y \to h(y, \xi)$ is non-decreasing;
(b) The function $(y, \xi) \to h(y, \xi)$ is convex (resp. convex and non-decreasing);
then, $(\eta, \xi_0, \xi_1, \ldots) \leq_{cx}$ (resp. $\leq_{icx}$) $(\widetilde{\eta}, \widetilde{\xi}_0, \widetilde{\xi}_1, \ldots)$ implies $(y_0, y_1, \ldots) \leq_{icx} (\widetilde{y}_0, \widetilde{y}_1, \ldots)$.

Proof: From Strassen's theorem (2.3.2), for all n, we can find random variables $(\eta', \xi'_0, \xi'_1, \ldots, \xi'_n)$ and $(\widetilde{\eta}', \widetilde{\xi}'_0, \widetilde{\xi}'_1, \ldots, \widetilde{\xi}'_n)$ defined on the same probability space, and such that if we denote $\mathcal{G}_n$ the σ-field generated by the variables $(\eta', \xi'_0, \xi'_1, \ldots, \xi'_n)$, then

α) The distribution of $(\eta, \xi_0, \xi_1, \ldots, \xi_n)$ (resp. $(\widetilde{\eta}, \widetilde{\xi}_0, \widetilde{\xi}_1, \ldots, \widetilde{\xi}_n)$) coincides with the distribution of $(\eta', \xi'_0, \xi'_1, \ldots, \xi'_n)$ (resp. $(\widetilde{\eta}', \widetilde{\xi}'_0, \widetilde{\xi}'_1, \ldots, \widetilde{\xi}'_n)$);

β-cx) $\eta' = E[\widetilde{\eta} \mid \mathcal{G}_n]$ a.s. and $\xi_i = E[\widetilde{\xi}_i \mid \mathcal{G}_n]$, for all $i = 0, 1, \ldots, n$.

β-icx) $\eta' \leq E[\widetilde{\eta}' \mid \mathcal{G}_n]$ a.s. and $\xi'_i \leq E[\widetilde{\xi}'_i \mid \mathcal{G}_n]$, for all $i = 0, 1, \ldots, n$.

We now prove that the relation

(2.5.3) $y'_i \leq E[\widetilde{y}'_i \mid \mathcal{G}_n]$ a.s. $(0 \leq i \leq n)$.

Since $\eta' = E[\widetilde{\eta} \mid \mathcal{G}_n]$ a.s. (resp. $\widetilde{\eta}' \leq E[\eta' \mid \mathcal{G}_n]$ a.s.), (2.5.3) holds for $i = 0$. Take as induction hypothesis that (2.5.3) holds true for some $i < n$. Jensen's inequality gives

$$E[\widetilde{y}'_{i+1} \mid \mathcal{G}_n] \geq h(E[\widetilde{y}'_i \mid \mathcal{G}_n], E[\widetilde{\xi}'_i \mid \mathcal{G}_n]),$$

since the function $h : \mathbb{R}^{K+M} \to \mathbb{R}^K$ is convex. Thus using the induction hypothesis and the fact that the function $y \to h(y, \xi)$ is non-decreasing

$$E[\widetilde{y}'_{i+1} \mid \mathcal{G}_n] \geq h(\widetilde{y}'_i, E[\xi'_i \mid \mathcal{G}_n]).$$

Using now the property that $E[\widetilde{\xi}'_i \mid \mathcal{G}_n] = \xi'_i$ a.s. (resp. $E[\widetilde{\xi}'_i \mid \mathcal{G}_n] \geq \xi'_i$ a.s. together with the assumption that the function $(y, \xi) \to h(y, \xi)$ is non-decreasing), we obtain that

$$(2.5.4) \quad E[\widetilde{y}'_{i+1} \mid \mathcal{G}_n] \geq h(y'_i, \xi'_i) = y'_{i+1},$$

and the property that $(y_0, y_1, \ldots, y_n) \leq_{\mathrm{icx}} (\widetilde{y}_0, \widetilde{y}_1, \ldots, \widetilde{y}_n)$ follows from Jensen's inequality. $\square$

2.6 Stability of Stochastic Orders by Limits

Let $\leq_{\mathcal{L}}$ be some integral stochastic order on $\mathcal{D}(\mathbb{R}^K)$, and let y_n and $\widetilde{y}_n$, $n \geq 0$, be two $\mathbb{R}^K$-valued sequences of random variables which converge weakly to the random variables y_∞ and $\widetilde{y}_\infty$ respectively.

The conditions under which the property

$$(2.6.1) \quad y_n \leq_{\mathcal{L}} \widetilde{y}_n,$$

for all $n \geq 0$, implies

$$(2.6.2) \quad y_\infty \leq_{\mathcal{L}} \widetilde{y}_\infty,$$

may be obtained analytically for most of the orders defined in this chapter (cf. D. Stoyan (1984) *Comparison Methods for Queues and Other Stochastic Models*).

Example 2.6.1 If the c.d.f. F_n and G_n on $\mathbb{R}$ converge weakly to F_∞ and G_∞ respectively, and if $F_n \leq_i G_n$ for all n, then $F_\infty \leq G_\infty$ (use (2.2.1)). Thus, $\leq_i$ is preserved by weak limits. $\square$

Consider now the case when the driving sequences $\{\xi_n\}$ and $\{\widetilde{\xi}_n\}$ are stationary and ergodic, and defined on the Palm space of some point process, $(\Omega, \mathcal{F}, P^0, \theta)$. Since the systems considered in (2.5.1) and (2.5.2) are such that the mapping $y \to h(y, \xi)$ is non-decreasing, Loynes' technique applies, provided this mapping is also continuous (see Remark 4.2.1, Chapter 2). Let $\{y_n^0\}$, $n \geq 0$, be the state variable sequence when the initial condition is 0. From Remark 4.1.1, Chapter 2, it is possible to define a sequence $\{z_n\}$, $n \geq 0$, such that $z_n =_i y_n^0$, (in what follows, we will often use the notation

$=_i$ to represent equality in distribution) for all $n \geq 0$, and such that z_n is non-decreasing in n. Let $\{\widetilde{z}_n\}$ be the sequence obtained in the same way from $\{\widetilde{y}_n^0\}$. Therefore, (2.6.1) is equivalent to

$$(2.6.3) \quad E^0[f(z_n)] \leq E^0[f(\widetilde{z}_n)] \quad \forall f \in \mathcal{L}.$$

Equation (2.6.3) provides another way of addressing the question. For instance, if $\mathcal{L} = \{\text{icx}\}$, when letting n go to ∞ in (2.6.3), a direct application of the monotone convergence theorem implies

$$E^0[f(z_\infty)] \leq E^0[f(\widetilde{z}_\infty)],$$

for all $f \in \{\text{icx}\}$ such that the expectations exist, which is equivalent to (2.6.2), for $\mathcal{L} = \{\text{icx}\}$.

Remark 2.6.1 Under the conditions of (2.5.1) (resp. (2.5.2)-icx), the existence of the monotone sequences $\{z_n\}$ and $\{\widetilde{z}_n\}$ implies the stronger property that for all $n \geq 1$, under P^0,

$$(2.6.4) \quad (z_\infty, z_\infty \circ \theta^1, \ldots, z_\infty \circ \theta^n) \leq_i (\text{resp. } \leq_{\text{icx}}) (\widetilde{z}_\infty, \widetilde{z}_\infty \circ \widetilde{\theta}^1, \ldots, \widetilde{z}_\infty \circ \widetilde{\theta}^n),$$

provided z_∞ and $\widetilde{z}_\infty$ are finite (resp. integrable).   □

2.7 Comparison of Basic Queues

We use the notations of Chapter 2. In what follows, the case when the initial condition W_0 and the vectors of service and inter-arrival times (σ_n, τ_n), $n \geq 0$, are mutually independent will be referred to as Assumption H_1 (thus H_1 allows σ_n and τ_n to be correlated); the case when, in addition to H_1, for all n, σ_n and τ_n are independent, will be referred to as Assumption H_2; if in addition the service times are all identically distributed, as well as the inter-arrival times, we will say that we have *renewal assumptions*.

Remark 2.7.1 From Remark 2.2.2, for $\mathcal{L} = \{i\}$, $\{\text{icx}\}$ or $\{\text{cx}\}$, under H_1,

$$(2.7.1) \quad (W_0, (\sigma_0, -\tau_0), (\sigma_1, -\tau_1), \ldots) \leq_{\mathcal{L}} (\widetilde{W}_0, (\widetilde{\sigma}_0, -\widetilde{\tau}_0), (\widetilde{\sigma}_1, -\widetilde{\tau}_1), \ldots)$$

is equivalent to $W_0 \leq_{\mathcal{L}} \widetilde{W}_0$ and $(\sigma_i, -\tau_i) \leq_{\mathcal{L}} (\widetilde{\sigma}_i, -\widetilde{\tau}_i)$ for all $i \geq 0$.
Similarly, (2.2.6) shows that under H_2, (2.7.1) holds if and only if $W_0 \leq_{\mathcal{L}} \widetilde{W}_0$, $\sigma_i \leq_{\mathcal{L}} \widetilde{\sigma}_i$ and $-\tau_i \leq_{\mathcal{L}} -\widetilde{\tau}_i$ for all $i \geq 0$.
Under renewal assumptions (2.7.1) reduces to $W_0 \leq_{\mathcal{L}} \widetilde{W}_0$, $\sigma_0 \leq_{\mathcal{L}} \widetilde{\sigma}_0$ and $-\tau_0 \leq_{\mathcal{L}} -\widetilde{\tau}_0$.   □

a) The $G/G/1/\infty$ Queue. The workload sequence in the $G/G/1/\infty$ queue, $\{W_n\}$, satisfies the recurrence equation

$$(2.7.2) \quad W_{n+1} = [W_n + \sigma_n - \tau_n]^+,$$

with initial condition W_0. Take $\xi_n = (\sigma_n, -\tau_n)$ and denote by h the function $h(W, \xi) = [W + \sigma - \tau]^+$.

$\leq_i$ **Monotonicity.** The function $(W, \xi) \rightarrow h(W, \xi)$ being non-decreasing, it follows from (2.5.1) and from the fact that Loynes' technique applies to (2.7.2) that both the transient and the stationary distributions of W_n are $\leq_i$-non-decreasing functions of the sequence $(W_0, \xi_0, \xi_1, \cdots)$.

Example 2.7.1 Consider the following two $GI/GI/1/\infty$ queues. Both queues have 0 initial workload. Queue 1 has its inter-arrival times $\{\tau_n\}$ exponentially distributed with parameter 1, and its service times $\{\sigma_n\}$ are distributed according to a Gamma distribution of parameters $\lambda = 1/4$, $n = 2$. Queue 2 has its service times $\{\tilde{\tau}_n\}$ uniformly distributed on $[0, 1]$ and its service times $\{\tilde{\sigma}_n\}$ are Γ of parameter $\lambda = 1/4$, $n = 3$. We immediately check from the analytical criteria of § 2.2 that $\tilde{\tau}_0 \leq_i \tau_0$ and $\sigma_0 \leq_i \tilde{\sigma}_0$. Let $\{W_n\}$ and $\{\tilde{W}_n\}$ denote the workload sequences in queue 1 and 2 respectively. Since we are under renewal assumptions, we conclude from Remark 2.7.1 that $W_n \leq_i \tilde{W}_n$ for all n. This results extends to the steady state regimes in view of Example 2.6.1. In particular, the steady state distributions W and $\tilde{W}$ satisfy the tail comparison property $P(W > x) \leq P(\tilde{W} > x)$ for all $x \in \mathbb{R}_+$. □

Example 2.7.2 Consider the following two $G/G/1/\infty$ queues. Both queues have 0 initial workload. The sequence (σ_n, τ_n) of queue 1 satisfies Assumption H_1, and the same property holds for the sequence $(\tilde{\sigma}_n, \tilde{\tau}_n)$ of queue 2. We have in addition $\sigma_n = \alpha_n + f(\tau_n)$ (resp. $\tilde{\sigma}_n = \tilde{\alpha}_n + f(\tilde{\tau}_n)$), where α_n and τ_n (resp. $\tilde{\alpha}_n$ and $\tilde{\tau}_n$) are independent and $f : \mathbb{R}_+ \rightarrow \mathbb{R}_+$ is non-increasing. Then $\alpha_n \leq_i \tilde{\alpha}_n$ and $\tilde{\tau}_n \leq_i \tau_n$ for all n imply that $(\sigma_n, -\tau_n) \leq_i (\tilde{\sigma}_n, -\tilde{\tau}_n)$, for all n, so that $W_n \leq_i \tilde{W}_n$ for all n. □

$\leq_{icx}$ **Monotonicity.** The function $(W, \xi) \rightarrow h(W, \xi)$ in (2.7.2) is non-decreasing and convex. The transient and the stationary distributions of W_n are hence $\leq_{icx}$-non-decreasing functions of the sequence (W_0, ξ_n), as a consequence of (2.5.2). In other words, any decrease of the variability of the initial condition and of the sequence $\sigma_n - \tau_n$ results in an increased variability of the transient and stationary workload.

Example 2.7.3 (Continuation of Example 2.3.1) Queue 1 and queue 2 are $GI/GI/1/\infty$ queues, with zero initial workload and with the same inter-arrival time c.d.f. The service times σ_n of queue 1 are Erlang k and those of queue 2 are exponentially distributed with the same mean as those of queue 1. Since we are under renewal assumptions, the fact that $\sigma_0 \leq_{cx} \tilde{\sigma}_0$ implies that $W_n \leq_{icx} \tilde{W}_n$ for all n. In particular $E[W_n^l] \leq E[\tilde{W}_n^l]$ for all $n \geq 0$ and $l \geq 0$ such that the expectations are finite. □

Example 2.7.4 Under renewal assumptions, we obtain from (2.5.2) that $\tau_0 \leq_{cx} \tilde{\tau}_0$ and $\sigma_0 \leq_{cx} \tilde{\sigma}_0$ imply $W_n \leq_{icx} \tilde{W}_n$, for all n. □

Extremal Properties of $G/G/1/\infty$ Queues. This subsection is a continuation of the example of the introduction and shows more precisely in what sense determinism is desirable. Let $\{W_n\}$ be workload sequence in a

$G/G/1$ queue, where $\{\sigma_n\}$, $\{\tau_n\}$ and the initial condition W_0 are mutually independent.

Let W_n^1 (resp. W_n^2), $n = 0, 1, \ldots$, be the workload in the $D/G/1$ (resp. $G/D/1$) queue obtained by keeping the same service (resp. inter-arrival) time sequence and the same initial condition, and by replacing the inter-arrival (resp. service) times by their mean value. The following property holds.

(2.7.3) $W_n \geq_{\mathrm{icx}} W_n^i, \quad i = 1, 2, \ n \geq 0.$

Proof: Let $\xi_n = (\sigma_n, -\tau_n)$, $\tilde{\xi}_n^1 = (\sigma_n, -E^0[\tau])$ and $\tilde{\xi}_n^2 = (E^0[\sigma], \tau_n)$, $n \geq 0$. If $(\Omega, \mathcal{F}, P^0)$ denotes the probability space on which these variables are defined let $\mathcal{G}^1$ and $\mathcal{G}^2$ denote the sub σ-field of $\mathcal{F}$ generated by the sequences $\{\tau_n\}$, $n \geq 0$, and $\{\sigma_n\}$, $n \geq 0$, respectively. It is clear from the independence assumptions that for all $n \geq 0$,

$$E^0[(\xi_0, \ldots, \xi_n) \mid \mathcal{G}^i] = (\tilde{\xi}_0^i, \ldots, \tilde{\xi}_n^i), \quad i = 1, 2,$$

so that

$$(\tilde{\xi}_0^i, \tilde{\xi}_1^i, \ldots) \leq_{\mathrm{cx}} (\xi_0, \xi_1, \ldots),$$

which completes the proof in view of (2.5.2).   □

The $G/G/s/\infty$ Queue. The notations are those of Chapter 2. Take $\xi_n = (\sigma_n, -\tau_n)$. The ordered workload vector satisfies the recurrence relation $W_{n+1} = h(W_n, \xi_n)$, where

(2.7.4) $h(W, \xi) = \mathcal{R}(W + \sigma e - \tau i)^+,$

$e = (1, 0, \ldots, 0), i = (1, \ldots, 1)$, and $\mathcal{R}$ is the operator arranging vectors of $\mathbb{R}^s$ in increasing order.

$\leq_i$ Monotonicity.

The function $h : \mathbb{R}^s \times \mathbb{R}^2 \to \mathbb{R}^s$ is non-decreasing, and it follows from (2.5.1) that the transient and the stationary distributions of W_n are $\leq_i$- non-decreasing functions of the sequence $(W_0, \xi_0, \xi_1, \ldots)$. Whenever Assumptions H_1 or H_2 are satisfied, this property translates into the same monotonicity properties with respect to $W_0, (\sigma_0, -\tau_0), \ldots$ as in the $G/G/1/\infty$ case.

2.8 Other Queueing Systems

Finite Capacity Queues in Tandem with Blocking. This section focuses on the queueing network defined in § 8 of Chapter 2. Let $\xi_n = (\sigma_n, \sigma_{n+1}, \tau_n)$, where σ_n is the vector of service times of customer n.

(2.8.1)   If $\{\xi_0, \xi_1, \ldots\} \leq_{cx} \{\widetilde{\xi}_0, \widetilde{\xi}_1, \ldots\}$, then the sequences of waiting times $(W_n^j)^0$ associated with the initial condition 0, are such that $(W_n)^0 \leq_{icx} (\widetilde{W}_n)^0$, for all $n \geq 0$.

Proof: The recurrence relation (7.2.3) of Chapter 2, that is,

$$W_{n+1}^k = \max_j (W_n^j + l_n^{j,k} - \tau_n)^+, \ n \geq 0, \ k = 1, \ldots, J,$$

with

$$l_n^{j,k} = \begin{cases} \sum_{i=1}^{j} \sigma_n^i - \sum_{i=1}^{j-1} \sigma_{n+1}^i, & \text{if } 1 \leq j \leq k+1; \\ -\infty & \text{otherwise} \end{cases}$$

is of the form $W_{n+1} = h(W_n, \xi_n)$, where the mapping h satisfies the assumptions of (2.5.2)-cx. $\square$

Under renewal type assumptions, namely the $(J+1)$ random sequences $\{\sigma_n^j\}$, $n \geq 0$ and $\{\tau_n\}$ are independent and each of them is an i.i.d. sequence, the condition $\{\xi_0, \xi_1, \ldots\} \leq_{cx} \{\widetilde{\xi}_0, \widetilde{\xi}_1, \ldots\}$ reduces to the two conditions $\tau_0 \leq_{cx} \widetilde{\tau}_0$ and $\sigma_0 \leq_{cx} \widetilde{\sigma}_0$.

Assume that the driving sequences $\{\xi_n\}$ and $\{\widetilde{\xi}_n\}$ are stationary and ergodic, and that the system is stable for both sequences (see § 8 of Chapter 2 for the stability condition). Since the unique stationary regimes are a.s. limits of the increasing sequences $(W_n)^0 \circ \theta^{-n}$ and $(\widetilde{W}_n)^0 \circ \theta^{-n}$, respectively, the comparison result on the stationary regimes follows from the considerations of § 2.6. $\square$

In this model, a $\leq_{icx}$-increase of the service times does not necessary result in an $\leq_{icx}$-increase of the vector of waiting times W_n.

Queues in a Random Environment. The setting is as in $G/G/1/\infty$ queues except now that the service is not given at unit rate, but at a random rate A_t. More precisely $(A_t, \ t \in \mathbb{R})$ is a non-negative process being compatible with the shift θ_t in the sense that $A_t \circ \theta_s = A_{t+s}$, $s, t \in \mathbb{R}$. The maximum amount of service which can be provided during the interval $[T_n, T_{n+1}]$ is

$$(2.8.3)   \widetilde{\tau}_n = \int_{T_n}^{T_{n+1}} A_s ds$$

and $\widetilde{\tau}_n = \widetilde{\tau} \circ \theta_n$, $n \in \mathbb{Z}$ on $\{T_0 = 0\}$. The evolution equation for the workload process is hence

$$\widetilde{W}_{n+1} = (\widetilde{W}_n + \sigma_n - \widetilde{\tau}_n)^+.$$

As we saw in Chapter 2, a sufficient condition for the existence of a finite stationary workload $\widetilde{W}$ is $E^0[\sigma] < E^0[\widetilde{\tau}]$. In addition $E^0[\sigma] > E^0[\widetilde{\tau}]$ implies that there exists no such finite stationary workload. Observe that

$$(2.8.4) \quad E^0[\widetilde{\tau}] = E^0\Big[\int_0^{T_1} A_s ds\Big] = E^0\Big[\int_0^{T_1} A_0 \circ \theta_s ds\Big]$$

and therefore, by the inversion formula (4.1.2a) of Chapter 1,

$$E^0\Big[\int_0^{T_1} A_0 \circ \theta_s ds\Big] = \frac{1}{\lambda} E[A_0],$$

where $\frac{1}{\lambda} = E^0[\tau]$. Thus

$$(2.8.5) \quad E^0[\widetilde{\tau}] = E[A_0]E^0[\tau].$$

Therefore if

$$(2.8.6) \quad E^0[\sigma] < E^0[\tau]E[A_0],$$

there exists a finite stationary workload $\widetilde{W} = \widetilde{M}_\infty$, where $\widetilde{M}_\infty = \lim_{n\to\infty} \uparrow \widetilde{M}_n$ and

$$(2.8.7) \quad \begin{aligned} &\widetilde{M}_0 = 0, \\ &\widetilde{M}_{n+1} \circ \theta = (\widetilde{M}_n + \sigma - \widetilde{\tau})^+. \end{aligned}$$

We wish to compare $\widetilde{W}$ to W, the stationary workload corresponding to a constant service rate $a = E[A_0]$. We have $W = M_\infty = \lim_{n\to\infty} \uparrow M_n$, where M_n is given by

$$M_0 = 0$$
$$M_{n+1} \circ \theta = (M_n + \sigma - a\tau)^+.$$

Notice that W will also be finite under condition (2.8.6).

(2.8.8) If $(A_t, \ t \in \mathbb{R})$ is independent of $(\sigma_n, \tau_n, \ n \in \mathbb{Z})$ (under P^0 or equivalently under P), then $\widetilde{W}_n \geq_{\mathrm{icx}} W_n$, for all n. If in addition (2.8.6) is satisfied, then $\widetilde{W} \geq_{\mathrm{icx}} W$.

Proof: In view of the results of § 2.7, it suffices to prove that for all n,

$$(\sigma_0, -a\tau_0, \sigma_1, -a\tau_1, \ldots, \sigma_n, -a\tau_n) \leq_{\mathrm{cx}} (\sigma_0, -\widetilde{\tau}_0, \sigma_1, -\widetilde{\tau}_1, \ldots, \sigma_n, -\widetilde{\tau}_n).$$

Let $\mathcal{G}_n$ be the σ-field generated by $\{\sigma_i, \tau_i\}$, $0 \leq i \leq n$. It suffices to show that $E^0[\widetilde{\tau}_i | \mathcal{G}_n] = a\tau_i$ a.s. But

$$E^0[\widetilde{\tau}_i | \mathcal{G}_n] = E^0\Big[\int_{T_i}^{T_{i+1}} A_s ds | \mathcal{G}_n\Big] = \int_{-\infty}^{+\infty} E^0[A_s 1_{(T_i, T_{i+1}]} | \mathcal{G}_n] ds \quad \text{a.s.}$$

But, using the measurability of T_i, T_{i+1} with respect to $\mathcal{G}_n$ and the independence assumption, we obtain the a.s. equalities

$$\int_{-\infty}^{+\infty} E^0[A_s 1_{(T_i, T_{i+1}]} | \mathcal{G}_n] ds = \int_{T_i}^{T_{i+1}} E^0[A_s | \mathcal{G}_n] ds = \int_{T_i}^{T_{i+1}} E^0[A_s] ds = a\tau_i,$$

where we have also used that $P = P^0$ on $\sigma\{(A_t, t \in \mathbb{R})\}$.   □

3 Association Properties of Queues

3.1 Association of Random Variables

The $\mathbb{R}$-valued random vector $X = (X_1, \ldots, X_n)$ is said to be *associated* if the inequality

(3.1.1) $E[f(X)g(X)] \geq E[f(X)]E[g(X)]$

holds for all *non-decreasing* mappings $f, g : \mathbb{R}^n \to \mathbb{R}$, for which the involved expectations exist. Thus, in particular, for all n-tuples of non-negative non-decreasing functions $f_i : \mathbb{R} \to \mathbb{R}_+$

$$E[\prod_{i=1}^{n} f_i(X_i)] \geq \prod_{i=1}^{n} E[f_i(X_i)] = E[\prod_{i=1}^{n} f_i(\overline{X}_i)].$$

Let γ be any permutation of $\{1, \ldots, n\}$; since the association of the vector $(X_1, \ldots, X_n)$ is equivalent to that of $(X_{\gamma(1)}, \ldots, X_{\gamma(n)})$, we will also speak of the association property of the *set* of random variables $\{X_1, \ldots, X_n\}$.

The sequence of $\mathbb{R}$-valued random variables $\{X_n\}$, $n \geq 1$, is said to be associated if the random variables $\{X_1, \ldots, X_n\}$ are associated for all $n \geq 1$. This notion is extended to $\mathbb{R}^k$ valued sequences by requiring that the set of all coordinates be associated.

The association property can often be established without computing explicitly the joint distribution of the variables. This can be done for instance by using the following 'calculus'

(a) *The set consisting of a single random variable is associated;*
(b) *The union of independent sets of associated random variables forms a set of associated random variables;*
(c) *Any subset of a set of associated random variables forms a set of associated random variables;*
(d) *For any non-decreasing function $\phi : \mathbb{R}^n \to \mathbb{R}$, and any set of associated random variables $\{X_1, \ldots, X_n\}$, the set of random variables $\{\phi(X_1, \ldots, X_n), X_1, \ldots, X_n\}$ is associated.*

As a direct consequence of (a) and (b), any set of mutually independent random variables is associated.

Proof: Properties (c) and (d) follow immediately from the definition.

Proof of (a).

Let X be a real-valued random variable. We have to prove that for all pairs of non-decreasing functions f and $g : \mathbb{R} \to \mathbb{R}$,

$$E[f(X)g(X)] \geq E[f(X)]E[g(X)],$$

at least whenever the involved expectations exist. This last relation is called Harris' Inequality. Let X' and X'' be two random variables defined on the same probability space and such that X' and X'' are independent and both variables are distributed like X. For all x' and x'' in $\mathbb{R}$ and for all f and g as above

$$\left(f(x') - f(x'')\right)\left(g(x') - g(x'')\right) \geq 0.$$

Therefore

$$E\left[\left(f(X') - f(X'')\right)\left(g(X') - g(X'')\right)\right] \geq 0,$$

which implies Harris' inequality in view of the statistical assumptions on X' and X'', provided the expectations on both sides of this inequality exist. $\square$

Proof of (b)

Let $X = (X_1, \dots, X_n)$ and $Y = (Y_1, \dots, Y_m)$ be associated and X and Y be independent. Let f and $g : \mathbb{R}^{m+n} \to \mathbb{R}$ be two non-decreasing functions. Writing f (resp. g) for $f(X_1, \dots, X_n, Y_1, \dots, Y_m)$ (resp. $g(X_1, \dots, Y_m)$), we have

$$E[fg] - E[f]E[g] = E\left[E[fg|Y]\right] - E\left[E[f|Y]E[g|Y]\right]$$
$$+ E\left[E[f|Y]E[g|Y]\right] - E\left[E[f|Y]\right]E\left[E[g|Y]\right].$$

In view of the assumption that X is a set of associated random variables, $E[fg|Y] - E[f|Y]E[g|Y] \geq 0$ and hence

$$E\left[E[fg|Y]\right] - E\left[E[f|Y]E[g|Y]\right] \geq 0.$$

The functions $Y \to E[f|Y]$ and $Y \to E[g|Y]$ are non-decreasing, so that

$$E\left[E[f|Y]E[g|Y]\right] - E\left[E[f|Y]\right]E\left[E[g|Y]\right] \geq 0,$$

since Y is associated. $\square$

The $\mathbb{R}$-valued random variables $\{\overline{X}_1, \dots, \overline{X}_n\}$ are said to form an *independent version* of the random variables $\{X_1, \dots, X_n\}$ if
   (a) The random variables $\{\overline{X}_1, \dots, \overline{X}_n\}$ are *mutually independent*, and
   (b) For every $1 \leq i \leq n$ the random variables X_i and $\overline{X}_i$ have the *same* probability distribution.

In view of the definition of association

(3.1.3) *If the random variables $\{X_1, \dots, X_n\}$ are associated, then $\overline{X} \leq_{\mathrm{ip}} X$.*

Example 3.1.1 Let $\{X_1, ..., X_n\}$ be associated. The fact that $f_t(x) = \prod_{i=1}^{n} 1_{x_i > t}$ belongs to {ip} implies the ordering relation

(3.1.4) $\min_{\{i=1,...,n\}} X_i \geq_i \min_{\{i=1,...,n\}} \overline{X}_i.$

In the same vein, if the random variables $\{X_1, ..., X_n\}$ are associated,

(3.1.5) $\max_{\{i=1,...,n\}} X_i \leq_i \max_{\{i=1,...,n\}} \overline{X}_i.$

□

These two relations suggest a natural way of generating *product form bounds* on extremal statistics, whenever the association property holds (see Example 3.2.2 below).

3.2 Bounds by Association

We now outline how the association properties can be established for the solutions of (2.4.1) and point out some instances where this property has interesting practical implications.

(3.2.1) *Assume that the function $(y, \xi) \rightarrow h(y, \xi)$ is non-decreasing. If the driving sequence $\{\xi_n\}$, $n \geq 0$ and the initial condition η forms a set of associated random variables , then the sequence $\{y_n\}$, $n \geq 0$, is also associated.*

Proof: The proof is based on the association calculus given in § 3.1 and on (2.4.1). Take as induction hypothesis that the random variables $\{y_k, 0 \leq k \leq n, \xi_k, k \geq 0\}$ be associated for some $n \geq 0$. Then rule (d) of the association calculus implies the association of the random variables $\{y_k, 0 \leq k \leq n+1, \xi_k, k \geq 0\}$, since the mapping $(y, \xi) \rightarrow h(y, \xi)$ is non-decreasing.

□

Example 3.2.1 *The $G/G/s/\infty$ queue.* A direct consequence of (3.2.1) above and of (3.1.1) of Chapter 2, is that the workload process $\{W_n\}$, in $GI/GI/s/\infty$ queues is associated, provided the initial condition is independent of the service and inter-arrival times. In particular, the components of W_n, that is, the workload of the servers at the n-th arrival time are associated. A similar property also holds when the sequence

$(W_0, \sigma_0, -\tau_0, \ldots, \sigma_1, -\tau_1, \ldots)$

has associated rather than independent components. Thus

$P^0[W_n^1 > t_1, \ldots, W_n^s > t_s] \geq P^0[W_n^1 > t_1] \ldots P^0[W_n^s > t_s], \quad (n \geq 0),$

for all $t_1, \ldots, t_s$ in $\mathbb{R}_+$. Using the associated Loynes' sequence, we obtain that this property also extends to the stationary workload.   □

Besides the characterization of the type of correlation of the workload process $\{W_n\}$, $n \geq 0$, the association property can also be used to obtain bounds on the solution of certain vectorial recurrences of the form (2.4.1).

Example 3.2.2 *Coupled $G/G/1/\infty$ queues.* Consider a network made of K $G/G/1/\infty$ FIFO queues which are coupled in that they share the same arrival process. Namely, at the arrival time T_n of some stationary and ergodic point process N, each of the K queues receives its n-th customer. Let $\sigma_n \overset{\text{def}}{=} (\sigma_n^1, \ldots, \sigma_n^K)$, where σ_n^k is the service time of the n-th customer of queue $k \in \{1, \ldots, K\}$. The waiting times of customer n in queue k satisfy the recurrence relations

$$W_{n+1}^k = \max(W_n^k + \sigma_n^k - \tau_n)^+,$$

where $\tau_n = T_{n+1} - T_n$. The global sojourn time of the n-th customer is defined as the duration between T_n and the time when all the customers arrived at T_n have completed their service times, that is,

$$(3.2.2) \quad B_n = \max_{k=1,\ldots,K} R_n^k,$$

where

$$(3.2.3) \quad R_n^k = W_n^k + \sigma_n^k.$$

If the initial condition, the inter-arrival times and the service times are associated (for instance independent), then $W_n = (W_n^1, \ldots, W_n^K)$ is also associated in view of (3.2.1). This association property extends to $R_n = (R_n^1, \ldots, R_n^K)$, so that by (3.1.5)

$$B_n \leq_i \max_{k=1,\ldots,K} \overline{R}_n^k, \quad (n \geq 0),$$

where $\overline{R}_n$ denotes the product form version of R_n. For instance, assume that the arrival process is Poisson of intensity λ and that the marks σ_n^k are independent of the arrival process, i.i.d. and exponentially distributed with parameter μ. Then, whenever $\lambda < \mu$, B_n couples in finite time with a stationary and ergodic sequence $B \circ \theta^n$ (because W_n couples with a stationary sequence). Therefore

$$B \leq_i \max_{k=1,\ldots,K} A_k,$$

where the random variables A_k are i.i.d. and exponentially distributed with parameter $\mu - \lambda$ (recall that the stationary sojourn times in queue k are exponentially distributed with parameter $\mu - \lambda$). In particular

$$(3.2.4) \quad E^0[B] \leq \frac{1}{\mu - \lambda} H(K),$$

with $H(k) = 1 + 1/2 + \ldots + 1/k$. $\qquad\qquad\qquad\qquad\qquad\qquad\quad \square$

Example 3.2.3 *Bounds for $GI/GI/1/\infty$ queues.* Due to the renewal assumption, the random variables $b_n = \sum_{i=1}^{n}(\sigma_{-i} - \tau_{-i})$, $n \geq 1$, are associated. From (2.2.3) of Chapter 2

$$M_\infty = \sup_{n \geq 0} b_n,$$

and using (3.1.5) plus a limit argument

$$P^0(M_\infty \leq x) \geq \prod_{n \geq 1} P(b_n \leq x), \quad (x \geq 0).$$

Now for all $s \geq 0$,

$$\exp(sx)P(b_n > x) \leq \exp(sb_n), \quad (n \geq 1).$$

Thus whenever the function $\Psi_\sigma = E(\exp(s\sigma))$ is finite in a right neighbourhood of 0 (for instance it is rational in s)

$$(3.2.5) \quad P(b_n > x) \leq \inf_{s \geq 0} (\Psi_\sigma(s)\Psi_\tau(-s))^n \exp(-sx) \overset{\text{def}}{=} K(n, x).$$

Thus

$$(3.2.6) \quad P^0(M_\infty \leq x) \geq \prod_{n \geq 1}(1 - K(n, x)).$$

Note that this bound is non-degenerate since the infinite product converges to a non-zero limit if $\rho < 1$. Indeed the infimum in (3.2.5) is reached for s_n such that

$$\frac{d}{ds}\log(\Psi_\sigma(s)\Psi_\tau(-s)) = \frac{x}{n}$$

and thus, when n tends to ∞ s_n tends to s^*, solution of

$$\frac{d}{ds}\log(\Psi_\sigma(s)\Psi_\tau(-s)) = 0.$$

But s^* is such that

$$\delta \overset{\text{def}}{=} \Psi_\sigma(s^*)\Psi_\tau(-s^*) < 1$$

because the function $\Psi_\sigma(s)\Psi_\tau(-s)$ is convex in the domain where $\Psi_\sigma(s)$ is finite, decreasing in $s = 0$ and tends to ∞ when we reach the first singularity. Thus

$$K(n, x) = O(\delta^n \exp(-s^*x))$$

from which we obtain that the infinite product of (3.2.6) is strictly positive.

Note that the same type of arguments can be used to prove instability in the case $\rho > 1$. $\qquad\square$

4 Stochastic Comparison of Time-Stationary Queues

4.1 Comparison of Point Processes

Let N and $\widetilde{N}$ be two stationary point processes, possibly defined on different probability spaces, both with finite intensity and no double points. Let P, P^0, $\widetilde{P}$ and $\widetilde{P}^0$ denote the corresponding stationary and Palm probabilities. The points of N and $\widetilde{N}$ will respectively be denoted T_n and $\widetilde{T}_n$, with the usual convention. Let X $[P]$ denote the c.d.f. of the random variable X under probability P.

Assume that T_1 $[P^0] \leq_{\mathcal{L}} \widetilde{T}_1$ $[\widetilde{P}^0]$. It is not true in general that this comparison property is preserved when passing from the Palm to the stationary probabilities; that is, it is not always true that T_1 $[P] \leq_{\mathcal{L}} \widetilde{T}_1$ $[\widetilde{P}]$, as shown by the following example, where $\mathcal{L} = \{i\}$.

Example 4.1.1 *Feller's paradox revisited.* Assume that N is a Poisson process of intensity 1 and that $\widetilde{N}$ is a renewal process with inter-arrival time c.d.f. equal to that of the random variable $X_u \stackrel{\text{def}}{=} X \vee u$, where X is exponentially distributed with parameter 1, and u is a real and positive constant. Thus T_1 $[P^0] \leq_i \widetilde{T}_1$ $[\widetilde{P}^0]$. However, we can check after some calculations that

$$E_{\widetilde{P}}[\widetilde{T}_1] = \frac{u^2 + 2(1+u)e^{-u}}{2(u + e^{-u})} < E_P[T_1] = 1,$$

for $0 \leq u < u^*$, where u^* is the positive root of the equation $u + 2\exp(-u) - 2 = 0$. Thus, for u in this interval, we cannot have T_1 $[P] \leq_i \widetilde{T}_1$ $[\widetilde{P}]$. $\square$

The preceding example shows that the property

(a) T_n $[P^0] \leq_i \widetilde{T}_n$ $[\widetilde{P}^0]$, for all $n \geq 1$,

does not imply that

(b) T_n $[P] \leq_i \widetilde{T}_n$ $[\widetilde{P}]$, for all $n \geq 1$;

note that for $n \geq 0$, the property $N([0, x)) > n$ is equivalent to $T_{n+1} < x$ P-a.s.; so (b) is equivalent to

(c) $N[0, x)$ $[P] \geq_i \widetilde{N}[0, x)$ $[\widetilde{P}]$, for all $x \in \mathbb{R}_+$.

However, for $\leq_{cx}$, we have:

(4.1.1) *The following two properties are equivalent:*

(d) T_n $[P^0] \leq_{cx} \widetilde{T}_n$ $[\widetilde{P}^0]$, *for all* $n \geq 1$;

(e) $N[0, x)$ $[P] \leq_{cx} \widetilde{N}[0, x)$ $[\widetilde{P}]$, *for all* $x \in \mathbb{R}_+$.

The proof of (4.1.1) is based on the following lemma:

(4.1.2) *Let N be a stationary point process with finite intensity. For all functions $f : \mathbb{R}_+ \to \mathbb{R}$ with $f(0) = 0$, and for all $x > 0$*

$$(4.1.3) \quad E_P\left[f(N[0,x))\right] = \sum_{n=0}^{\infty} (f(n+1) - 2f(n) + f((n-1)^+))\, \lambda E_{P^0}(x - T_n)^+.$$

Proof: When adopting the convention $N[a,b) = 0$ for $a \geq b$, Mecke's formula ((3.3.1), Chapter 1) applied to the function

$$v(\omega, t) = f([N[0, x-t)) - f(N[T_1, x-t))\mathbf{1}_{0 \leq t \leq x}$$

gives

$$\lambda E_{P^0}\left[\int_0^x (f(N[0, x-t)) - f(N[T_1, x-t)))dt\right] = E_P\left[f(N[T_1, x))\right]$$
$$= E_P\left[f(N[0,x))\right],$$

since $v(\theta_t \omega, t) = f(N[t, x)) - f(N[T_1, x))$. From this, it suffices to observe that

$$\int_0^x (f(N[0, x-t)) - f(N[T_1, x-t))) \, dt$$
$$= \sum_{n=0}^{\infty} (f(n+1) - 2f(n) + f((n-1)^+))(x - T_n)^+, \quad P^0 - \text{a.s.}$$

□

Proof of (4.1.1). Assume that (d) holds. This implies that $\lambda = \widetilde{\lambda}$. In addition, $E_{P^0}[(x - T_n)^+] \leq \widetilde{E}_{\widetilde{P}^0}[(x - \widetilde{T}_n)^+]$, for all $x > 0$ and $n \geq 1$, since the function $t \to (x - t)^+$ is convex. If f is a non-decreasing convex function $\mathbb{R}_+ \to \mathbb{R}$, with $f(0) = 0$, the coefficients of the sum in the right-hand side of (4.1.3) are non-negative, and so $E_P[f(N[0,x))] \leq E_{\widetilde{P}}[f(\widetilde{N}[0,x))]$.

For the converse implication, we first observe that (e) also implies $\lambda = \widetilde{\lambda}$. The functions $f_k(x) = (x - k)^+$, $k = 0, \ldots$, are non-decreasing convex and null at the origin. For all $n \geq 1$,

$$f_k(n+1) - 2f_k(n) + f_k((n-1)^+) = \begin{cases} 1, & n = k \\ 0, & \text{otherwise.} \end{cases}$$

Therefore, $E_P[f_k(N[0,x))] \leq E_{\widetilde{P}}[f_k(\widetilde{N}[0,x))]$, for all x implies that

$$E_{P^0}[(x - T_k)^+] \leq E_{\widetilde{P}^0}[(x - \widetilde{T}_k)^+], \quad (x \in \mathbb{R})$$

From (2.2.5), this implies that $-T_k\, [P^0] \leq_{cx} -\widetilde{T}_k\, [\widetilde{P}^0]$, which is equivalent to (d). □

Remark 4.1.1 If N is a renewal process, then (d) is equivalent to $\tau_0 \leq_{cx} \widetilde{\tau}_0$. □

The preceding result also gives the following corollary:

(4.1.4) *For all non-decreasing convex functions* $f : \mathbb{R}_+ \rightarrow \mathbb{R}$, *the function* $\phi(x) = E_P f(N(0, x])$ *is non-decreasing and convex on* $\mathbb{R}_+$.

Proof: Formula (4.1.3) shows that $\phi(x)$ is the sum of convex non-decreasing functions.   □

Example 4.1.2 *Number of customers in the* $M/GI/1/\infty$ *queue.* Let $X(t)$ and $\widetilde{X}(t)$ denote the corlol congestion processes in two FIFO $M/GI/1/\infty$ queues, with the same arrival intensity λ, and with respective service time c.d.f. G and $\widetilde{G}$. Let $W(t)$ and $\widetilde{W}(t)$ denote the corresponding workload processes. We show that

(4.1.5) $G \leq_{\text{icx}} \widetilde{G}$ *implies* $X(0) \leq_{\text{icx}} \widetilde{X}(0)$ *under* P.

We first prove the following equality in distribution:

(4.1.6) $X(0)\ [P] = N(0, W(0+)]\ [P_A^0]$,

where P_A^0 denotes the Palm probability with respect to the arrival process. Due to the PASTA property (see Formula (3.1.5) in Chapter 3), $X(0)\ [P] = X(0-)\ [P_A^0]$. But $X(0-)\ [P_A^0] = X(0+)\ [P_D^0]$, where P_D^0 denotes the Palm distribution of the departure process (see (4.1.5), Chapter 3). Therefore $X(0)\ [P] = X(0+)\ [P_D^0]$. Now, due to the FIFO assumption, the number of customers left by a departing customer coincides with the number of arrivals during its sojourn time. That is $X(0+) = N(S, 0]\ P_D^0$-a.s., where S denotes the (negative) arrival time of the customer which leaves at time 0. The proof of (4.1.6) is concluded from the fact that $N(S, 0]\ [P_D^0] = N(0, W(0+)]\ [P_A^0]$, which follows from a direct pathwise identification and from the cross ergodic theorem of § 7.3, Chapter 1.

For proving (4.1.5), it is thus sufficient to show that

$$N(0, W(0+)]\ [P_A^0] \leq_{\text{icx}} \widetilde{N}(0, \widetilde{W}(0+)]\ [\widetilde{P}_A^0].$$

Since the arrival process is Poisson, $N(0, t]$ is P_A^0-independent of $W(0-)$ for all $t > 0$, with a similar property for the other queue. Therefore the proof will be concluded if we show that

$$\int E_P\left[f(N(0, x])\right] dP_A^0(W(0+) \leq x) \leq \int E_P\left[f(N(0, x])\right] d\widetilde{P}_A^0(\widetilde{W}(0+) \leq x),$$

for all f non-decreasing and convex (in the last equation, we used the fact that both arrival processes have the same law, and that $E_{P_A^0}\left[f(N(0, x])\right] = E_P\left[f(N(0, x])\right]$. Under the foregoing assumptions,

$$W(0-)\ [P_A^0] \leq_{\text{icx}} \widetilde{W}(0-)\ [\widetilde{P}_A^0],$$

provided both queues are stable (see §§ 2.6-2.7). This implies that

$$W(0+)\ [P_A^0] \leq_{\text{icx}} \widetilde{W}(0+)\ [\widetilde{P}_A^0],$$

since $W(0+) = W(0-) + \sigma$, where $W(0-)$ and σ are P_A^0-independent. Thus the proof is concluded from (4.1.4). □

Example 4.1.3 *Finite capacity queues with blocking.* Let $\{X(t)\}$ denote the total number of customers in the tandem queueing system of § 8, Chapter 2. Using the FIFO property of the system, whenever the input process is Poisson and service times are independent and i.i.d., with c.d.f. G^i at queue i, arguments similar to those used in the preceding example show that (with obvious notations) $G^i \leq_{cx} \widetilde{G}^i$ for all i implies $X(0) \leq_{icx} \widetilde{X}(0)$ under P, provided both systems are stable. □

For point processes, determinism is also extremal: let $\widetilde{N}$ be a point process on $(\widetilde{\Omega}, \widetilde{\mathcal{F}}, \widetilde{P})$, with intensity λ. Let N^λ be a *deterministic stationary point process* with intensity λ, defined on $(\Omega, \mathcal{F}, P)$, that is, a point process with all its inter-arrival times equal to $1/\lambda$ (either under the Palm or the stationary probability).

(4.1.7) *For $\widetilde{N}$ and N^λ as above, $N^\lambda([0, x))$ $[P] \leq_{cx} \widetilde{N}([0, x))$ $[\widetilde{P}]$, $\forall x > 0$.*

Proof: The proof follows from (4.1.1) and from the fact that the deterministic distribution with mean n/λ is a $\leq_{cx}$-lower bound for T_n $[P^0]$. □

So in particular, for all stationary point processes N with intensity λ, for all increasing convex functions $f : \mathbb{R} \to \mathbb{R}$,

$$(4.1.8) \quad E\left[f\left(N[0, x)\right)\right] \geq \int_0^1 f\left(\lceil \lambda x - u \rceil\right) du,$$

where $\lceil a \rceil$ is the smallest integer larger than or equal to a.

4.2 Stochastic Comparison under Time-Stationary Probabilities

Let N and $\widetilde{N}$ be two point processes as above. Let $T \stackrel{\text{def}}{=} T_1$ (resp. $\widetilde{T} \stackrel{\text{def}}{=} \widetilde{T}_1$) denote the first positive point of N (resp. $\widetilde{N}$) and X (resp $\widetilde{X}$) be some $\mathbb{R}^n$-valued mark associated with T_0 (resp. $\widetilde{T}_0$). Let $\leq_{\mathcal{L}}$ be one of the integral orderings defined in § 2.1. The aim of the present subsection is to analytically characterize the stochastic comparison properties which should hold between the c.d.f. (T, X) $[P^0]$ and $(\widetilde{T}, \widetilde{X})$ $[\widetilde{P}^0]$ in order to have (T, X) $[P] \leq_{\mathcal{L}} (\widetilde{T}, \widetilde{X})$ $[\widetilde{P}]$. For $t \geq 0$, $x \in \mathbb{R}^n$, let

$$F^0(t, x) \stackrel{\text{def}}{=} P^0[T \leq t, X \leq x], \qquad \widetilde{F}^0(t, x) \stackrel{\text{def}}{=} \widetilde{P}^0[\widetilde{T} \leq t, \widetilde{X} \leq x],$$

and

$$F(t, x) \stackrel{\text{def}}{=} P[T \leq t, X \leq x], \qquad \widetilde{F}(t, x) \stackrel{\text{def}}{=} \widetilde{P}[\widetilde{T} \leq t, \widetilde{X} \leq x].$$

Let $\{I - \mathcal{L}\}$ be the set of functions $\phi : \mathbb{R}^{n+1} \to \mathbb{R}$ which admit an integral representation of the form

$$(4.2.1) \quad \phi(t, x_1, \ldots, x_n) = \int_0^t f(u, x_1, \ldots, x_n) du,$$

for some mapping f in $\mathcal{L}$. We will also use the notation $I - \mathcal{L}^+$ for the set of functions ϕ which admit the representation (4.2.1), with $f \geq 0$. For $n = 0$ (or equivalently for the T-marginal), the set $I - i$ coincides with the set of cx functions on $\mathbb{R}_+$ which vanish at the origin. Similarly $I - i^+$ is just the set of icx functions which vanish at the origin.

(4.2.2) $F \leq_{\mathcal{L}} \tilde{F}$ if and only if for all ϕ in $I - \mathcal{L}$

$$(4.2.3) \quad \frac{E_{P^0}[\phi(T, X)]}{E_{P^0}[T]} \leq \frac{E_{\tilde{P}^0}[\phi(\tilde{T}, \tilde{X})]}{E_{\tilde{P}^0}[\tilde{T}]}.$$

Proof: From the very definition, $F \leq_{\mathcal{L}} \tilde{F}$ if $E_P[f(T, X)] \leq E_{\tilde{P}}[f(\tilde{T}, \tilde{X})]$, for all f in $\mathcal{L}$. From the Palm inversion formula, and since X (resp. $\tilde{X}$) is a mark of N (resp. $\tilde{N}$), this inequality reads

$$\lambda E_{P^0} \left[\int_0^T f(T - u, X) du \right] \leq \tilde{\lambda} E_{\tilde{P}^0} \left[\int_0^{\tilde{T}} f(\tilde{T} - u, \tilde{X}) du \right],$$

or equivalently

$$\lambda E_{P^0} \left[\int_0^T f(u, X) du \right] \leq \tilde{\lambda} E_{\tilde{P}^0} \left[\int_0^{\tilde{T}} f(u, \tilde{X}) du \right].$$

$\square$

For the marginal distributions $F_T(t) = F(t, \infty)$ and $F_T^0 = F^0(t, \infty)$, in view of Formula (4.2.4b) of Chapter 1, (4.2.2) takes the following simplified form:

(4.2.4) $F_T \leq_i \tilde{F}_T$ if and only if for all $x \geq 0$,

$$\frac{1}{E_{P^0}[T]} \int_x^\infty (1 - F_T^0(u)) du \leq \frac{1}{E_{\tilde{P}^0}[\tilde{T}]} \int_x^\infty (1 - \tilde{F}_T^0(u)) du$$

(4.2.5) $F_T \leq_{icx} \tilde{F}_T$ if and only if for all $x \geq 0$,

$$\frac{1}{E_{P^0}[T]} \int_x^\infty \int_u^\infty (1 - F_T^0(v)) dv du \leq \frac{1}{E_{\tilde{P}^0}[\tilde{T}]} \int_x^\infty \int_u^\infty (1 - \tilde{F}_T^0(v)) dv du.$$

Remark 4.2.1 Inequality (4.2.4) is equivalent to

$$\frac{E_{P^0}[(T - x)^+]}{E_{P^0}[T]} \leq \frac{E_{\tilde{P}^0}[(\tilde{T} - x)^+]}{E_{\tilde{P}^0}[\tilde{T}]}, \quad (x \geq 0),$$

and (4.2.5) is equivalent to

$$\frac{1}{E_{P^0}[T]} E_{P^0}[((T-x)^+)^2] \le \frac{1}{E_{\widetilde{P}^0}[\widetilde{T}]} E_{\widetilde{P}^0}[((\widetilde{T}-x)^+)^2], \quad (x \ge 0).$$

$\square$

Similarly, for marks, let $F_X(x) = F(\infty, x)$ and $F_X^0 = F^0(\infty, x)$.

(4.2.6) $F_X \le_{\mathcal{L}} \widetilde{F}_X$ if and only if for all $f : \mathbb{R}^n \to \mathbb{R}$ in $\mathcal{L}$

$$\frac{E_{P^0}[Tf(X)]}{E_{P^0}[T]} \le \frac{E_{\widetilde{P}^0}[\widetilde{T}f(\widetilde{X})]}{E_{\widetilde{P}^0}[\widetilde{T}]},$$

Remark 4.2.2 If X and T are P-independent, and $\widetilde{X}$ and $\widetilde{T}$ are $\widetilde{P}$-independent, then obviously $(T, X) [P] \le_{\mathcal{L}} (\widetilde{T}, \widetilde{X}) [\widetilde{P}]$ if and only if $T [P] \le_{\mathcal{L}} \widetilde{T} [\widetilde{P}]$ and $X [P] \le_{\mathcal{L}} \widetilde{X} [\widetilde{P}]$ (see (2.2.6)). In addition, in view of (4.2.6). $X [P] \le_{\mathcal{L}} \widetilde{X} [\widetilde{P}]$ if and only if $X [P^0] \le_{\mathcal{L}} \widetilde{X} [\widetilde{P}^0]$. $\square$

Relations with Integral Orders. For $\mathcal{L}$ any set of functions as in § 2.1, let $\le_{S-\mathcal{L}}$ be the partial semi-order on $\mathcal{D}(\mathbb{R}^{n+1})$ defined by $F^0 \le_{S-\mathcal{L}} \widetilde{F}^0$ if, for all ϕ in $I - \mathcal{L}$.

$$\frac{\int_{\mathbb{R}^{n+1}} \phi(t, x) F^0(dt, dx)}{\int_{\mathbb{R}} t F_T^0(dt)} \le \frac{\int_{\mathbb{R}^{n+1}} \phi(t, x) \widetilde{F}^0(dt, dx)}{\int_{\mathbb{R}} t \widetilde{F}_T^0(dt)}$$

or equivalently if $F \le_{\mathcal{L}} \widetilde{F}$.

Unlike the integral orders defined in § 2, $\le_{S-\mathcal{L}}$ does not apply to any c.d.f., but only to those of the form $(T, X) [P^0]$, as defined above. In particular, $T [P^0]$ should have its support on $\mathbb{R}_+$ and be such that $P^0(T = 0) = 0$.

The relationships between the $\le_{S-\mathcal{L}}$ orders and the integral orders of § 2.1 are summarized below:

(4.2.7)
$$
\begin{array}{ccccc}
\le_{I-i} & \Rightarrow & \le_{S-i} & \Rightarrow & \le_{S-I-i+} \\
 & & \Downarrow & & \\
\le_i & \Rightarrow & \le_{I-i+} & &
\end{array}
$$

The proof of (4.2.7) uses the following result:

(4.2.8) $F^0 \le_{S-i} \widetilde{F}^0$ implies $E_{P^0}[T] \le E_{\widetilde{P}^0}[\widetilde{T}]$.

Proof: The assumption implies $F_T^0 \le_{S-i} \widetilde{F}_T^0$. From (4.2.4)

$$\frac{1}{E_{P^0}[T]} \frac{1}{x} \int_0^x (1 - F_T^0(u)) du \ge \frac{1}{E_{\widetilde{P}^0}[\widetilde{T}]} \frac{1}{x} \int_0^x (1 - \widetilde{F}_T^0(u)) du.$$

We conclude the proof by letting x tend to zero and by using the assumption that $F_T^0(0) = \widetilde{F}_T^0(0) = 0$. $\square$

We now prove the properties stated in (4.2.7).

(4.2.9) $F^0 \leq_{\text{I}-\text{i}} \widetilde{F}^0 \Rightarrow F^0 \leq_{\text{S}-\text{i}} \widetilde{F}^0$.

Proof: $F^0 \leq_{\text{I}-\text{i}} \widetilde{F}^0$ implies $F_T^0 \leq_{\text{cx}} \widetilde{F}_T^0$, which in turn implies $E_{P^0}[T] = E_{\widetilde{P}^0}[\widetilde{T}]$. From the very definition, $F^0 \leq_{\text{I}-\text{i}} \widetilde{F}^0$ reads

$$\int_{\mathbb{R}^{n+1}} f(t,x) F^0(dt,dx) \leq \int_{\mathbb{R}^{n+1}} f(t,x) \widetilde{F}^0(dt,dx),$$

for all $f \in \text{I}-\text{i}$. Dividing both terms by $E_{P^0}[T] = E_{\widetilde{P}^0}[\widetilde{T}]$, we obtain $F^0 \leq_{\text{S}-\text{i}} \widetilde{F}^0$. $\qquad\square$

(4.2.10) $F^0 \leq_{\text{S}-\text{i}} \widetilde{F}^0 \Rightarrow F^0 \leq_{\text{I}-\text{i}^+} \widetilde{F}^0$.

Proof: If $f \in \text{I}-\text{i}^+$, then

$$E_{P^0}[f(T,X)] \leq \frac{E_{P^0}[T]}{E_{\widetilde{P}^0}[\widetilde{T}]} E_{\widetilde{P}^0}[f(\widetilde{T},\widetilde{X})] \leq E_{\widetilde{P}^0}[f(\widetilde{T},\widetilde{X})],$$

where the last inequality follows from (4.2.8). $\qquad\square$

The remaining implications of (4.2.7) follow from

(4.2.11) $F^0 \leq_{\text{i}} \widetilde{F}^0 \Rightarrow F^0 \leq_{\text{I}-\text{i}^+} \widetilde{F}^0$.

Proof: Use the inclusion $I - \text{i}^+ \subset \text{i}$. $\qquad\square$

When restricting the above relations to the marginal c.d.f. F_T, we obtain the following relations (for c.d.f. in $\mathcal{D}(\mathbb{R})$):

(4.2.12) $\quad \leq_{\text{cx}} \Rightarrow \leq_{\text{S}-\text{i}} \Rightarrow \leq_{\text{icx}}$.

In words, for $F_T \leq_{\text{i}} \widetilde{F}_T$ to hold, it is enough to have $F_T^0 \leq_{\text{cx}} \widetilde{F}_T^0$. However, it is possible to have $F_T^0 \leq_{\text{icx}} \widetilde{F}_T^0$ and not $F_T \leq_{\text{i}} \widetilde{F}_T$, as exemplified below.

Example 4.2.1 *Example of c.d.f. in $\mathcal{D}(\mathbb{R}+)$ such that $F^0 \leq_{\text{icx}} \widetilde{F}^0$, but F^0 and $\widetilde{F}^0$ do not compare for $\leq_{\text{S}-\text{i}}$.* Let Φ be a c.d.f. in $\mathcal{D}(\mathbb{R}_+)$ and let u_0 be a real number such that $\Phi(u_0-) > 0$. Let Ψ be the c.d.f. in $\mathcal{D}(\mathbb{R}_+)$ defined by

$$\Psi(x) = \Phi(x) 1_{x \geq u_0}.$$

It is clear that $\Phi \leq_{\text{i}} \Psi$ and hence $\Phi \leq_{\text{icx}} \Psi$. However, the relation $\Phi \leq_{\text{S}-\text{i}} \Psi$ does not hold. Indeed, if this were true, using (4.2.4), we would have

$$\frac{\int_x^\infty (1 - \Phi(u)) du}{\int_0^\infty (1 - \Phi(u)) du} \leq \frac{\int_x^\infty (1 - \Psi(u)) du}{\int_0^\infty (1 - \Psi(u)) du},$$

for all x. But this is not possible for $x \geq u_0$ since $\int_x^\infty (1 - \Phi(u)) du = \int_x^\infty (1 - \Psi(u)) du$, whereas $\int_0^\infty (1 - \Psi(u)) du > \int_0^\infty (1 - \Phi(u)) du$. $\qquad\square$

Example 4.2.2 *Example of c.d.f. in $\mathcal{D}(\mathbb{R}_+)$ such that $F^0 \leq_{\text{S}-\text{i}} \widetilde{F}^0$, but F^0 and $\widetilde{F}^0$ do not compare for $\leq_{\text{cx}}$.* Take $F^0 = F_T^0$ deterministic with mean λ^{-1}

and $\widetilde{F}^0 = \widetilde{F}_T^0$ exponential with mean μ^{-1}, and assume that $\lambda > \mu$. The last assumption precludes the property $F^0 \leq_{\mathrm{cx}} \widetilde{F}^0$. F_T is uniform on $[0, \lambda^{-1}]$, and $\widetilde{F}_T$ is exponential with parameter μ. Thus

$$F(x) = (\lambda x) \wedge 1 \geq \widetilde{F}(x) = 1 - \exp^{-\mu x}, \quad (x \geq 0),$$

so that $F^0 \leq_{\mathrm{s-i}} \widetilde{F}^0$. □

4.3 Comparison of Queues

The results which are proved in §§ 2.4-2.8, on the stochastic monotonicity of queues, are mainly based on the recurrence relations satisfied by imbedded sequences. Typically, we used these recurrences to show how a 'stochastic increase' of the Palm distribution of the driving sequence leads to an increase of the Palm distribution of the imbedded sequence. The latter is usually imbedded in a continuous time process like for instance the workload process in the $G/G/1/\infty$ queue. The aim of the present section is to investigate the conditions which guarantee a similar stochastic increase for this continuous time process.

Example 4.3.1 Let $W(t)$ and $\widetilde{W}(t)$ denote the workload processes in two $G/G/1/\infty$ queues, with associated arrival point process (N, P) and $(\widetilde{N}, \widetilde{P})$, respectively. It is not true in general that $W(0)$ $[P^0] \leq_{\mathrm{i}} \widetilde{W}(0)$ $[\widetilde{P}^0]$ implies that $W(0)$ $[P] \leq_{\mathrm{i}} \widetilde{W}(0)$ $[\widetilde{P}]$, as shown by the following counter-example: the driving sequence of the first queue is $\{\tau_n, \sigma_n\}$, with $\sigma_n = \tau_n$, and that of the second queue is $\{\widetilde{\tau}_n, \widetilde{\sigma}_n\}$, also with $\widetilde{\sigma}_n = \widetilde{\tau}_n$. We have $W(0) = T_1$ and $\widetilde{W}(0) = \widetilde{T}_1$, so that a simple counter-example is obtained from Example 4.1.1. □

Let $y \in \mathbb{R}^K$ be a finite solution of the equation

(4.3.1) $y \circ \theta = h(y, \eta)$,

associated with a stochastic recurrence defined as in (2.4.1). This solution is defined on the Palm space $(\Omega, \mathcal{F}, P^0, \theta)$ of a stationary point process N. Let $y(t)$, $t \in \mathbb{R}$ be the $\mathbb{R}^K$-valued stochastic process on $(\Omega, \mathcal{F}, P^0)$ defined by

(4.3.2) $y(t) = g(t - T_n, y \circ \theta^n, \xi \circ \theta^n), \quad T_n \leq t < T_{n+1}, \quad P^0-\text{a.s.}$,

where ξ is some integrable $\mathbb{R}^M$-valued random variable, and where g is assumed to admit left-hand limits with respect to the variable t. It is assumed that the consistency relation

$$g(T-, y, \xi) = h(y, \eta)$$

holds, or equivalently that $y(T_n-) = y \circ \theta^n$, P^0-a.s. The stochastic process $y(t)$, initially defined on the Palm space of N, also admits a time stationary version such that $y(\omega, t) = y(\theta_t(\omega), 0)$, P-a.s.

Example 4.3.2 The workload in the $G/G/1/\infty$ queue (see § 1.2, Chapter 2), is obtained when taking $\eta = (\sigma, \tau) \in \mathbb{R}^2$, and $h(y, \eta) = (y + \sigma - \tau)^+$, where σ_n is the n-th service time and τ_n the n-th inter-arrival time. The sequence $\{y_n\}$ is imbedded in the continuous time workload process which is obtained when taking $\xi = \sigma \in \mathbb{R}$, and $g(t, y, \xi) = (y + \sigma - t)^+$, $0 \le t < T$. □

Let $\widetilde{N}$ be a second point process defined on a possibly different probability space $(\widetilde{\Omega}, \widetilde{\mathcal{F}}, \widetilde{P}, \widetilde{\theta}_t)$, on which are also defined a stationary sequence $\{\widetilde{y}_n\}$ satisfying the relation

$$\widetilde{y} \circ \widetilde{\theta} = h(\widetilde{y}, \widetilde{\xi}),$$

with the *same* function h as in (4.3.1), and a stochastic process $\{\widetilde{y}(t)\}$ such that

$$\widetilde{y}(t) = g(t - \widetilde{T}_n, \widetilde{y} \circ \widetilde{\theta}^n, \widetilde{\xi} \circ \widetilde{\theta}^n), \quad \widetilde{T}_n \le t < \widetilde{T}_{n+1}, \ \widetilde{P}^0 \text{ -a.s.,}$$

also with the same function g as in (4.3.2). All the objects initially defined for the first processes are also supposed to exist for the second ones, and will be denoted by the same symbol with a tilde.

Strong Bounds. If $(t, y, \xi) \to g(-t, y, \xi)$ is non-decreasing, and if

$$(4.3.3) \quad (T_0, y, \xi) \ [P] \le_i (\widetilde{T}_0, \widetilde{y}, \widetilde{\xi}) \ [\widetilde{P}],$$

then since $y(0) = g(-T_0, y, \xi)$, $y(0) \ [P] \le_i \widetilde{y}(0) \ [\widetilde{P}]$.
If T_0 and (y, ξ) (resp. $\widetilde{T}_0$ and $(\widetilde{y}, \widetilde{\xi})$) are P (resp. $\widetilde{P}$)-independent, from Remark 4.2.2, (4.3.3) is equivalent to

$$(4.3.4) \quad (y, \xi) \ [P^0] \le_i (\widetilde{y}, \widetilde{\xi}) \ [\widetilde{P}^0] \quad \text{and} \quad T_1 \ [P^0] \ge_{s-i} \widetilde{T}_1 \ [\widetilde{P}^0].$$

Example 4.3.2 (cont'd) The function g involved in the workload process $W(t)$, $t \in \mathbb{R}$, of the $G/G/1/\infty$ queue, satisfies the above assumptions with

$$g(t, W, \xi) = (W + \sigma - t)^+,$$

so that the ordering of the workload at arrival times extends to the continuous time stationary workload provided (4.3.3) holds. Under renewal assumptions (see § 2.7), if the relations

$$(4.3.5) \quad \sigma_0 \le_i \widetilde{\sigma}_0$$

and

$$(4.3.6) \quad (a) \quad \tau_0 \ [P^0] \ge_i \widetilde{\tau}_0 \ [\widetilde{P}^0] \quad \text{and} \quad (b) \quad \tau_0 \ [P^0] \ge_{s-i} \widetilde{\tau}_0 \ [\widetilde{P}^0]$$

hold, then in view of (4.3.5) and (4.3.6a), $W \ [P^0] \le_i \widetilde{W} \ [\widetilde{P}^0]$, provided the stationary regimes exist (see §§ 2.6-2.7). Since in addition, T_0 and (W, σ) are independent, (4.3.6b) implies that $W(0)\ [P] \leq_i \widetilde{W}(0)\ [\widetilde{P}]$ in view of the above remarks.

Note that conditions (4.3.6a-b) are for instance simultaneously satisfied for τ_0 and $\widetilde{\tau}_0$ such that $\widetilde{\tau}_0 \leq_i \tau_0$, whenever the Palm distributions of both variables are deterministic, or both are Erlang with the same number of stages, or both are uniform on intervals of the form $(0, x)$, etc.   □

Example 4.3.3 Similar conclusions hold for $G/G/s/\infty$ queues since the ordered workload process $W(t) \in \mathbb{R}^s$ is given by

$$W(t) = g(t, W \circ \theta^n, \xi \circ \theta^n, t), \quad T_n \leq t < T_{n+1},$$

where $\xi = \sigma$ and

$$g(t, W, \xi) = \mathcal{R}(W + \sigma e - ti)^+.$$

□

Convex Ordering Bounds. If $(t, y, \xi) \to g(-t, y, \xi)$ is {icx} and

$$(4.3.7) \quad (T_0, y, \xi)\ [P] \leq_{icx} (\widetilde{T}_0, \widetilde{y}, \widetilde{\xi})\ [\widetilde{P}],$$

then, since {icx} is stable by composition, $y(0)\ [P]\leq_{icx} \widetilde{y}(0)\ [\widetilde{P}]$. Assume in addition that the random variables T_0 and (y, ξ) (resp. $\widetilde{T}$ and $(\widetilde{y}, \widetilde{\xi})$) are P (resp. $\widetilde{P}$)-independent. Then in view of Remark 4.2.2 and Equation (2.1.5), (4.3.7) is equivalent to

$$(4.3.8) \quad (y, \xi)\ [P^0] \leq_{icx} (\widetilde{y}, \widetilde{\xi})\ [\widetilde{P}^0] \quad \text{and} \quad T_1\ [P^0] \leq_{S-dcx} \widetilde{T}_1\ [\widetilde{P}^0],$$

where {dcx} denotes the set of decreasing convex functions.

Example 4.3.2 (cont'd) Thus, under renewal assumptions, if $\sigma_0 \leq_{icx} \widetilde{\sigma}_0$, $\tau_0\ [P^0] \leq_{dcx} \widetilde{\tau}_0\ [\widetilde{P}^0]$ and $\tau_0\ [P^0] \leq_{S-dcx} \widetilde{\tau}_0\ [\widetilde{P}^0]$, then $W(0)\ [P] \leq_{icx} \widetilde{W}(0)\ [\widetilde{P}]$, provided the stationary regime exists.   □

Bounds by Association.

(4.3.9)   *Assume that* $(y, \xi) \to g(t, y, \xi)$ *is non-decreasing and that* $t \to g(t, y, \xi)$ *is monotone. Assume in addition that* $T = T_1$ *and* (y, ξ) *are* P^0-*independent. If* (y, ξ) *is* P^0-*associated then* $y(0)$ *is* P-*associated.*

Proof: Let f_1 and f_2 be two non-decreasing functions $\mathbb{R}_+^K \to \mathbb{R}$ such that $f_1(y(0))f_2(y(0))$, $f_1(y(0))$ and $f_2(y(0))$ are P-integrable. The Palm inversion formula reads

$$E_P[f_1(y(0))f_2(y(0))] = \lambda E_{P^0}\left[\int_0^\infty 1(t \leq T) f_1 \circ g(t, y, \xi) f_2 \circ g(t, y, \xi) dt\right].$$

since $(y, \xi) \to g(t, y, \xi)$ is non-decreasing and in view of (d) of association, the random variables $f_1 \circ g(t, y, \xi)$ and $f_2 \circ g(t, y, \xi)$ are P^0 associated. This and the independence assumption imply

$$E_P[f_1(y(0))f_2(y(0))] \geq \lambda \int_0^\infty P^0[t \leq T]\phi_1(t)\phi_2(t),$$

where $\phi_i(t) \stackrel{\text{def}}{=} E_{P^0}[f_i \circ g(t, y, \xi)]$. The right hand side of the last inequality also reads $= E_P[\phi_1(T)\phi_2(T)]$. Since the functions $\phi_1(t)$ and $\phi_2(t)$ are either both non-decreasing or non-increasing, and since the set consisting of the single variable T is associated

$$E_P[\phi_1(T)\phi_2(T)] \geq E_P[\phi_1(T)]E_P[\phi_2(T)] = E_P[f_1(y(0))]E_P[f_2(y(0))].$$

$\square$

Example 4.3.3 (cont'd) Under renewal assumptions, the assumptions of (4.3.9) are satisfied, so that for instance, the vector $W(0)$ has associated components under P, whenever the stationary regime exists. $\square$

5 Proof of Strassen's Theorem

Let Λ be a convex subset of the set of c.d.f. in $\mathcal{D}(\mathbb{R}^{2n})$, which is closed for the topology of the weak convergence. Let p and q denote the projections of $\mathbb{R}^{2n}$ onto the first n and the last n coordinates, respectively, and let $\mathcal{C}$ be the space of continuous and bounded functions from $\mathbb{R}^n$ to $\mathbb{R}$.

(5.1) *Let F and G be c.d.f. in $\mathcal{D}(\mathbb{R}^n)$. A necessary and sufficient condition for the existence of a distribution function H in Λ such that $F = H \circ p^{-1}$ and $G = H \circ q^{-1}$ is that*

$$(5.2) \quad \int_{\mathbb{R}^n} f(t)F(dt) + \int_{\mathbb{R}^n} g(t)G(dt) \leq \sup_{H \in \Lambda} \int_{\mathbb{R}^{2n}} (f \circ p(u) + g \circ q(u)) H(du),$$

for all bounded and continuous functions in $\mathcal{C}$.

Proof: The necessary part is obvious. Let M_Λ be the subset of $\mathcal{D}(\mathbb{R}^n) \times \mathcal{D}(\mathbb{R}^n)$:

$$M_\Lambda = \{(F, G) \mid \exists H \in \Lambda, \ F = H \circ p^{-1}, \ G = H \circ q^{-1}\}.$$

The set M_Λ, is closed and convex. The convexity is clear. The fact that M_Λ is closed follows from the observation that if K_1 and K_2 are two compact subsets of $\mathbb{R}^n$, then

$$H\left((K_1 \times K_2)^c\right) \leq H \circ p^{-1}\left(K_1^c\right) + H \circ q^{-1}\left(K_2^c\right).$$

So if (F_n, G_n) is a tight sequence in M_Λ, then the corresponding H_n sequence is also tight. Therefore, if (F_n, G_n) converges weakly to (F_∞, G_∞), then H_n also has a converging subsequence. Let H_∞ be its limit. It is easily checked that $H_\infty \circ p^{-1} = F_\infty$, $H_\infty \circ q^{-1} = G_\infty$ (the projection mappings are continuous) and that $H_\infty \in \Lambda$ (because Λ is closed). Therefore M_Λ is closed.

A continuous, linear functional from $\mathcal{D}(\mathbb{R}^n) \times \mathcal{D}(\mathbb{R}^n)$ to $\mathbb{R}$ is represented by (f, g), where f and g are in $\mathcal{C}$ and where $(f, g) \cdot (F, G) \stackrel{\text{def}}{=} \int_{\mathbb{R}^n} f \, dF + \int_{\mathbb{R}^n} g \, dG$. Then, owing to the Hahn-Banach Theorem, (F, G) belongs to closed the convex set M_Λ, if and only for all (f, g) as above,

$$\int_{\mathbb{R}^n} f(t) F(dt) + \int_{\mathbb{R}^n} g(t) G(dt) \leq \sup_{(F', G') \in M_\Lambda} f(t) F'(dt) + g(t) G'(dt)$$

$$= \sup_{H \in \Lambda} \int_{\mathbb{R}^{2n}} (f \circ p(u) + g \circ q(u)) \, H(du).$$

$\square$

Proof of (2.3.1). The sufficient part is obvious. Let F and G be distribution functions on $\mathcal{D}(\mathbb{R}^n)$, such that $F \leq_i G$. For any open set $U \in \mathbb{R}^n$, let $U^+ = \{s \in \mathbb{R} \mid \exists \, t \in U, t \leq s\}$. For all such sets, we have

(5.3) $P_F(U) \leq P_F(U^+) \leq P_G(U^+),$

where P_F and P_G respectively denote the probability measures on $\mathbb{R}^n$ associated with F and G. The second inequality in (5.3) comes from the fact that the set U^+ has a non-decreasing indicator function. Let

$$\Lambda = \{ H \in \mathcal{D}(\mathbb{R}^{2n}) \mid \text{support}(H) \subset \{(t, s) \in \mathbb{R}^n, t \leq s\} \}.$$

The set Λ is closed and convex, so that it is enough to prove that (5.2) holds for all f and g in $\mathcal{C}$ in order to conclude the proof of (2.3.2) (in view of the above theorem). There is no loss of generality in assuming that f and g are non-negative. In view of (5.3), we have

$$\int_{\mathbb{R}^n} f(t) F(dt) = \int_0^{\sup f} P_F(\{t \mid f(t) > r\}) dr$$

$$\leq \int_0^{\sup f} P_G(\{s \mid \exists t \leq s, f(t) > r\}) dr$$

$$= \int_0^{\sup f} P_G(\{s \mid f_0(s) > r\}) dr = \int_{\mathbb{R}^n} f_0(s) G(ds),$$

where $f_0(s) \stackrel{\text{def}}{=} \sup_{t \leq s} f(t)$ is bounded and non-negative. Therefore

$$\int f(t) F(dt) + \int g(t) G(dt) \leq \int (f_0(t) + g(t)) \, G(dt)$$

$$\leq \sup_{t \in \mathbb{R}^n} (f_0(t) + g(t))$$

$$= \sup_{H \in \Lambda} \int_{\mathbb{R}^{2n}} (f \circ p(u) + g \circ q(u)) \, H(du).$$

$\square$

Proof of (2.3.2). The sufficient part follows immediately from Jensen's inequality for conditional expectations. In order to prove the converse implication, it is enough to prove that if two distribution functions F and G on $\mathbb{R}^n$ satisfy the relation

$$\int f(t)F(dt) \leq \int f(t)G(dt),$$

for all convex functions f, then there is a distribution function H in $\mathcal{D}(\mathbb{R}^{2n})$, with marginals F and G, and such that the conditional expectation of the last n coordinates given the first n is the first n coordinates. Let

$$\Lambda = \{H \in \mathcal{D}(\mathbb{R}^{2n}), \int g \circ q(t)f \circ p(t)H(dt) = \int g \circ p(t)f \circ p(t)H(dt)\ \forall f, g \in \mathcal{C}$$

This integral relation is no more than the martingale relation which was mentioned above, written in a form which makes it transparent that Λ is closed. Since Λ is also convex, the preceding theorem shows that it is enough to prove that (5.2) holds for all f and g in $\mathcal{C}$.

Let $g_0(t)$ be the smallest concave function such that $g_0(t) \geq g(t)$, where $g_0(t) = \infty$ if no such function exists. Then

$$\int_{\mathbb{R}^n} f(t)F(dt) + \int_{\mathbb{R}^n} g(t)G(dt) \leq \int_{\mathbb{R}^n} f(t)F(dt) + \int_{\mathbb{R}^n} g_0(t)G(dt)$$

$$\leq \int_{\mathbb{R}^n} (f(t) + g_0(t))\, F(dt)$$

$$\leq \sup_{t \in \mathbb{R}^n} (f(t) + g_0(t)),$$

where we used our assumption that $F \leq_{\mathrm{cx}} G$. Let $r < \sup_{t \in \mathbb{R}^n}(f(t) + g_0(t))$. Then for some t^*, $r < f(t^*) + g_0(t^*)$. Let us show that

$$r < \sup_{H \in \Lambda} \int_{\mathbb{R}^{2n}} (f \circ p(t) + g \circ q(t))\, H(dt).$$

For t in $\mathbb{R}^n$, let B_t be the set of distribution functions of $\mathcal{D}(\mathbb{R}^n)$ with first moment equal to t. The function $g_1 : \mathbb{R}^n \to \mathbb{R}$ defined by

$$g_1(t) = \sup_{G \in B_t} \int_{\mathbb{R}^n} g(u)G(du),$$

is concave and $g_1 \geq g$, so that $g_1 \geq g_0$ and hence $r < f(t^*) + g_1(t^*)$. By definition of g_1, there exists a distribution function G^* in B_{t^*} with

$$r < f(t^*) + \int_{\mathbb{R}^n} g(u)G^*(du) = \int_{\mathbb{R}^{2n}} (f \circ p(t) + g \circ q(t))\, H(dt),$$

with $H(t) = 1_{p(t) \leq t^*} G^*(q(t)) \in \Lambda$.   □

Bibliographical Comments

The notion of majorization of § 1 was introduced by Muirhead [100] and Schur [118]. A recent survey on the matter together with bibliographical notes can be found in the monograph of Arnold [1] and in the comprehensive book of Marshall and Olkin [89]. Besides the connection with Schur-convexity, most of the results of § 1.2 on the SRPT discipline are taken from Flipo [43]; this reference also contains many more interesting details and historical references. The optimality of the FIFO discipline in GI/GI-input queues was addressed by several authors, including Kingman [72] and, more recently, Foss [45], Berg and Posner [15], and Shanthikumar and Sumita [119]; we found it useful to prove that the interchange argument of § 1.3 preserves the law of the point process, although this is intuitively clear. Here also, the expression of optimality in terms of majorization was chosen because it leads to the strongest results. Basic analytical and stability properties of the integral stochastic orders of § 2, mainly in dimension 1, and bibliographical notes are collected in the first chapter of the book of Stoyan [125]. The key paper on the pointwise representation of integral orders (§ 2.3) is due to Strassen [126]. The proofs of § 5 are borrowed from this reference. Extensions of this type of pointwise representation can be found in a paper of Rüschendorf [113], where the pathwise and projection orders associated with majorization are considered. Such pointwise representations are often referred to as couplings (like for instance in the book of Lindvall [83]). The comparison results of § 2.4-6 on stochastic recurrences were given by Baccelli and Makowski in [11]. The results of § 2.7 were obtained with different levels of generality by several authors, including Rogozin [109], Humblet [56], Hajek [52] and Whitt [131], to name a few. The example given in the introduction is taken from [56]. The book of Stoyan [125] contains a review of the literature on the comparison of queues. The approach of this book is mainly based on stability properties of orders by convolution, maximization etc., which only apply to the renewal case. The analysis of the $G/G/1/\infty$ queue in random environment is related to Ross' conjecture [112], which states that a $G/G/1/\infty$ queue in a random environment should be bounded from below by the corresponding queue where the environment process is 'frozen' to its mean values. A first proof of this conjecture was given by Rolski [111]; the proof for the stationary ergodic case given in § 2.8 is that of [10]. The notion of association, also known as *Positive Correlation*, was introduced by Esary, Proschan, and Walkup [42]. The two basic references on association are the book of Barlow and Proschan [14], and that of Marshall and Olkin [89]. The relation between association and integral orders was studied in [12]. It is shown in particular that, for $\mathcal{L} \in \{i, icx, cx\}$, one cannot have $X = (X_1, \ldots, X_n)$ associated and $X \leq_{\mathcal{L}} \overline{X}$ ($\overline{X}$ denotes the product form version of X), unless $X = \overline{X}$ in distribution. Other applications of association to systems generalizing those of Example 3.2.2 are considered in the review article [11], which also contains bibliographical notes on the matter. Property (4.1.4) was proved analytically by Jean-Marie and Liu [60], for renewal processes. The equivalence stated in Lemma (4.1.1) is new. Property (4.1.7) is due to Hajek [53], where more general results based on multimodular functions are given. The stochastic order $\leq_{S-i}$ of § 4.2 was first considered by Whitt in [132]. The results of § 4.2-3 are mainly taken from Baccelli and Makowski [13].

References

[1]   Arnold, B. C. (1987) *Majorization and the Lorenz Order: A Brief Introduction*, Lecture Notes in Statistics, 43, Springer-Verlag, New York.

[2]   Asmussen, S. (1987) *Applied Probability and Queues*, Wiley, New York.

[3]   Asmussen, S. (1992) *On Coupling and Weak Convergence to Stationarity*, Ann. Appl. Proba., 2, 3, pp. 739-751.

[4]   Baccelli, F. and Brémaud, P. (1987) *Palm probabilities and stationary queueing systems*, Lect. Notes in Stat. 41, Springer-Verlag, New York.

[5]   Baccelli, F. and Brémaud, P. (1993) *Virtual Customer in Sensitivity Analysis via Campbell's Formula for Point Processes*, Adv. App. Proba., 25, pp. 221-234.

[6]   Baccelli, F., Cohen, G., Olsder, G.J. and Quadrat, J.P. (1992) *Synchronization and Linearity*, Wiley, New York.

[7]   Baccelli, F. and Foss, S. (1993) *Stability of Jackson-Type Queueing Networks*, INRIA Report 1945, to appear in QUESTA.

[8]   Baccelli, F. and Foss, S. (1993) *On the Saturation Rule for the Stability of Queues*, INRIA Report 2015.

[9]   Baccelli F. and Liu, Z. (1992) *On a Class of Stochastic Recursive Equations Arising in Queuing Theory*, Ann. of Prob., 20, 1, pp. 350-374.

[10]   Baccelli, F. and Makowski, A.M. (1986) *Queues in Random Environment, Stability and Bounds*, Commun. Statist. Stoch. Models, 2.

[11]   Baccelli, F. and Makowski, A.M. (1989) *Queueing Models for Systems with Synchronization Constraints*, Proceedings of the IEEE, 77, 1, pp. 138-161.

[12]   Baccelli, F. and Makowski, A.M. (1989) *Multidimensional Stochastic Ordering and Associated Random Variables*, Oper. Res. 37, 3, pp. 478-487.

[13]   Baccelli, F. and Makowski A.M. (1992) *Stochastic Orders Related with Renewal Processes*, University of Maryland, SRC-TR-92-3.

[14]   Barlow, R.E. and Proschan, F. (1975) *Statistical Theory of Reliability and Life Testing*, Holt Rinehart and Winston, New York.

[15]   Berg, M. and Posner, M.J.M. (1986) *On the Regulation of Queues*, Oper. Res. Letters, 4, 5, pp. 221-224.

[16]   Billingsley, P. (1965) *Ergodic Theory and Information*, Wiley, New York.

[17]   Billingsley, P. (1968) *Convergence of Probability Measures*, Wiley, New York.

[18]   Blaszczyszyn, B. (1993) *Factorial Moment Expansion for Stochastic Systems*, preprint, Math. Inst., University of Wroclaw.

[19]   Borovkov, A.A. (1976) *Stochastic Processes in Queueing Theory*, Springer-Verlag, New York.

[20]   Borovkov, A.A. (1984) *Asymptotic Methods in Queueing Theory*, Wiley, New York.

[21]   Borovkov, A.A. and Foss, S. (1992) *Stochastic Recursive Sequences and their Applications*, Siberian Advances in Mathematics, 2, 1, pp. 16-81.

[22]   Bramson, M. (1993) *Instability of FIFO Queueing Networks*, preprint Mathematics Department, University of Wisconsin.

[23]   Brandt, A. (1985) *On Stationary Waiting Times and Limiting Behavior of Queues with Many Servers I: the General $G/G/m/\infty$ Case*, Elektron. Inform. u. Kybernet., 21, pp 47-64.

[24]   Brandt, A., Franken, P. and Lisek B. (1992) *Stationary Stochastic Models*, Wiley, New York.

[25]   Brémaud, P. and Jacod, J. (1977) *Processus ponctuels et martingales : résultats récents sur la modélisation et le filtrage*, Adv. Appl. Proba., 9, pp. 362-416.

[26]   Brémaud, P. (1981) *Point Processes and Queues : Martingale Dynamics*, Springer-Verlag, New York.

[27]   Brémaud, P. (1989) *Characteristics of Queueing Systems Observed at Events and the Connection Between Stochastic Intensity and Palm Probabilities*, Queueing Systems, 5, pp. 99-112.

[28]   Brémaud, P. (1993) *A Swiss Army Formula of Palm Calculus*, J. Appl. Proba., 30, pp. 40-51.

[29]   Brémaud, P. and Kannurpatti, R. Mazumdar, R. (1992) *Events And Time Averages: A review*, Adv. Appl. Proba., 24, pp. 377-411.

[30]   Brémaud, P. and Massoulié, L. (1993) *Imbedding and Coupling in the Construction of Stationary Point Processes*, preprint, Laboratoire des Signaux et Systèmes, CNRS.

[31]   Brill, P.H. and Posner, M.J.M (1977) *Level Crossings in Point Process Applied to Queues: Single Server Case*, Oper. Res., 25, pp. 662-674.

[32]   Brumelle, D. (1971) *On the Relation Between Customer and Time Average in Queues*, J. Appl. Proba. 2, pp. 508-520.

[33]   Brumelle, D. (1972) *A Generalization of $L = \lambda W$ to Moments of Queue Length and Waiting Times*, Oper. Res., 20, pp. 1127-1136.

[34]   Campbell, N.R. (1909) *The Study of Discontinuous Phenomena*, Proc. Cambridge Philos. Soc. 15, pp. 117-136.

[35]   Cobham, A. (1954) *Priority Assignment in Waiting Line Problems*, Oper. Res., 2, pp. 470-76.

[36]   Dacunha-Castelle, D. and Duflo, M. (1982) *Probabilités et Statistiques: II Problèmes à temps mobile*, Masson, Paris.

[37]   Daley, D.S. and Vere-Jones, D. (1988) *An Introduction to the Theory of Point Processes*, Springer-Verlag, New York.

[38]   Delasnerie, M. (1977) *Flots mélangeants et mesures de Palm*, Ann. Inst. H. Poincaré, Section B 8, pp. 357-369.

[39]   Doshi, B.T. (1986) *Queueing Systems with Vacations – A survey*, Queueing Systems 5, pp. 99-112.

[40]   Doshi, B.T. (1990) *Single Server Queues with Vacations*, in Stoch. Anal. of Comp. and Comm. Systems, H. Takagi editor, North-Holland, pp. 217-265.

[41]   Dumas, V. (1992) *Stabilité des réseaux de Jackson*, Mémoire de DEA, CMAP, Ecole Polytechnique, Paris.

[42]   Esary, J. D., Proschan, F. and Walkup, D. W. (1967) *Association of Random Variables, with Applications*, Ann. Math. Stat. 38, pp. 1466-1474.

[43]   Flipo, D. (1981) *Comparaison des disciplines de service des files d'attente $G/G/1$*, Annales de l'IHP, Paris, 7, 2, pp. 191-212.

[44]   Flipo, D. (1983) *Steady State of Loss Systems*, Comptes rendus de l'Académie des Sciences, 297, 6, Paris.

[45]   Foss, S. (1981) *Comparison of Multi-Server Queues*, Sibirsk. Math. J. 22, pp. 190-197 (in Russian).

[46]   Franken, P. and Streller, A. (1979) *Generalized Stationary Renewal Processes* (in Russian), Probability Theory and its Applications, 24, pp. 78-80.

[47]   Franken, P., König, D., Arndt, U. and Schmidt, V. (1981) *Queues and point processes*, Akademie-Verlag, Berlin (American edition: Wiley, New York, 1982).

[48]   Fuhrmann, S.W. and Cooper, R.B. (1985) *Stochastic Decomposition in the $M/GI/1$ queue with generalized vacations*, Oper. Res., 33, pp. 1117-1129.

[49]   Garsia, A. (1965) *A Simple Proof of Eberhard Hopf's Maximal Ergodic Theorem*, J. Math. and Mech. 14, pp. 381-382.

[50]   Geman, D. and Horowitz, J. (1973) *Remarks on Palm Measures*, Ann. Inst. H. Poincaré, Section B. 9, pp. 215-232.

[51]   Halfin, S. and Whitt, W. (1989) *An Extremal Property of the FIFO Discipline via and Ordinal Version of $L = \lambda W$*, Commun. Statist. Stoch. Models, 5, pp. 515-529.

[52]   Hajek, B. (1983) *The Proof of a Folk Theorem on Queueing Delay with Applications to Routing in Networks*, Journal Assoc. Comp. Mach. 30, pp. 834-851.

[53]   Hajek, B. (1985) *Extremal Splittings of Point Processes*, Math. of Operations Research 10, 4, pp. 543-556.

[54]   Heyman, D.P. and Stidham, S. (1980) *The Relation Between Customer and Time Averages in Queues*, Oper. Res., 28, pp. 983-994.

[55]   Heyman, D. and Sobel, M (1982) *Stochastic Models in Operations Research* (I,II), Mc Graw Hill, New York.

248   References

[56]   Humblet, P. (1982) *Determinism Minimizes Waiting Times in Queues*, Technical Report, LIDS - Department of Electrical Engineering and Computer Science, MIT, (MA).

[57]   Jacod, J. (1975) *Multivariate Point Processes : Predictable Projections, Radon-Nikodým Derivatives, Representation of Martingales*, Z. Wahrs. 31, pp. 235-253.

[58]   Jaibi, M.R. (1984) *Charges stationnaires d'une file d'attente avec blocages*, preprint.

[59]   Jansen, U., König, D., Nawrotzki, K. (1979). *A Criterion of Insensitivity for a Class of Queueing Systems with Random Marked Point Processes*, Math. Operationsforsch. Stat., Ser. Optimization, 10, pp. 379-403.

[60]   Jean-Marie, A. and Liu, Z. (1992) *Stochastic Comparisons for Queueing Models via Random Sums and Intervals*, Adv. Appl. Proba., 24, pp. 960-985.

[61]   Jewell, W.S. (1967) *A Simple Proof of $L = \lambda W$*, Oper. Res., 15, pp. 1109-1116.

[62]   Kalähne, U. (1976) *Existence, Uniqueness and some Invariance Properties of Stationary Distributions for General Single Server Queues*, Math. Operationsforsch. Stat. 7, pp. 557-575.

[63]   Kalashnikov, V.V., and Rachev, S.T. (1990) *Mathematical Methods for Construction of Queueing Models*, Wadsworth & Brooks, Pacific Grove, Cal.

[64]   Kallenberg, 0. (1983) *Random Measures*, 3rd ed. Akademie-Verlag, Berlin, and Academic Press, London. (first. ed., 1975).

[65]   Kallenberg, 0. (1984) *An Informal Guide to the Theory of Conditioning in Point Processes*, Int. Statist. Review 52, pp. 151-164.

[66]   Karr, A.F. (1986) *Point Processes and their Statistical Inference*, Marcel Dekker, New York.

[67]   Karr, A.F. (1988) *Palm Distributions of Point Processes and their Application to Statistical Inference*, Contemporary Mathematics, 80, pp. 331-358.

[68]   Kella, O. and Whitt, W. (1991) *Queues with Server Vacations and Lévy Processes with Secondary Jump Input.*, The Annals of Appl. Proba., 1, pp. 104-117.

[69]   Kelly, F. (1979) *Reversibility and Stochastic Networks*, Wiley, New York.

[70]   Khinchin, A.Ya. (1955) *Mathematical Methods in the Theory of Queueing* (in Russian), Trudy Mat. Inst. Steklov 49, [Translated (1960) Griffin, London].

[71]   Khinchin, A. Ya. (1932) *Mathematical Theory of Stationary Queues* (in Russian), Mat. Sbornik 39, pp. 73-84.

[72]   Kingman, J.F.C. (1970) *Inequalities in the Theory of Queues*, Journal Roy. Stat. Soc. B 32, pp. 102-110.

[73]   Kingman, J.F.C. (1973) *Subadditive Ergodic Theory*, Annals of Proba. 1, pp. 883-909.

[74]   Kingman, J.F.C. (1976) *Subadditive Processes*, Ecole d'Eté de Probabilité de Saint-Flour, Springer-Verlag, New York.

[75]   Kleinrock, L. (1975,1976) *Queueing Systems* (I, II), John Wiley & Sons, New York.

[76]   König, D. and Schmidt, V. (1980) *Imbedded and Non-imbedded Stationary Characteristics of Queueing Systems with Varying Service Rate and Point Process*, J. Appl. Proba., 17, pp. 753-767.

[77]   Konstantopoulos, P. and Walrand, J. (1989) *Stationarity and Stability of Fork-Join Networks*, J. Appl. Proba. 26, pp. 604-614.

[78]   Kummer, G. and Matthes, K. (1970) *Verallgemeinerung eines Satzes von Sliwnyak*, II. Rev. Roumaine Math. Pures Appl. 15, pp. 845-870.

[79]   Kunita, H. and Watanabe, S. (1967) *On Square-Integrable Martingales*, Nagoya Math. Journal 30, pp. 209-245.

[80]   Lazar, A. and Hsiao, H. (1990) *An Extension to Norton's Equivalent*, QUESTA 5, pp. 401-412.

[81]   Lazar, A. and Ferrandiz J. (1990) *Rate Conservation for Stationary Point Processes*, J. Appl. Proba. 28, pp. 146-158.

[82]   Lindvall, T. (1988) *Ergodicity and Inequalities in a Class of Point Processes*, Stoch. Process. Appl., 30, pp. 121-131.

[83]   Lindvall, T. (1992) *Lectures on the Coupling Method*, Wiley, New York.

[84]   Liptser, R.S. and Shiryayev, A.N. (1978) *Statistics of Random Processes, II : Applications*, Springer Verlag, New York.

[85]   Lisek, B. (1982) *A Method for Solving a Class of Recursive Stochastic Equation*, Zeitschrift für Wahrsch. 60, pp. 151-162.

[86]   Little, J. (1961) *A Proof for the Queueing Formula* $L = \lambda W$, Oper. Res., 9, pp. 383-387.

[87]   Loynes, R. M. (1962) *The Stability of Queues with non Independent Interarrival and Service Times*, Proc. Camb. Ph. Soc. 58, pp. 497-520.

[88]   Mairesse, J. (1993) *Products of Random Matrices in the* (max, +) *Algebra*, INRIA Report 1939.

[89]   Marshall, A.W. and Olkin, I. (1979) *Inequalities: Theory of Majorization and its Applications*, Academic Press, New York.

[90]   Massoulié, L. (1993) *Stability of a non-Markovian Polling System*, Preprint, Laboratoire des Signaux et Systèmes, CNRS.

[91]   Matthes, K. (1962) *Zur Theorie des Bedienungsprozesses*, Trans. 3-rd Prague Conf. Information Theory, Prague 1964, pp. 513-528.

[92]   Matthes, K., Kerstan, J. and Mecke, J. (1978) *Infinitely Divisible Point Processes*, 2nd ed. Wiley, New York.

[93]   Mecke, J. (1967) *Stationäre zufällige Masse auf lokal kompakten Abelschen Gruppen*, Z. Wahrs. 9, pp. 36-58.

[94]   Mecke, J. (1968) *Eine charakteristische Eigenschaft der doppelt stochastischen Poissonschen Prozesse*, Zeitschrift für Wahrs. 11, pp. 74-81.

[95]   Mitrani, I. (1987) *Modeling of Computer and Communications Systems*, Cambridge Univ. Press.

[96]   Miyazawa, M. (1977) *Time and Customer Processes in Queues with Station-ary Inputs*, J. Appl. Proba., 14, pp. 349-357.

[97]   Miyazawa, M. (1979) *A Formal Approach to Queueing Processes in the Steady State and their Applications*, J. Appl. Proba., 16, pp. 332-346.

[98]   Miyazawa, M. (1983) *The Derivation of Invariance Relations in Complex Queueing Systems with Stationary Inputs*, Adv. Appl. Proba., 15, pp. 874-885.

[99]   Miyazawa, M. (1985) *The Intensity Conservation Law for Queues with Ran-domly Changed Service Rate*, J. Appl. Proba, 22, pp. 408-418.

[100] Muirhead, R.F. (1903) *Some Methods Applicable to Identities and Inequal-ities of Symmetric Algebraic Functions of n Letters*, Proceedings of Edim-burgh Mathematical Society 21, pp. 144-157.

[101] Neveu, J. (1976) *Processus ponctuels*, in Ecole d'Eté de St. Flour, Springer-Verlag Lect. Notes in Math. 598, pp. 249-445.

[102] Neveu, J. (1976). *Sur les mesures de Palm de deux processus ponctuels sta-tionnaires*, Zeitschrift für Wahrsch. 34, pp. 199-203.

[103] Neveu. J. (1983) *Construction de files d'attente stationnaires*, in Lecture Notes in Control and Information Sciences 60, Springer-Verlag, Berlin Hei-delberg, pp. 31-41.

[104] Palm, C. (1943) *Intensitätsschwankungen im Fernsprechverkehr*, Ericsson Techniks 44, pp. 1-189.

[105] Papangelou, F. (1972) *Integrability of Expected Increments and a Related Random Change of Time Scale*, Trans. Amer. Math. Soc. 165, pp. 483-506.

[106] Phipps, T. (1956) *Machine Repair as a Priority Waiting Line Problem*, Oper. Res., 4, pp. 76-85.

[107] Pollaczek, F. (1930) *Ueber Aufgabe der Warscheinlichkeitstheorie* (I,II), Math. Zeitschr., 32, pp. 65-99 and 729-750.

[108] Reiman, M.I. and Simon, B. (1989) *Open Queueing Systems in Light Traffic*, Mathematics of Oper. Res., 14, 1, pp. 26-59.

[109] Rogozin, B.A. (1966) *Some Extremal Problems in Queueing Theory*, Theor. Prob. Appl. and its Appl. 11, pp. 144-151.

[110] Rolski, T. (1981) *Stationary Random Processes Associated with Point Pro-cesses*, Springer-Verlag Lecture Notes Statist. 5, Springer-Verlag, Berlin Hei-delberg.

[111] Rolski, T. (1983) *Comparison Theorems for Queues with Dependent Inter-Arrival Times*, in Springer Verlag, Lecture Notes in Control and Information Sciences 60, pp. 42-71.

[112] Ross, S.M. (1978) *Average Delay in Queues with non-stationary Poisson Arrivals*, J. Appl. Proba., 15, pp. 602-609.

[113] Rüschendorf, L. (1981) *Ordering of Distributions and Rearrangement of Functions*, The Annals of Probability, 2, pp. 276-283.

[114] Ryll-Nardzeweki, C. (1961) *Remarks on Processes of Calls*, Proc. Fourth Berkeley Symp. Math. Statist. Probab. 2, pp. 455-465.

[115] Schassberger, R. (1977) *Insensitivity of Steady State Distribution of Generalized semi-Markov Processes I*, Ann. Proba. $\underline{5}$, pp. 87-99.

[116] Schassberger, R. (1978) *Insensitivity of Steady State Distribution of Generalized semi-Markov Processes II*, Ann. Proba. $\underline{6}$, pp. 85-93.

[117] Schassberger, R. (1978) *Insensitivity of Steady State Distribution of Generalized semi-Markov Processes with Speeds*, Adv. Appl. Proba., $\underline{10}$, pp. 836-851.

[118] Schur, I. (1923) *Über eine Klasse von Mittelbildungen mit Anwendungen der Determinanten*, Theorie Sitzung. Berlin Math. Gesellschaft, $\underline{22}$, pp. 9-20.

[119] Shanthikumar, G.J. and Sumita, U. (1987) *Convex Ordering of Sojourn Times in Single Server Queues: Extremal Properties of FIFO and LIFO Disciplines*, J. Appl. Probability, $\underline{24}$.

[120] Shanthikumar, G.J. (1988) *On Stochastic Decomposition in $M/GI/1$ Type Queues with Generalized Server Vacations*, Oper. Res., $\underline{36}$, pp. 566-569.

[121] Shanthikumar, G.J. (1989) *Level Crossing Analysis of Priority Queues and Conservation Identity for Vacation Models*, Naval. Res. Logist. Quart., $\underline{36}$, pp. 797-806.

[122] Slivnyak, I.M. (1962) *Some Properties of Stationary Flows of Homogeneous Random Events*, Theory Proba. Appl.. $\underline{7}$, pp. 347-352.

[123] Slivnyak, I.M. (1966) *Stationary Streams of Homogeneous Random Events*, Vest. Harkov. Gos. Univ. Ser. Mech. Math. $\underline{32}$, pp. 73-116.

[124] Smith, W.L. (1955) *Regenerative Stochastic Processes*, Proc. Roy. Soc., Ser. A $\underline{232}$, pp. 66-31.

[125] Stoyan, D. (1983) *Comparison Methods for Queues and Other Stochastic Models*, English Edition, Wiley, New York.

[126] Strassen, V. (1965) *The Existence of Probability Measures with Given Marginals*, Ann. Math. Statist. $\underline{36}$, pp. 423-439.

[127] Thorisson, H. (1992) *On Time and Cycle Stationarity* , Stoch. Proc. Appl., to appear.

[128] Totoki, H. (1966) *Time Changes of Flows*, Mem. Fac. Sci. Kyushu Univ., Ser. A, $\underline{20}$, pp. 27-55.

[129] Walrand, J. (1988) *An Introduction to Queueing Networks*, Prentice-Hall, Englewood Cliffs, N.J.

[130] Watanabe, S. (1964) *On Discontinuous Additive Functionals and Lévy Measures of a Markov Process*, Japan J. Math. $\underline{34}$, pp. 53-70.

[131] Whitt, W. (1984) *Minimizing Delays in the $GI/GI/1$ Queue*, Oper. Res., $\underline{32}$, pp. 41-51.

[132] Whitt, W. (1985) *The Renewal-Process Stationary Excess Operator*, J.A.P. $\underline{22}$, pp. 156-167.

[133] Whitt, W. (1991) *A Review of $L = \lambda W$ and Extensions*, Queueing Systems, $\underline{9}$, pp. 235-268.

[134] Wolff, R.W. (1970) *Work Conserving Priorities*, J. Appl. Proba., $\underline{7}$, pp. 327-337.

[135]   Wolff, R.W. (1982) *Poisson Arrivals See Time Average*, Oper. Res., <u>30</u>.

[136]   Wolff, R.W. (1989) *Stochastic Modeling and the Theory of Queues*, Prentice-Hall, Englewood Cliffs, N.J.

Index